Farming Systems
and Poverty

IMPROVING FARMERS' LIVELIHOODS
IN A CHANGING WORLD

John Dixon and Aidan Gulliver with David Gibbon

Principal Editor: Malcolm Hall

FAO and World Bank
Rome and Washington D.C.
2001

ISBN 92-5-104627-1

PREFACE

...

Small farmers produce much of the developing world's food. Yet they are generally much poorer than the rest of the population in these countries, and are less food secure than even the urban poor. Furthermore, although the majority of the world's population will live in urban areas by 2030, farming populations will not be much smaller than they are today. For the foreseeable future, therefore, dealing with poverty and hunger in much of the world means confronting the problems that small farmers and their families face in their daily struggle for survival.

Investment priorities and policies must take into account the immense diversity of opportunities and problems facing small farmers. The resources on which they draw, their choice of activities, indeed the entire structure of their lives, are linked inseparably to the biological, physical, economic and cultural environment in which they find themselves and over which they only have limited control. While every farmer is unique, those who share similar conditions also often share common problems and priorities that transcend administrative or political borders.

These broad patterns of similar production systems, practices and external conditions are used in this book as a basis for defining more than 70 major farming systems throughout the six developing regions of the world. While recognizing the heterogeneity that inevitably exists within such broad systems, it is a central tenet of this book that the farming systems approach, as used here, offers a useful framework for understanding the needs of those living within a system, the likely challenges and opportunities that they will face over the next thirty years, and the relative importance of different strategies for escaping from poverty and hunger.

To offer a basis for comparative analysis, this book looks in detail at some 20 farming systems that are judged to have the greatest potential for poverty and hunger reduction and economic growth in the next few decades. They are considered in the light of five possible broad household strategies for escape from poverty and hunger: (a) intensification of production; (b) diversification of agricultural activities for increased output value; (c) increased farm size; (d) expansion in off-farm income; and (e) complete exit or departure from the farming system. The book asks the crucial question: What are likely to be the most successful strategies for small farmers in each system, and what sort of initiatives can best help farmers to realize them?

The material for this book is derived from a study originally undertaken at the request of the World Bank in order to provide a specifically agricultural perspective to the revision of the Bank's Rural Development Strategy. It has drawn on many years of specialised work within FAO and the World Bank, as well as in a number of other national and international institutions. Findings were supported by more than 20 case studies from around the world which analysed innovative approaches to small farm or pastoral development. This book is intended for a wider audience than the original study, and it is hoped that policy makers, researchers, NGOs and the agribusiness sector will all find its conclusions and recommendations interesting and thought provoking; and that they will carry the analysis further by applying the approach at national level to assist in the formulation of rural development strategies.

Jacques Diouf
Director-General
Food and Agriculture Organization
of the United Nations

James D. Wolfensohn
President
World Bank Group

ACKNOWLEDGEMENTS

...

The preparation of this book was carried forward by FAO under the overall co-ordination of E. S. Funes (Director, Rural Development Division) and the technical leadership of J. Dixon (Senior Officer, Farming Systems, Farm Management and Production Economics Service, Agricultural Support Systems Division) and A. Gulliver (Senior Economist, Investment Centre Division), with support from D. Gibbon (consultant). This work was conducted to contribute to the preparation of the World Bank Rural Development Strategy, *Reaching the Rural Poor*, which was prepared under the leadership of Robert L. Thompson. The research benefited from the guidance of D. Forbes Watt (Director, Investment Centre Division), J. Monyo (Director, Agricultural Support Systems Division), A. MacMillan (Principal Adviser, Project Advisory Unit, Investment Centre Division) and D. Baker (Chief, Farm Management and Production Economics Service, Agricultural Support Systems Division) in FAO and of C. Csaki (Senior Advisor/Team Leader-Rural Strategy) and S. Barghouti (Research Advisor) of the Rural Development Department, World Bank.

The authors wish to acknowledge the major contributions made by the persons principally responsible for the six regional analyses, the results of which were originally issued as separate documents, and on which the current regional chapters are based. Africa – A. Carloni (Investment Centre Division); Middle East and North Africa – D. Gibbon; Eastern Europe and Central Asia – S. Tanic (Sub-Regional Office for Central and Eastern Europe) and F. Dauphin (Investment Centre Division); South Asia – J. Weatherhogg (Investment Centre Division), J. Dixon and K. d'Alwis (Consultant); East Asia and the Pacific – D. Ivory (Regional Office for Asia and the Pacific); and Latin America and Caribbean – A. Gulliver, J. de Grandi, C. Spehar, G. Majella (Consultants). Among these, D. Ivory also made important contributions to the global conclusions.

The regional analyses were reviewed by the regional Rural Development Strategy task teams within the World Bank led by S. Ganguly (AFR), M. Bale (EAP), L. Tuck

(ECA), M. Cackler (LAC), P. Aklilu (MNA) and R. Ali (SAS). The comments and suggestions received from these teams, and especially the assistance of I. Tsakok (LAC regional team), are gratefully acknowledged. C.Csaki and S. Barghouti provided feedback on the entire study at several points. R. Schurmann (FAO/World Bank Technical Services Coordinator) assisted in liaison as well as providing review comments.

More than twenty supporting case studies were prepared by M. Bazza (FAO Regional Office for the Near East), L. Fe'D'Ostiani (Economic and Social Department); C. Batello, W. Fiebig, F. Hoque, H. Le, N. Nguyen & D. Tran (Agriculture Department); A. Gulliver, Y. Ishihara & T. Bachmann, A. Mascaretti (Technical Co-operation Department); A. Agarwal, R. Brinkman, J de Grandi, B. Dugdill & A. Bennett, E. Kiff & B. Pound, D. Kopeva, A. Martinenko, E. Meng, G. Mitti, R. de Sagun, C. Spehar, C. Tanner, Z. Wang and J. Zethraeus (Consultants).

The Data and GIS Team, responsible for generating the farming systems specific data and developing the GIS-based maps used in the study, was led by C. Auricht (consultant) with the support of P. Aguilar (WAICENT/FAOSTAT Data Management Branch), L. Hein (Investment Centre), M. Zanetti (Land and Water Development Division), G. Agostini, S. Accongiagico, M. Lespine and T. Rosetti.

The content of the book benefited from the contributions of numerous FAO staff (in addition to those mentioned above), including: T. Bachmann, L. Clarke, R. Florin, P. Koohafkan, E. Kueneman, S. Mack, J. Maki-Hokkonen, F. Moukoko-N'Doumbé, F. Nachtergaele, M. Porto, J. Poulisse, S. Reynolds, R. Roberts, A. Rottger, P. Santacoloma, A. Shepherd, J. Slingenberg, P. Steele and N. Urquia (Agriculture Department); G. Boedeker, J. Bruinsma, F. Egal, Y. Lambrou, K. Stamoulis and J. Schmidthuber (Economic and Social Department); M. Halvart (Fisheries Department); M. Gauthier and K. Warner (Forestry Department); L. Collette, J. Dey-Abbas, P. Groppo, A. Herrera, J. Juhasz, J. Latham, P. Munro-Faure and D. Palmer (Sustainable Development Department); C. Bevan, M. Bral, G. Evers, A. Jumabayeva, D. Khan, D. LeLievre, P. Lucani, T. Tecle, B. Veillerette, M. Wales and F. Yriarte (Technical Co-operation Department); D. Kunze (Regional Office for Africa); B. D'Avis, R. Jehle and D. Sedik (Regional Office for Europe); N. Deomampo and R. Singh (Regional Office for Asia and the Pacific); and H. Bamman (Sub-Regional Office for the Pacific).

The exceptional review and editorial efforts of E. Kueneman and A. Macmillan are gratefully acknowledged. Further, R. Brinkman contributed greatly to the clarity of the regional analyses. P. Hollingworth was responsible for graphic design and layout of the publication. Special thanks are due to support staff, including: C. Bianchi, A. Biolley, M. Cullinan, J. Francis, B. Grani-Polidori, B. Hall, S. Lami, S. Peppicelli, and R. Smith.

The comments from reviewers are gratefully acknowledged. The external reviewers were: T. Aldington, S. Barraclough, M. Cox, D. Norman, B. Roitman and Vo-Tong Xuan. The internal reviewers were J. Bruinsma, P. Munro-Faure and S. Keya. Any remaining mistakes are the responsibility of the authors.

TABLE OF CONTENTS

• • •

1

INTRODUCTION

• • •

THE CONTEXT

The vision that underlies this book is one of a world without hunger and poverty. Most poor people live in rural areas of developing countries and are dependent on agriculture for their livelihood. The authors are convinced that the key to eradicating current suffering is to focus upon the creation of dynamic rural communities founded upon prosperous farming. A central tenet of this book is that the analysis of the farming systems within which the rural poor live and work can provide powerful insights into strategic priorities for the reduction of the poverty and hunger now affecting so many of their lives.

The availability of food has always been a central preoccupation of mankind. Despite a doubling of the global population during the past four decades, farmers have produced sufficient food to allow average per capita food intake to grow gradually. Yet hunger persists and food reserves have fluctuated markedly during this period, sometimes falling to critically low levels. In order to address these concerns, the World Food Conference was organised in 1974, followed by the International Conference on Nutrition in 1992 and the World Food Summit in 1996. At the Summit, Heads of State reaffirmed ... *the right of everyone to have access to safe and nutritious food, consistent with the right of everyone to be free from hunger.* They also committed themselves to reducing the number of undernourished people to half their present level no later than 2015[1]. The achievement of this goal is central to the Strategic Framework of the Food and Agriculture Organization of the United Nations (FAO)[2].

The eradication of poverty[3] is another international commitment, made originally in 1995 at the World Summit for Social Development held in Copenhagen, Denmark. At the Social Summit +5 (June 2000) this commitment was

---

[1] FAO 1996a.
[2] FAO 1999a.
[3] At an international level, the term 'poverty' is applied with respect to those earning less than US$1 per day.

1

translated into the target of halving the proportion of people living in extreme poverty by the year 2015. Both the World Food Summit and Social Summit +5 targets are reflected in the Millennium Declaration[4] adopted by the United Nations General Assembly (UNGA) in September 2000.

Many other development organisations have committed themselves to similar visions of reduced hunger or poverty. For instance, in 1997 the World Bank issued a new strategy for rural development entitled *Rural Development: From Vision to Action*[5]. Similarly, after its pathbreaking global poverty survey of the early 1990s, the International Fund for Agricultural Development (IFAD) has recently renewed its commitment to poverty reduction with the publication of its *Rural Poverty Report 2001 – The Challenge of Ending Rural Poverty*[6]. A majority of bilateral aid organisations have also focused on poverty reduction as a major theme in their programmes of development co-operation. Both food and income security are emphasised in the planning and policy documents of a great many governments.

This book takes a new look at the old problem of hunger and poverty through the lens of farming systems analysis. It recognises the diversity of the livelihoods of poor farmers, pastoralists and fishing families, and explores various pathways that may offer them an escape from poverty. The analysis also charts the expected directions of change in the major farming systems throughout the developing world during the coming 30 years. Rural development ultimately depends on the outcomes of the daily decisions of millions of individual women and men. The challenge for governments, civil society organisations and the private sector is to provide the public goods, institutional environment and incentives that will enable farm households themselves to accelerate agricultural growth and poverty reduction.

Unfortunately, the best available existing projections[7] suggest only a slow decline in hunger and poverty in developing regions. Accordingly, the book outlines, for leaders in the fields of development policy and science, the key strategic priorities for action – for different farming systems, for each developing region and for the developing world as a whole. These priorities focus upon closing the gap between the projected slow reduction in hunger and poverty and the goals set by the international community in the Millennium Declaration.

In this Chapter the current extent of rural hunger and poverty in the developing world is highlighted and the contribution of agricultural growth to poverty alleviation is discussed. Subsequently, the farming systems concept is introduced and the ways in which farming systems have been defined in this book are explained. The likely evolution of farming systems over the next 30 years is then outlined, and the main factors influencing the process are reviewed. The Chapter ends with a reader's guide to the rest of the book.

---

[4] United Nations General Assembly 2000.
[5] World Bank 1997.
[6] International Fund for Agricultural Development 2001.
[7] Comprehensive projections to 2015 and to 2030 are summarised in FAO (2000a). These projections by FAO are referred to extensively throughout this book.

HUNGER, POVERTY AND AGRICULTURE

POPULATION

In the last four decades of the 20th century, the population of developing regions[8] has approximately doubled – to 5.1 billion in 1999. At present, about 60 percent of these people are classed as rural; of whom around 85 percent are agricultural[9] (see Table 1.1). Women constitute 44 percent of the approximately 1.3 billion persons in the agricultural labour force of these regions. In some areas there is a high percentage of female-headed households. Women play a vital role in many aspects of farming systems, including production, processing, marketing and domestic responsibilities, and their contribution to the evolution of these systems is of the greatest importance.

Table 1.1 Rural and Agricultural Populations by Developing Region, 1999

Developing Region	Total Population (million)	Rural Population (million)	Agricultural Population (million)	Females Economically Active (%) [1]/
Sub-Saharan Africa	626	417	384	47
Middle East and North Africa	296	121	84	44
Eastern Europe and Central Asia	478	154	86	44
South Asia	1 344	970	750	39
East Asia and Pacific	1 836	1 184	1 119	47
Latin America and Caribbean	505	126	110	17
All Developing Regions	5 085	2 971	2 534	44

Source: FAOSTAT.

Note: [1]/ Indicates the proportion of those economically active in agriculture who are women.

Over the next thirty years, it is estimated that the total population of developing regions will continue to grow, but the rate of growth is projected to decline – from the current level of 1.8 percent per annum to an estimated 1.2 percent per annum in 2030[10]. However, as a result of the constantly increasing proportion of urban

[8] World Bank classifies developing countries into six developing regions, which are used to organise the analysis underlying this book. Annex 3 lists the membership of each region.
[9] FAO defines the agricultural population as all persons depending for their livelihood on agriculture, hunting, fishing or forestry. This estimate comprises all persons actively engaged in agriculture and their non-working dependants.
[10] United Nations Population Division 2000.

3

dwellers (40 percent in 2000 rising to 56 percent in 2030[11]), the total rural population is actually expected to decline after 2020 (see Figure 1.1). Based on these estimates, the agricultural population of developing countries in 2030 will be little changed from its present level. Despite these forecasts, it should be emphasised that the actual future numbers of people engaged in agriculture in any developing region will depend upon the way that constituent farming systems evolve.

Figure 1.1 Population Trends in Developing Regions

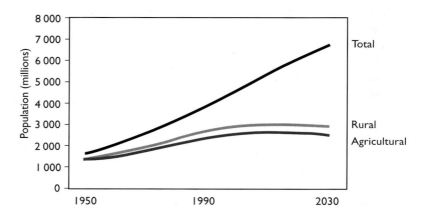

Source: United Nations Population Division 2000.

Among the factors causing uncertainty over future population trends, two are particularly noteworthy. First, the prognosis for the HIV/AIDS pandemic is uncertain. At present the rates of infection are already extremely high in Africa, and the scale of infection is growing alarmingly in Asia, especially South Asia. In Africa, a few countries appear to have contained AIDS through an effective series of measures to combat its spread. It is difficult, however, to predict whether other countries will be able to emulate this experience. Also, should affordable treatments become available – either through new drugs, lowered costs of production of existing drugs, or subsidised provision of drugs to developing countries – mortality rates could be reduced significantly. The second area of uncertainty concerns the migration of people engaged in agriculture to rural towns and other urban areas. Migration rates reflect, *inter alia*, relative poverty rates in urban and rural areas, and hence are affected by factors such as international commodity prices, urban employment growth, and real exchange rates.

---

[11] United Nations Population Division 2000.

THE INCIDENCE OF HUNGER AND POVERTY

Hunger is still prevalent in many developing countries, especially in South Asia and Africa. Although, as indicated in Figure 1.2, the number of undernourished people[12] actually increased in the above two developing regions[13], the overall total has fallen since the late 1960s – from 959 million in 1969-1971 to 790 million in 1995-1997. Since total population has grown substantially, this represents a halving of the actual proportion of undernourished people – from 37 to 18 percent.

Projections indicate a further fall in the incidence of undernourishment, to around 576 million people in 2015 and 400 million in 2030[14], but this decline could be accelerated if the requisite measures are taken to reduce hunger, as foreseen in the World Food Summit. The most dramatic fall in the incidence of undernourishment has occurred in East Asia. Estimates of the 2030 situation indicate that this trend will continue, with strong declines also taking place in South Asia and the Latin America and Caribbean regions.

Figure 1.2 Incidence of Undernourishment by Developing Region

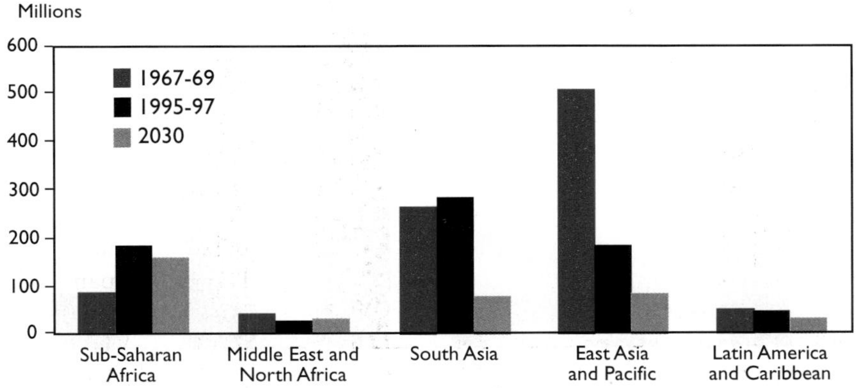

Source: FAO 2000a.

Hunger and poverty are closely related. While the lack of sufficient income to purchase food is clearly a major factor causing household food insecurity, hunger itself contributes to poverty by lowering labour productivity, reducing resistance to disease and depressing educational achievements.

---

[12] Undernourishment is defined as a situation in which an individual's food intake does not meet basic energy requirements.

[13] Regions correspond to those used in FAO (2000a) – see Annex 3 for country groupings. Data for Eastern Europe and Central Asia are not available.

[14] FAO 2000a.

It is estimated that, across the developing world, a total of 1.2 billion people live in poverty [15] – as defined by the international poverty line of average daily consumption equivalent to US$1 per day per capita National data from a large number of countries suggest that the incidence of poverty in urban areas is less than in rural areas [16]. Although the relative importance of rural poverty varies substantially from one country to another, in developing countries as a whole more than 70 percent of total poverty is found in rural areas. Similarly, hunger is also concentrated in rural areas despite the fact that they are the locus of food production.

Recent changes in the incidence and distribution of dollar poverty by developing region are shown in Figure 1.3. Poverty is concentrated in South Asia – where it has been increasing gradually during the 1990s – and Africa, where it has been growing at an alarming rate. Conversely, there has been a major decline in poverty in East Asia and Pacific, mainly as a result of economic growth in China.

Figure 1.3 Poverty Incidence by Developing Region

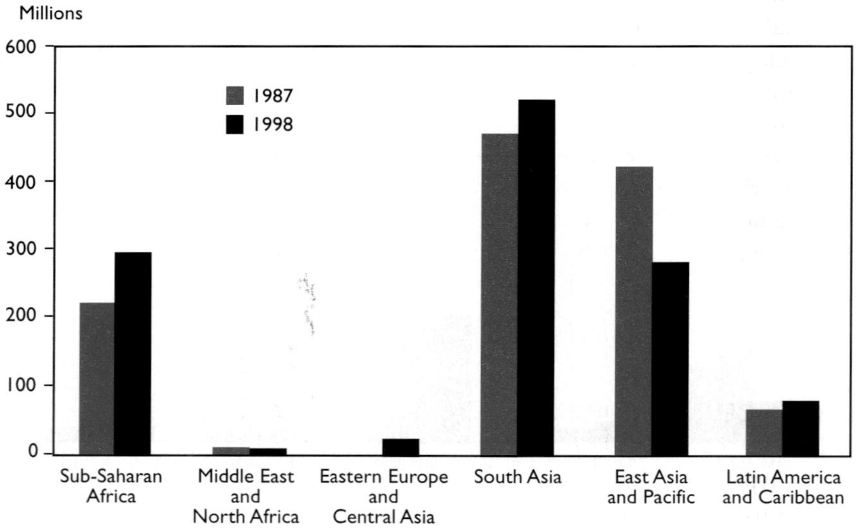

Source: World Bank 2001b.

THE CONTRIBUTION OF AGRICULTURAL GROWTH TO POVERTY ALLEVIATION

The evidence is quite clear that broad-based agricultural development provides an effective means for both reducing poverty and accelerating economic growth. This is normally achieved not only by increasing incomes for producers and farm

---

[15] World Bank 2001b.

[16] However, a number of ex-centrally planned countries (e.g. Mongolia, Georgia) display higher urban than rural poverty rates.

workers, but also by creating demand for non-tradable goods – namely services and local products. It is this indirect effect on demand, and the associated employment creation in the off-farm sector of rural areas and market towns, that appears to be the main contributing factor to the reduction of rural poverty. Furthermore, as other studies show[17], agricultural growth can reduce urban poverty more rapidly than does urban growth itself, largely because of the consequent reduction in urban food costs and lower rates of in-migration from rural areas. Mellor concludes that *... the evidence is overwhelming that it is essential to accelerate agricultural growth if poverty is to decline rapidly.*[18]

While overall agricultural growth is undoubtedly an effective engine for both economic development and poverty reduction, the form that this growth takes has a bearing on its effectiveness in reducing rural poverty. Thus, rising productivity within labour-intensive small farms, which generates extra demand for local goods and services, can be expected to have a broader effect on poverty reduction than equivalent productivity increases on large, mechanised holdings, which typically generate less additional demand for local goods and services.

The challenge for developing countries is to identify specific agricultural and rural development needs and opportunities, and to focus investment in areas where the greatest impact on food insecurity and poverty will be achieved. This identification and resource allocation process can be facilitated by analysing farming systems in order to develop an understanding of local factors and linkages. In the course of this analytical process it is also extremely helpful to be able to aggregate locations with similar development constraints and investment opportunities through the application of a farming systems framework.

FARMING SYSTEMS AND THEIR CHARACTERISTICS

THE CONCEPT OF FARMING SYSTEMS

Farmers typically view their farms, whether small subsistence units or large corporations, as systems in their own right. The following systems diagram (see Figure 1.4) of a typical farm system, drawn by Bangladeshi farmers, illustrates the structural complexity and interrelationships between various components of a smallholding. It also shows the variety of natural resources available to farm families. These resources normally include different types of land, various water sources and access to common property resources – including ponds, grazing areas and forest. To these basic natural resources may be added climate and biodiversity, as well as human, social and financial capital. The diagram also illustrates the diversity which characterises the livelihoods of most smallholders.

---

[17] For example, Datt and Ravallion 1998.
[18] Mellor 2000.

Each individual farm has its own specific characteristics arising from variations in resource endowments and family circumstances. The household, its resources, and the resource flows and interactions at this individual farm level are together referred to as a *farm system* [19]. The biophysical, socio-economic and human elements of a farm are interdependent, and thus farms can be analysed as systems from various points of view.

The resource endowment of any particular farm depends, *inter alia*, on population density, the distribution of resources among households and the effectiveness of institutions in determining access to resources. Regardless of their size, individual farm systems are organised to produce food and to meet other household goals through the management of available resources – whether owned,

Figure 1.4 Farmers' View of a Farm System, Bangladesh [20]

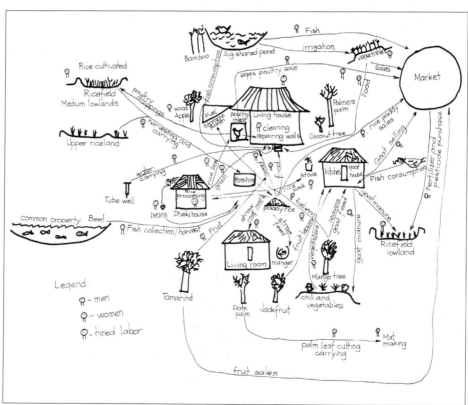

---

[19] In the literature a wide variety of definitions of farm system and farming system are found, which emphasise different aspects of a system. For example, systems components and systems interrelationships (see Dillon *et al* 1978 and Shaner *et al* 1982) and complementary biophysical and socio-economic processes (see Norman *et al* 1982).

[20] Lightfoot *et al* 1991.

rented or jointly managed – within the existing social, economic and institutional environment. They often consist of a range of interdependent gathering, production and post-harvest processes, so that besides cropping and livestock keeping[21], household livelihoods can encompass fishing, agro-forestry, as well as hunting and gathering activities. Off-farm incomes, which make a significant contribution to the livelihoods of many poor rural households, are also included. Farm systems are not found only in rural areas; significant levels of urban agriculture exist in many cities and towns in a wide range of developing countries.

The functioning of any individual farm system is strongly influenced by the external rural environment, including policies and institutions, markets and information linkages. Not only are farms closely linked to the off-farm economy through commodity and labour markets, but the rural and urban economies are also strongly interdependent. For example, as noted above, it is quite common for small farm households to derive a significant part of their income – often 40 percent or more – from off-farm activities. Farm women and men are also linked to rural communities and social networks, and this social capital influences the management of farms.

A *farming system*, by contrast, is defined as a population of individual farm systems that have broadly similar resource bases, enterprise patterns, household livelihoods and constraints, and for which similar development strategies and interventions would be appropriate[22]. Depending on the scale of the analysis, a farming system can encompass a few dozen or many millions of households.

Over the past 30 years, the original approach to analysing farming systems has evolved markedly, as illustrated in Table 1.2. Essentially, the scope of the analysis has gradually expanded, placing increasing emphasis on horizontal and vertical integration, on multiple sources of household livelihoods, and on the role of the community, the environment and support services[23]. The use of the Farming System Approach (FSA) as an analytical framework became common in the 1970s, and it has contributed to a paradigm change in rural development thinking.

From a predominantly top-down, reductionist view of agricultural development dominated by technical productivity considerations, there has been a marked shift to a more holistic perspective. This is based upon a broader goal of improved livelihoods and greater household food security, where household structure, gender, social networks, local institutions, information, policies and markets all play a role. Concurrently, analytical techniques have become more participatory, with an increasing stress on indigenous knowledge, and upon group planning, experimentation and monitoring. There is now also a greater insistence on the

---

[21] Households of refugees and agricultural workers, who lack land or livestock, are generally not considered to be farm households.

[22] See also footnote 19 on diversity of definitions of farming systems.

[23] Collinson (2000) provides a comprehensive history of Farming Systems Research.

prime responsibility for change and initiative residing within the farming community, and with this shift in emphasis, the underlying importance of human resource capacity has become more widely recognised. The current FSA approach, with its focus on the farm household as the centre of a network of resource allocation decisions, has much in common with the Sustainable Livelihoods Approach (SLA)[24].

Table 1.2 Evolution of the Farming Systems Approach

Characteristics	1970s	1980s	1990s	2000s
System Level:				
Farm				
Household				
Groups/Community				
District/Zones/Catchments or Sector				
Livelihood Focus:				
Crops				
Crop-Livestock				
Multiple Household Livelihoods				
Functional Focus:				
Research				
Research & Extension				
Research, Extension & Support Services				
Multi-sectoral, incl. Infrastructure				
Stakeholder Focus:				
Public				
Public & Civil Society				
Public, Civil Society & Private				
Other Foci:				
Gender				
Household Food Security				
Productivity & Resource Management				

Source: Adapted from Dixon and Anandajayasekeram (2000).
Note: Darker squares indicate greater focus on the element in that period.

[24] While both approaches are farmer-centred approaches, which recognise diverse livelihoods, Sustainable Livelihoods (see Ellis [2000] for a comprehensive overview) places greater emphasis on vulnerability.

MAJOR CATEGORIES OF FARMING SYSTEM

As stated earlier, the delineation of the major farming systems provides a useful framework within which appropriate agricultural development strategies and interventions can be determined. The decision to adopt very broad farming systems inevitably results in a considerable degree of heterogeneity within any single system. However, the alternative of identifying numerous, discrete, micro-level farming systems in each developing country – which could result in hundreds or even thousands of systems worldwide – would complicate the interpretation of appropriate regional and global strategic responses and detract from the overall impact of the analysis. Only the major farming systems have, therefore, been identified and then mapped in order to estimate the magnitudes of their populations and resource bases. Each of these broad systems is characterised by a typical farm type or household livelihood pattern[25], although significant sub-types are described where appropriate.

The classification of the farming systems of developing regions, as specified in this book, has been based on the following criteria:

- available natural resource base, including water, land, grazing areas and forest; climate, of which altitude is one important determinant; landscape, including slope; farm size, tenure and organization; and

- dominant pattern of farm activities and household livelihoods, including field crops, livestock, trees, aquaculture, hunting and gathering, processing and off-farm activities; and taking into account the main technologies used, which determine the intensity of production and integration of crops, livestock and other activities.

Based on these criteria, the following eight broad categories of farming system have been distinguished:

- Irrigated farming systems, embracing a broad range of food and cash crop production;

- Wetland rice based farming systems, dependent upon monsoon rains supplemented by irrigation;

- Rainfed farming systems in humid areas of high resource potential, characterised by a crop activity (notably root crops, cereals, industrial tree crops – both small scale and plantation – and commercial horticulture) or mixed crop-livestock systems;

- Rainfed farming systems in steep and highland areas, which are often mixed crop-livestock systems;

- Rainfed farming systems in dry or cold low potential areas, with mixed crop-livestock and pastoral systems merging into sparse and often dispersed systems with very low current productivity or potential because of extreme aridity or cold;

---

[25] Farm type in the case of commercial or large-scale agriculture.

- Dualistic (mixed large commercial and small holder) farming systems, across a variety of ecologies and with diverse production patterns;
- Coastal artisanal fishing, often mixed farming systems; and
- Urban based farming systems, typically focused on horticultural and livestock production.

The above criteria and broad grouping of farming systems were applied to the six main regions of the developing world in a pragmatic fashion, with a view to drawing conclusions with regard to poverty reduction and agricultural growth. This exercise resulted in the identification of 72 farming systems with an average agricultural population of about 40 million inhabitants, although individual systems range from less than one million to several hundred million agricultural inhabitants. Sometimes, sufficient differences exist within a farming system to justify reference to distinct sub-types; for example, small-scale farms and plantations or commercial farms, or low altitude and high altitude areas. The names chosen for the farming systems reflect the eight main types outlined above. Nevertheless, the name of each system is expressed in the singular form, emphasising commonality within the system for purposes of this analysis[26].

The names also reflect key distinguishing attributes, notably: (i) water resource availability, e.g. irrigated, rainfed, moist, dry; (ii) climate, e.g. tropical, temperate, cold; (iii) landscape relief/altitude, e.g. highland, lowland; (iv) farm size, e.g. large scale; (v) production intensity, e.g. intensive, extensive, sparse; (vi) dominant livelihood source, e.g. root crop, maize, tree crop, artisanal fishing, pastoral; (vii) dual crop livelihoods, e.g. cereal-root, rice-wheat (note that crop-livestock integration is denoted by the term mixed); and (viii) location, e.g. forest based, coastal, urban based.

The spatial mapping of farming systems presented in this study represents a compromise between the usefulness of showing farming system areas in a graphical manner and the dangers of implying sharp boundaries between neighbouring systems. With a large degree of variation inevitable among individual farm households within any one system, there are seldom sharp boundaries between systems. In most cases transitions occur as one farming system gradually merges into another. In some cases, systems may be separated by narrow zones with quite distinct characteristics (e.g. on lower slopes of mountain areas), the identification of which would not be useful in a study of this nature and on this global scale.

Irrigation constitutes a special case in relation to the heterogeneity of farming systems. Where irrigation-based production is the dominant agricultural characteristic within an area, as in the case of large-scale irrigation schemes, the entire zone has been classified as an irrigation-based farming system. However, significant amounts of irrigation appear as small yet important areas of otherwise

---

[26] In this respect, previous authors have followed different conventions. Ruthenberg (1971) refers to families of farming systems across the world, e.g. shifting cultivation systems. Fresco (1986) provides farming system names in the singular.

rainfed farming systems, and the implications of this situation are reflected in the analysis of constraints and opportunities. Because irrigated agriculture is so different from rainfed – not only in farming system characteristics, but also in terms of priorities and strategic approaches – substantial localised concentrations of irrigation within predominantly rainfed systems have been identified through cross hatching on the farming system maps.

Of the 72 identified farming systems, from three to five systems were identified within each region for in-depth analysis. The main variables influencing the selection were: (i) potential for poverty reduction; (ii) potential for agricultural growth; and (iii) demographic and economic importance within the region. The selection includes some farming systems with few opportunities for a rapid advance in one or both of the above variables, but a majority exhibit a potential for achieving growth and/or reducing poverty levels. Rapid and sustained agricultural growth in a major farming system – even one not currently associated with high levels of poverty – could be expected to have a significant impact on aggregate poverty through migration and market linkages. Nevertheless, the emphasis in this analysis is placed, in so far as feasible, on the prospects for the *in situ* reduction of poverty levels. Factors determining a system's apparent growth potential include: (i) suitable resource endowments, including underlying agro-climatic and soil conditions, a relatively high ratio of land and other resources (water, forest) to human population, and a currently low intensity of exploitation; (ii) favourable access to infrastructure and services, including markets; and (iii) the identification of broader development constraints whose removal is considered to be feasible.

DEVELOPMENT OF FARMING SYSTEMS AND REDUCTION OF HUNGER AND POVERTY

In broad terms, there are five main farm household strategies to improve livelihoods. These can be summarised as:

- intensification of existing production patterns;
- diversification of production and processing;
- expanded farm or herd size;
- increased off-farm income, both agricultural and non-agricultural; and
- a complete exit from the agricultural sector within a particular farming system.

These strategic options are not mutually exclusive, even at the individual household level; any particular household will often pursue a mixed set of strategies.

The first of these two strategies – intensification and diversification – form important components of the FAO Special Programme for Food Security[27].

[27] FAO 1999c.

13

Intensification is defined in this book as increased physical or financial productivity of existing patterns of production; including food and cash crops, livestock and other productive activities. Although intensification is frequently associated with increased yields as a result of greater use of external inputs, it may also arise from improved varieties and breeds, utilisation of unused resources, improved labour productivity, and better farm management – for example improved irrigation practices or better pest control.

Diversification is defined as an adjustment to the farm enterprise pattern in order to increase farm income, or to reduce income variability. It exploits new market opportunities or existing market niches. Diversification may take the form of completely new enterprises, or may simply involve the expansion of existing, high value, enterprises. The addition or expansion of enterprises refers not only to production, but also to on-farm processing and other farm-based, income generating activity.

Some households escape poverty by expanding farm size – in this context size refers to managed rather than to owned resources. Beneficiaries of land reform are the most obvious examples of this source of poverty reduction. Increased farm size may also arise through incursion into previously non-agricultural areas, such as forest – often termed expansion of the agricultural frontier. Although this option is not available within many systems, it is of relevance particularly in parts of Latin America and Sub-Saharan Africa. Increasingly, however, such 'new' lands are marginal for agricultural purposes, and may not offer sustainable pathways to poverty reduction.

Off-farm income represents an important source of livelihood for many poor farmers. Seasonal migration has been one traditional household strategy for escaping poverty and remittances are often invested in land or livestock purchases. In locations where there is a vigorous off-farm economy, many poor households augment their incomes with part-time or full-time off-farm employment. Where opportunities for improved livelihoods are perceived, a proportion of farm households will abandon their land altogether, and move into other farming systems, or into off-farm occupations in rural or urban locations. This means of escaping agricultural poverty is referred to in the following Chapters as *exit from agriculture*.

The above five household strategies for reducing hunger and poverty will be referred to frequently in the following Chapters, in which the relative importance of the different sources is assessed. The assessment for each farming system is based on the judgement of groups of experts knowledgeable about each particular region. Table 1.3 illustrates this type of assessment for two farming systems in Sub-Saharan Africa.

The data indicate that in the irrigated farming system intensification is extremely important in terms of potential for reducing poverty, whereas exit from agriculture has relatively little attraction as a poverty reduction pathway. Conversely, in the pastoral farming system the greatest potential lies in households leaving the system

Table 1.3 Relative Importance of Different Household Strategies[28]

Source of Hunger and Poverty Reduction	Intensification	Diversification	Increased Farm Size	Increased off-farm Income	Exit from Agriculture
Irrigated Farming System	3.5	2	2.5	1.5	0.5
Pastoral Farming System	1	1	1	2	5

Source: Table 2.4.
Note: Scores add to 10 for each farming system.

altogether – the so-called exit strategy. In this particular farming system, the poverty reduction potential of intensification, diversification and increasing farm size, is considered to be low.

ASPECTS OF THE EVOLUTION OF FARMING SYSTEMS

The Farming System Approach considers both biophysical dimensions (such as soil nutrients and water balances) and socio-economic aspects (such as gender, food security and profitability) at the level of the farm – where most agricultural production and consumption decisions are taken. The power of the approach lies in its ability to integrate multi-disciplinary analyses of production and its relationship to the key biophysical and socio-economic determinants of a farming system.

In order to present the analysis of farming systems and their future development within a framework that is broadly comparable between systems and across different regions, the above key biophysical and socio-economic determinants have been grouped together into five categories:

- natural resources and climate;
- science and technology;
- trade liberalisation and market development;
- policies, institutions and public goods; and
- information and human capital.

In the opinion of a range of experts[29], these categories represent the major areas in which farming system characteristics, performance and evolution are likely to be significantly affected over the next thirty years.

---

[28] It should be noted that safety nets are excluded from this assessment, being viewed as transitory relief measures which are not generally intended to lift households out of poverty.

[29] The experts were mostly staff and consultants of FAO.

Figure 1.5 represents schematically the interrelationship of these key determinants of farm systems and, by extension, farming systems. Some of these factors are internal to, or part of, the farming system, whereas others are external. The principal exogenous (external) factors which influence the development of farming systems – policies, institutions, public goods, markets, and information – are indicated on the left side of the Figure, lying outside the dotted line that marks the system boundary. The availability of markets and the prices on offer influence farmers' decisions on enterprise pattern, on purchases of inputs and on the timing of produce sales. The availability of economic and social infrastructure in rural areas determines the transport costs and the availability of services to the household – notably human and animal health. Similarly, information and educational services affect household strategies and decisions. Technologies, which determine the

Figure 1.5 Schematic Representation of Farming Systems

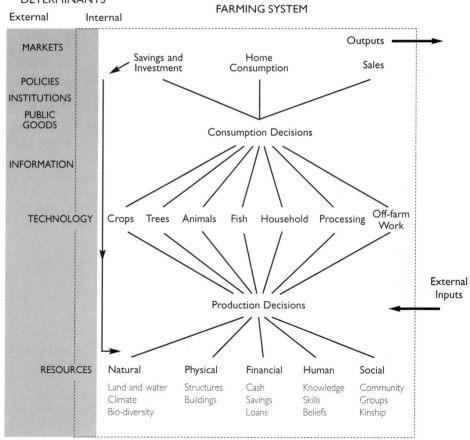

nature of production and processing, and natural resources, are largely endogenous (internal) factors and are therefore depicted as lying mainly within the boundary of the farming system. In general terms, the biophysical factors tend to define the set of *possible* farming systems, whilst the socio-economic factors determine the *actual* farming system which can be observed at a given time.

Often, the evolution of a farming system follows a predictable direction. For example, a system originally dependent solely on the use of hand hoes may face constraints as market-driven diversification occurs. This could lead to the increasing use of cattle for draught power, replacing some manual operations and, if land is available, an expansion of the cultivated area. Later, the intensification of crop production may be driven by population expansion and land shortages. Market-driven evolution sometimes leads to specialisation in production and often involves greater use of external inputs. Further stages may include partial mechanisation of crop production and substantial market integration. Ultimately, a high degree of production intensity is likely – perhaps with an export orientation – and is usually characterised by intensive use of purchased inputs, land aggregation and a high degree of mechanisation. In certain circumstances intensive mixed systems may develop. In all cases, enabling infrastructure and the availability of technical and market information will be important influences on system evolution.

The five key categories of determinants influencing farming system evolution – already listed above – are described in the following sections.

NATURAL RESOURCES AND CLIMATE

The interaction of natural resources, climate and population determines the physical basis for farming systems. During the early stages of development, increased population generally leads to an expansion in cultivated area and, in many cases, conflict between the different users of land and water resources. Once most good quality land is already exploited, further population increases tend to lead to the intensification of farming systems. As forests and woodlands come under greater pressure, biodiversity is threatened and there may be growing tension between development and conservation goals. These trends have often been exacerbated by colonial and

Box 1.1 Population Pressure on Annual and Permanent Cropland by Region – 1995-1997 (pers/ha)		
Region	Agric.	Total
Sub-Saharan Africa	2.2	3.6
Middle East and North Africa	3.1	4.5
East Europe and Central Asia	0.3	1.6
South Asia	3.5	6.3
East Asia and Pacific	4.9	7.9
Latin America and Caribbean	0.7	3.2
Average	2.3	4.5
Source: FAO 2000a.		

post-colonial forces that have concentrated indigenous or minority peoples on poorer quality land – thus aggravating the degradation problem.

Over the past four decades the amount of land under cultivation, including permanent crops, has increased by more than one quarter – to just over one billion ha. However, the rapid growth of population in recent years has meant that the area of cultivated land per capita in developing countries has declined by almost half since the 1960s.

Since the 1960s, pasture and grazing land has expanded by a total of 15 percent in developing regions, to around 2.2 billion ha in 1994. Much of this expansion was achieved at the expense of forest and woodland, which declined to about 2.3 billion ha over the same period. Annual growth rates in cultivated area vary considerably between the regions, as shown in Box 1.2. By far the highest growth rates were experienced in Latin America and Caribbean – 1.26 percent

Box 1.2 Average Annual Expansion in Cultivated Area 1961-1997	
Region	% p.a.
Sub-Saharan Africa	0.73
Middle East and North Africa	0.42
South Asia	0.18
East Asia	0.91
Latin America and Caribbean	1.26
Average	0.67
Source: FAO 2000a.	

per annum as compared with only 0.18 percent per annum in South Asia. It is worth noting that, during this period, average cropping intensity rose in total by only five percent; suggesting that growth in output has resulted mainly from yield increases and area expansion rather than from higher cropping intensity.

It is estimated that an additional 1.8 billion ha of land of 'acceptable' quality remains available for future agricultural use, but this seemingly favourable scenario is seriously constrained by a number of factors. Much of the land categorised as suitable for agriculture is only suited to a narrow range of crops (e.g. olive trees in North Africa). Secondly, more than 90 percent of available land is in Latin America and Sub-Saharan Africa, which means that further expansion is simply not an option for most of North Africa, Eastern Europe, Asia and Middle East. Even in those areas where potential for expansion does appear to exist, over 70 percent of available land is estimated to suffer from one or more soil or terrain constraints. As a result of these factors, the projected expansion[30] in cultivated area in developing regions to 2030 is only half the historic rate – adding about 120 million ha to the current total[31]. Strikingly, however, by the year 2030, and despite the addition of well over two billion people to the population of developing countries, the average amount of cultivated land available for each person engaged in agriculture may actually increase[32] due to the stabilisation of agricultural populations.

[30] FAO 2000a. Of course, the actual rate of expansion will depend upon the nature of the evolution of these farming systems.
[31] FAO 2000a.
[32] Changes in per capita cultivated land availability will vary widely from one region to another. Almost all additional cultivated land is expected to derive from expansion of agricultural frontiers in Africa and Latin America, while cultivated land area may actually decline in areas such as Middle East.

Despite the typically high cost of developing irrigation systems, irrigated land use has risen at three times the rate of overall expansion of farmland; total irrigated area in developing countries has doubled since 1961 – to 197 million ha. This supports the contention that many areas of the developing world have already faced constraints to further expansion for several decades, if not longer. However, intensification through irrigation has its limits. At present, it consumes about 70 percent of the total volume of fresh water used by humans, but this proportion is likely to decline during the coming 30 years as urban and industrial use grows. Despite the fact that only seven percent of total renewable water resources in developing countries are currently exploited, these competing demands, together with the fact that much of the available water is not located in areas of agricultural need, is expected to reduce current rates of irrigation growth.

The expansion of agriculture, plus changes in production technologies, has resulted in a decrease in agro-biodiversity in recent decades. In addition to the well publicized disappearance of indigenous flora and fauna, there has been a considerable reduction in the number of varieties cultivated, which has affected in particular the main cereal crops: wheat, maize and rice. A similar loss of biodiversity has occurred among domestic animals. However, modern plant breeding may go some way to reversing this trend by making it easier to maintain genetic material, and by creating a wider gene pool of modern varieties.

Agriculture currently contributes about 30 percent of the global anthropogenic emission of greenhouse gases. Growth in the production of these gases by crops is expected to slow down in future, but methane production by livestock could increase substantially. Accumulated evidence[33] now strongly suggests that impacts from global climate change will be significant. Average global surface temperatures are expected to rise by an estimated 1.4 to 5.8°C in the next 100 years, while the frequency of climatic extremes (temperatures, precipitation and winds) is expected to increase dramatically. Models based on the Intergovernmental Panel on Climate Change (IPCC) scenario of a one percent increase in greenhouse gases annually, predict that within 80 years extremes currently experienced only once a century will become normal. Higher temperatures will inevitably lead to a rise in sea levels – estimated at between 0.1 and 0.9 metres over this century.

There is little doubt that both agriculture and food security will be affected by climate change. Not only will crop yields change, but huge investments in infrastructure could also be required. Among the impacts predicted by the IPCC Working Group is a reduction in potential crop yields in most tropical and sub-tropical regions and, if temperature increases are towards the higher end of the predicted range, also in mid-latitudes[34]. Another recent study has estimated that crop yields could decline by one-fifth in many developing countries[35]. Water

[33] Intergovernmental Panel on Climate Change 2001.
[34] It should be stressed, however, that these are declines in potential yields. In many farming systems, other factors may be more limiting than the impact of global warming.
[35] Fischer et al 2001.

availability – particularly in the sub-tropics – is expected to diminish; although some areas such as South East Asia, may have to cope with greater volumes of water as a result of more intense monsoon activity. A widespread increase in the risk of flooding is anticipated, as a result of rises in sea level and increased severity of precipitation from storms, hurricanes and monsoons. Labour availability may be affected by the expected increase in the transmission of diseases; both vector borne (e.g. malaria), and water borne (e.g. cholera). Overall, the increased variability of climate, and thus agricultural productivity, substantially increases the risk faced by farmers, with concomitant reduction in investment and input use.

SCIENCE AND TECHNOLOGY

Investments in agricultural science and technology have expanded rapidly during the last four decades. During this period, major technical and institutional reforms occurred, which shaped the pattern of technology development and dissemination. In the early 1970s, the Consultative Group on International Agricultural Research (CGIAR) was established and National Agricultural Research Systems (NARS) were greatly strengthened. During the 1980s and 1990s partnerships among CGIAR centres and NARS were established, including the eco-regional consortia. During the past decade, however, many NARS have been under budget pressure as macro-economic reforms were implemented.

Box 1.3 Average Cereal Yield (1961-1997) in Developing Countries (t/ha)

	1961-63	1995-97
Wheat	0.9	2.5
Rice (paddy)	1.8	3.5
Maize	1.2	2.6
All cereals	1.2	2.5

Source: FAO 2000a.

The historical focus of research by CGIAR and NARS centres on food crop production technologies, with its emphasis on improved yielding varieties, has undeniably been successful. Nearly three-quarters (71 percent) of production growth since 1961 have been due to yield increases. Increased yields have contributed to greater food security within developing regions and have contributed to declining real prices for food grains. It is significant that FAO projections to 2030[36] indicate a continuing rise in average cereal yields in developing countries, under both rainfed and irrigated conditions.

However, many poor smallholder farmers in marginal areas have not benefited from these cereal yield increases, and investments in technology development for non-cereal crops have usually received a low priority. Although the private sector and large farmers' organisations have invested heavily in research for commercially important cash crops – examples include coffee, tea, sugar cane and

[36] FAO 2000a.

bananas – many tropical staples and minor cash crops have received relatively little attention. Similarly, investment in livestock research has generally not been commensurate with the contribution of the sub-sector to household income or Gross Agricultural Domestic Product (GADP). Only one CGIAR research centre – the International Livestock Research Institute (ILRI) – concentrates on livestock, although other centres have animal production programmes. In contrast, agricultural research in industrialised countries has been relatively well funded with some of the work being led by the private sector. Consequently, a much greater range of new technologies is available for production systems and crops of interest to developed countries than for smallholder production systems in developing countries.

Overall, research has been focused principally upon intensifying crop and livestock production, usually by means of purchased inputs. There has been far less research on integrated technologies for diversifying the livelihoods of small farmers in developing countries and increasing the sustainability of land use. Little is understood, for instance, about the role of organic matter in soils, the development of reduced tillage systems, the use of on-farm organic resources in combination with inorganic fertilisers and the role of legumes in biological nitrogen fixation. Similarly, there has been limited research in Integrated Pest Management (IPM) and in weed and pest control. These are topics of little interest to the private sector, but also ones which are in danger of neglect by public research institutions.

Despite these weaknesses, the global research agenda is gradually moving from a focus on individual crop performance to a growing acceptance of the importance of increased system productivity. This is viewed largely in terms of better-managed interactions among diversified farm enterprises, sustainable resource management, and improved targeting of technologies towards women farmers and poorer households. Perhaps even more importantly in the long term, institutional modalities are now shifting. From a public sector focus, largely led by the international system, more emphasis is now being given to public-private partnerships driven mainly by the demands of clients. These changes are being accompanied by a growing understanding of farmers' problems and opportunities and a greater willingness to blend indigenous knowledge and modern information.

Growing investments in biotechnology are likely to increase agricultural research productivity and have the potential to revolutionise production practices through the generation of customised crop varieties. Whilst there has been a gradual decrease in national and international public funding available for agricultural research and extension systems, private sector biotechnology research has attracted ample support, although not generally for tropical food crops. Most of this research is likely to focus on profit-generating inputs, export crops and agro-processing.

TRADE LIBERALISATION AND MARKET DEVELOPMENT

Of the broad and all-encompassing processes included under the term *globalisation*, the emphasis in this document is placed on economic reform and trade liberalisation. By the end of the 1970s, the economies of many developing countries had become highly distorted as a result of excessive government intervention and control. Most were in serious economic difficulties, with high inflation, unmanageable balance of payments and fiscal deficits, high external debt ratios and Gross Domestic Product (GDP) growth rates that were negative or failing to match the rate of population increase. To address these problems, the International Monetary Fund (IMF), and subsequently the World Bank and other international institutions and bilateral donors, initiated lending programmes under which balance of payments support was provided to a range of developing countries conditional upon the adoption of programmes of structural reform. These Structural Adjustment Programmes (SAPs) have resulted in liberalised trade and exchange rate regimes and radically reduced subsidies in many developing countries. Structural adjustment, however, has not eliminated the urban bias in policies.

Many SAPs have embodied reforms specific to the agricultural sector. These include measures to: (i) end marketing monopolies; (ii) reduce parastatal involvement in the supply of inputs, marketing and processing; (iii) reduce or remove subsidies, price controls and impediments to private sector activities; (iv) remove restraints on foreign trade; and (v) promote the private sector. Small-scale activities, requiring limited management, technical knowledge and with limited capital requirements, have been rapidly adopted. The most notable is grain milling. In many countries, the marketing of grains has been the first major agricultural service to be privatised, due to the prior existence of parallel markets and because grain marketing boards have imposed major financial burdens on governments.

More recently, international agreements and the establishment of the World Trade Organization (WTO) have further boosted trade liberalisation. Markets have a critical role to play in agricultural development, as they form the linkages between farm, rural and urban economies upon which the development processes outlined by Mellor (see above) depend. As a result of the reduction of impediments to international trade and investment, the process of trade liberalisation is already generating changes in the structure of production at all levels – including smallholder-farming systems in many developing countries. Not only is market development accelerating, but patterns of production and natural resource usage are also changing profoundly in response to market forces. The speed of change engendered by this transition has, however, also had important negative effects. Poverty increased, at least temporarily, in many farming systems during the 1980s and early 1990s, as a result of reductions in government support and declining prices for major smallholder products.

In the longer run as barriers to trade between countries diminish, and if subsidies to producers in industrialised countries are removed, developing country products that are competitive in world markets will benefit, replacing those that have hitherto relied on protection. Broad social, economic and cultural trends will also contribute to a profound reshaping of market demand, as increased urbanisation, rising incomes, improved communications and the diffusion of cultural preferences exert their effect. The availability of new production, post-harvest and transport technologies will also change demand patterns, by making possible the delivery of new products – or established products in new forms – to markets where they have been previously unattainable.

POLICIES, INSTITUTIONS AND PUBLIC GOODS

The development of dynamic farming systems requires a conducive policy environment. Moreover, the establishment of the farm-rural-urban linkages described by Mellor[37] requires effective demand. The greatest change in this environment during the past 30 years has been structural adjustment, the widespread introduction of which marked another step in a key policy trend that can be discerned over the last few decades; the decline of national food self-sufficiency as a dominant element in the shaping of policies for rural areas. In the 1960s, the perceived need to ensure national food security was paramount for many governments and was used to justify direct intervention in agricultural marketing, storage, import licensing, input subsidies and other areas. Although national food self-sufficiency is no longer an overriding policy aim, food security remains a key policy issue for developing countries and indeed for the whole world. This was emphasised in the FAO-sponsored World Food Summit of 1996 and the follow-up development activities.

As structural adjustment programmes have progressed, policy makers have increasingly shifted their attention to the potential to increase the efficiency of service delivery through the restructuring of institutions. This has led to several results with enormous long-term impact: the shift of many traditionally public sector roles to civil society and the private sector; the decentralisation of remaining government services; and an increasing reduction of government investment in the provision of public services.

The first two trends fit well within the growing tendency, at a broader social level, to encourage more local participation in decision making and resource allocation. The third is largely an outcome of the shedding of many previous governmental responsibilities to the private sector. These tendencies will probably continue to gain importance during the next one or two decades. However, while such trends offer significant benefits in terms of mobilisation of non-governmental resources and a better alignment of public activities to local needs, they have also created constraints. There has been a generally slow or erratic supply response

---

[37] Mellor 2000.

from the private sector, which in many countries has experienced difficulties in effectively replacing public services in finance, research, extension, education, health and even in infrastructure development and maintenance – particularly in rural areas where poverty is widespread. Smaller farmers and female-headed households have suffered disproportionately. The missing element has been the creation of the new public services required to create a supportive environment for the growth of private sector activities and to ensure equity and environmental sustainability.

Despite this critical omission, the strengthening of local institutions – including decentralisation and democratisation at local levels – is noticeable in many countries. In recent years, the role of women in local governance has been strengthened in some countries, although long-term outcomes are not yet clear. These trends have exposed rifts between central and local authorities in setting development priorities and budgetary allocations, as well as in developing oversight mechanisms. Other policy shifts have had a dramatic effect on production incentives in some farming systems. For example, the introduction of the individual household incentive policies boosted food and agricultural production almost overnight in Vietnam – which was transformed from a food deficit country to a food exporter. Similarly, the introduction of the individual household responsibility system in China stimulated a dramatic production response and signalled a major change in production structures.

A further policy area that is growing in importance is that of access to, and control of, natural resources – particularly land and water. As populations continue to grow and marginal lands suffer increasing levels of degradation, the demands of poorer, minority and indigenous populations for more equitable access to resources will continue to intensify. Although accelerating rates of urbanisation will relieve some of the pressure, governments that are unable to develop and implement effective policies on land ownership, water management and taxation reform, will face the risk of serious social conflict.

INFORMATION AND HUMAN CAPITAL

The evolution of farming systems based upon increasing specialisation (e.g. large-scale broiler units) or integrated intensification (e.g. rice-fish-ducks) has required extra knowledge on the part of farm operators. The need for better information and enhanced human capital has also increased, as production systems have become more integrated with regional, national and international market systems. Many farmers in developed countries now have a much better understanding of the nature of the demand that they are responding to – in terms of its implications for varieties, timing, packaging and permitted chemicals. As a result, they have progressively modified their production practices and their portfolio of products in response to changing patterns of demand. This knowledge-based approach has not yet been adopted widely in developing countries, beyond a relatively small group of educated commercial producers. However, the experiences of some small producers have shown that this approach is possible, even among producers facing severe poverty. Depending on the speed and form of evolution of farming systems, knowledge-based adjustments are likely to intensify during the coming 30 years.

Lack of education, information and training is frequently a key limiting factor to smallholder development. Many observers anticipate an information revolution that will provide large volumes of technological, market and institutional information to these farmers. However, it is unlikely that much of this information will reach most producers in low income countries in the near future; although commercial operations could benefit. Inevitably, issues of equitable access and dissemination will arise as marginalized populations are bypassed.

One of the major achievements in many developing countries during the past three decades has been the extension of literacy training and primary education to the majority of the rural population. Given the high returns to primary education that have been repeatedly demonstrated, it is considered likely that rural education will expand considerably in those countries where gender discrimination is minimal, civil conflict is absent and economic stability can be maintained. This development may leave the next generation better equipped to participate in knowledge-based agriculture and to utilise the expanding information base.

In parallel with the extension of primary education, tertiary education has expanded in most developing countries. Thus, governments, private sector and civil society, in many countries, now have a steady supply of agricultural graduates who can provide technical services to farmers. However, many observers are convinced that the agricultural education system should be overhauled and the quality and relevance of such training radically improved.

Armed conflict, migration of men in search of paid employment and rising mortality rates attributed to HIV/AIDS, have led to a rise in the number of female-headed households and placed a considerable burden on women's capacity to produce, provide and prepare food. Despite their increasingly prominent role in agriculture, they remain severely disadvantaged in terms of their access to commercial activities. A FAO survey showed that female farmers receive only seven percent of all agricultural extension services world-wide and that only 11 percent of extension agents are women[38]. Throughout the developing world women are denied the full legal status necessary to give them access to loans. This lack of access to rural financial services hampers women's efforts to improve their farm activities. Improvements in these areas can be expected in the coming decades, as women become better organised to assert their rights.

[38] FAO 1990b.

Whilst in the past many development efforts failed women – because planners had a poor understanding of the role women play in farming and household food security – greater efforts are being made to take account of their actual situation. A gradual improvement is also expected to result from improved primary education, as a higher proportion of women farmers being able to communicate directly in the same language as extension advisors, bankers or agribusiness managers. Notwithstanding the increased sensitivity to gender roles, however, there is still a widespread failure to reach women with effective services.

It is increasingly recognised and acknowledged by development workers that the empowerment of women is the key to raising levels of child and family nutrition, improving the production and distribution of food and agricultural products, and enhancing the living conditions of rural populations. It has been concluded that if women in Africa received the same amount of education as men, farm yields would rise by between seven and 22 percent[39]. Similarly, better access to credit, land and extension services would enable women to make an even greater contribution to eliminating rural hunger and poverty. As gender bias is progressively eliminated during the coming 30 years – often in the face of severe cultural and religious barriers – productivity within many farming systems will be transformed.

READER'S GUIDE

This document provides an outline of future challenges, opportunities and proposed agricultural development strategies for the developing world. The relevance of farming systems analysis has been discussed in this Chapter, and particular attention paid to describing the key trends that are expected to influence farming system evolution over the next thirty years. Drawing on FAO projections[40], and utilising a range of databases, the book delineates and analyses the main farming systems of the six major developing regions of the world in Chapters 2 to 7. As a single region may contain as many as 16 identified farming systems, from three to five systems have been selected for detailed analysis in each region. Detailed discussion of the selected key systems is divided into three sections: (i) characteristics; (ii) trends and issues; and (iii) priorities. The regional analyses each conclude with a discussion of overall strategic priorities for the region. Commonalities, challenges and crosscutting priorities emerging from these analyses are presented in Chapter 8. Conclusions and ways forward are presented in Chapter 9.

[39] FAO 1990b.
[40] FAO 2000a.

2

SUB-SAHARAN

AFRICA

...

REGIONAL SETTING

CHARACTERISTICS OF THE REGION

Sub-Saharan Africa[1] contains a total population of 626 million people of whom 384 million (i.e. 61 percent) are classified as agricultural. The region is relatively well endowed with natural resources. Total land area is 2 455 million ha, of which 173 million ha are under annual cultivation or permanent crops[2] – about one quarter of the potentially arable area. In the region as a whole, the arid and semiarid agro-ecological zones[3] encompass 43 percent of the land area; the dry subhumid zone is equivalent to 13 percent and the moist subhumid and humid zones jointly account for 38 percent. In West Africa, 70 percent of the total population live in the moist subhumid and humid zones, whereas in East and Southern Africa only about half the population lives in these areas.

Despite the abundance of natural resources, the average Gross Domestic Product (GDP) per capita in constant prices was lower at the end of the 1990s than in 1970[4]. Nineteen of the 25 poorest countries[5] in the world are found in Sub-Saharan Africa and income inequality is high. Approximately 16 percent of the region's population lives in countries that have an average GDP per capita of less than US$200; 36 percent live in countries with an average GDP per capita of less than US$300 and as many as 75 percent live in countries with an average GDP per capita below US$400. In the region as a whole, an estimated 43 percent of the total population fall below either the international dollar poverty line or below nationally defined poverty lines. In East and Southern Africa, it is estimated that rural poverty

---

[1] See Annex 3 for a list of countries.

[2] FAOSTAT.

[3] See Annex 5 for an explanation of agro-ecological zones.

[4] World Bank 2000b.

[5] Among those countries ranked by the World Bank (2000a) (excludes small island countries and those with incomplete data).

accounts for as much as 90 percent of total poverty. Although remote areas with marginal agricultural resources are poorer than other places, they have a low population density and hence account for a relatively low proportion of total poor people.

Agriculture accounts for 20 percent[6] of the region's GDP, employs 67 percent of the total labour force and is the main source of livelihood for poor people. Although the share of agricultural GDP is declining in more than one third of regional countries, in a further one quarter it is actually increasing[7]. In most cases, a declining share of GDP is the result of rapid growth in non-agricultural sectors, whereas increases in the contribution of agriculture to national GDP stem from either growth of agricultural value added or, more commonly, from declines in non-agricultural sector output.

Although Sub-Saharan Africa accounts for barely one percent of global GDP and only two percent of world trade (down from nearly four percent in 1970), international trade contributes a relatively large share of regional GDP. Agriculture is the dominant export sector for East Africa (47 percent of total exports), and a significant source of exports in other areas of the region (14 percent of exports in Southern Africa and 10 percent in West Africa)[8]. The region's main agricultural export commodities are cocoa, coffee and cotton. In the region as a whole agricultural exports make up 16 percent of total exports, while agricultural imports – mainly cereals – account for around 11 to 15 percent of total imports. During the past three decades, the region has suffered massive losses from the erosion of its share of world trade, aggravated by substantially worsening terms of trade.

In the next sub-section of this Chapter, the major regional farming systems are briefly described. After a discussion of region-wide trends influencing the evolution of these systems, the principal systems are described. The final section summarises the strategic priorities for the region.

MAJOR FARMING SYSTEMS IN SUB-SAHARAN AFRICA

For the purpose of this analysis, 15 broad farming systems have been identified (see Map)[9]. The main characteristics of the major farming systems, including the land area and agricultural population as a proportion of regional totals, principal livelihoods and the prevalence of poverty, are shown in Table 2.1. The Urban Based

---

[6] Calculated on the basis of totals published in World Bank (2000f), for countries with data available.

[7] The sharpest declines were reported in Eritrea, Angola, Uganda, Ghana, Côte d'Ivoire, Mozambique, Mauritania and Lesotho and the greatest increases in the Congo Republic, Cameroon, Rwanda, Togo, Niger, Benin, Namibia, Central African Republic, Zimbabwe and Mali.

[8] In West Africa, agriculture's contribution to export earnings has declined over the past three decades due to expansion of the petroleum industry. In Southern Africa it declined due to expansion of non-agricultural sectors.

[9] See Chapter 1 for an explanation of the approach to delineation of farming systems.

Major Farming Systems
SUB-SAHARAN AFRICA

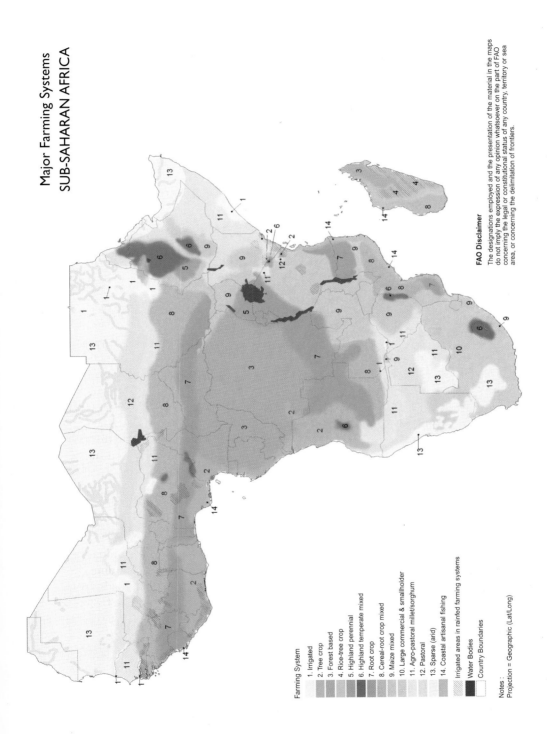

Farming System

1. Irrigated
2. Tree crop
3. Forest based
4. Rice-tree crop
5. Highland perennial
6. Highland temperate mixed
7. Root crop
8. Cereal-root crop mixed
9. Maize mixed
10. Large commercial & smallholder
11. Agro-pastoral millet/sorghum
12. Pastoral
13. Sparse (arid)
14. Coastal artisanal fishing

Irrigated areas in rainfed farming systems

Water Bodies

Country Boundaries

Notes :
Projection = Geographic (Lat/Long)

FAO Disclaimer

The designations employed and the presentation of the material in the maps do not imply the expression of any opinion whatsoever on the part of FAO concerning the legal or constitutional status of any country, territory or sea area, or concerning the delimitation of frontiers.

Farming System is not mapped. A brief description of each farming system appears in the following paragraphs, and five are analysed in greater depth in subsequent sections.

Irrigated Farming System

This farming system comprises large-scale irrigation schemes such as the Gezira Scheme in Sudan, extensive riverine and flood recession-based irrigation, West African *fadama* areas and the Wabi Shebelle in Somalia. It covers only 35 million ha (1.4 percent) of the land area in the region, but accounts for nearly 2 million ha (29 percent) of the irrigated surface[10] and supports an agricultural population of 7 million (nearly 2 percent of the regional total). The remainder of the irrigated area in the region occurs within other farming systems – notably the Large Commercial and Smallholder System in South Africa and Namibia, and the Rice-Tree Crop System in Madagascar.

The Irrigated Farming System is quite complex, especially in respect of institutional aspects. In many cases, irrigated cropping is supplemented by rainfed cropping or animal husbandry (the Gezira is one notable exception). Water control may be full or partial. Irrigated holdings vary in size from 22 ha per household in the Gezira scheme to less than 1 ha. Crop failure is generally not a problem, but livelihoods are vulnerable to water shortages, scheme breakdowns and deteriorating input/output price ratios. Many state-run schemes are currently in crisis, but if institutional problems can be solved, future agricultural growth potential is good. The incidence of poverty is lower than in other farming systems and absolute numbers of poor are small.

Tree Crop Farming System

This farming system runs from Côte d'Ivoire to Ghana, and from Nigeria and Cameroon to Gabon, with smaller pockets in Congo and Angola, largely in the humid zone. The system occupies 73 million ha (three percent) of the region's land area, but accounts for 10 million ha (6 percent) of total cultivated area and supports an agricultural population of nearly 25 million (7 percent of the regional total).

The backbone of the system is the production of industrial tree crops; notably cocoa, coffee, oil palm and rubber. Food crops are inter-planted between tree crops and are grown mainly for subsistence; few cattle are raised. There are also commercial tree crop estates (particularly for oil palm and rubber) in these areas, providing services to smallholder tree crop farmers through nucleus estate and outgrower schemes. Since neither tree crop nor food crop failure is common, price fluctuations for industrial crops constitute the main source of vulnerability. Socio-economic differentiation is considerable. The incidence of poverty is limited to moderate, and tends to be concentrated among very small farmers and agricultural workers, but growth potential is moderately high.

---

[10] Area of irrigation generally refers, herein, to area equipped for irrigation, which exceeds the operated area in some cases.

Table 2.1 Major Farming Systems of Sub-Saharan Africa

Farming Systems	Land Area (% of region)	Agric. Popn. (% of region)	Principal Livelihoods	Prevalence of Poverty
Irrigated	1	2	Rice, cotton, vegetables, rainfed crops, cattle, poultry	Limited
Tree Crop	3	6	Cocoa, coffee, oil palm, rubber, yams, maize, off-farm work	Limited-moderate
Forest Based	11	7	Cassava, maize, beans, cocoyams	Extensive
Rice-Tree Crop	1	2	Rice, banana, coffee, maize, cassava, legumes, livestock, off-farm work	Moderate
Highland Perennial	1	8	Banana, plantain, enset, coffee, cassava, sweet potato, beans, cereals, livestock, poultry, off-farm work	Extensive
Highland Temperate Mixed	2	7	Wheat barley, tef, peas, lentils, broadbeans, rape, potatoes, sheep, goats, livestock, poultry, off-farm work	Moderate-extensive
Root Crop	11	11	Yams, cassava, legumes, off-farm work	Limited-moderate
Cereal-Root Crop Mixed	13	15	Maize, sorghum, millet, cassava, yams, legumes, cattle	Limited
Maize Mixed	10	15	Maize, tobacco, cotton, cattle, goats, poultry, off-farm work	Moderate
Large Commercial and Smallholder	5	4	Maize, pulses, sunflower, cattle, sheep, goats, remittances	Moderate
Agro-Pastoral Millet/Sorghum	8	8	Sorghum, pearl millet, pulses. sesame, cattle, sheep, goats, poultry, off-farm work	Extensive
Pastoral	14	7	Cattle, camels, sheep, goats, remittances	Extensive
Sparse (Arid)	17	1	Irrigated maize, vegetables, date palms, cattle, off-farm work	Extensive
Coastal Artisanal Fishing	2	3	Marine fish, coconuts, cashew, banana, yams, fruit, goats, poultry, off-farm work	Moderate
Urban Based	little	3	Fruit, vegetables, dairy, cattle, goats, poultry, off-farm work	Moderate

Source: FAO data and expert knowledge.
Note: Prevalence of poverty refers to number in poverty, not depth of poverty, and is a relative assessment for this region.

Forest Based Farming System

This farming system occupies 263 million ha (11 percent) of the total land in the region, accounts for six million ha (4 percent) of cultivation and supports an agricultural population of 28 million (7 percent of the region). It is found in the humid forest zone of the Congo Democratic Republic, the Congo Republic, Southeast Cameroon, Equatorial Guinea, Gabon, Southern Tanzania and the northern tips of Zambia, Mozambique and Angola.

Farmers practice shifting cultivation; clearing a new field from the forest every year, cropping it for 2 to 5 years (first cereals or groundnuts, then cassava) and then abandoning it to bush fallow for 7 to 20 years. With increasing population density, however, the fallow periods are progressively being reduced. Cassava is the main staple, complemented by maize, sorghum, beans and cocoyams. Cattle and small ruminant populations are low, as is human population density. Physical isolation plus lack of roads and markets pose serious problems. Forest products and wild game are the main source of cash, which is in very short supply because few households have cash crops and market outlets are distant. Poverty is extensive, and in places very severe. Agricultural growth potential is moderate, thanks to the existence of large uncultivated areas and high rainfall, but yield increases in the near future are expected to be modest. Development requires careful management of environmental risks, including soil fragility and loss of wildlife habitats.

Rice-Tree Crop Farming System

This farming system is located in Madagascar – mostly in the moist subhumid and humid agro-ecological zones. It accounts for only 31 million ha of land area and 2.2 million ha of cropland (both one percent of the total in the region), yet it supports an agricultural population of seven million (two percent of the regional total). Though farm size is small, there is a significant amount of irrigation – equivalent to 10 percent of the region's total irrigated area. Banana and coffee cultivation is complemented by rice, maize, cassava and legumes. Cattle numbers are relatively low.

Poverty is of moderate prevalence. From a resource and climatic perspective the agricultural growth potential is high. However, actual agricultural growth and the poverty reduction potential are both considered fairly low in the short term, due to small farm size, shortage of appropriate technologies, and poor development of markets and off-farm activities.

Highland Perennial Farming System

This farming system, found in Ethiopia, Uganda, Rwanda and Burundi, covers 32 million ha (only 1 percent) of the land area of the region, mostly in the subhumid and humid agro-ecological zones, but accounts for 6 million ha (4 percent) of the cultivated area and has an agricultural population of 30 million (8 percent of the regional total). This system supports the highest rural population density (more than one person per ha of land) in the region. Land use is intense and holdings are very small (average cultivated area per household is just under one ha, but more than 50 percent of holdings are smaller than 0.5 ha). The farming system is based on perennial crops such as banana, plantain, *enset*[11] and coffee, complemented by cassava, sweet potato, beans and cereals. Eleven million cattle are kept, for milk, manure, bridewealth, savings and social security. The main trends are diminishing farm size, declining soil fertility, and increasing poverty and hunger. People cope by working the land more intensively, but returns to labour are low.

Poverty is high, both in terms of severity and absolute numbers. Despite favourable natural resources and climate, both the overall agricultural growth potential and the poverty reduction potential are considered fairly low, due to very small farm size, absence of under-utilised resources, shortage of appropriate technologies, poor infrastructure, and markets and few opportunities for off-farm activities.

Highland Temperate Mixed Farming System

This farming system occupies 44 million ha (only two percent) of the land area of the region and accounts for six million ha (4 percent) of cultivated area, but supports an agricultural population of 28 million (7 percent of the total in the region). Most of the system is located at altitudes between 1 800 and 3 000 metres in the highlands and mountains of Ethiopia. Smaller areas are found in Eritrea, Lesotho, Angola, Cameroon and Nigeria, generally in subhumid or humid agro-ecological zones. Average population density is high and average farm size is small (1 to 2 ha). Cattle are numerous (estimated population of 17 million) and are kept for ploughing, milk, manure, bridewealth, savings and emergency sale. Small grains such as wheat and barley are the main staples, complemented by peas, lentils, broad beans, rape, *tef* (in Ethiopia) and Irish potatoes. The main sources of cash are from the sale of sheep and goats, wool, local barley beer, Irish potatoes, pulses and oilseeds. Some households have access to soldiers' salaries (Ethiopia and Eritrea) or remittances (Lesotho), but these mountain areas offer few local opportunities for off-farm employment. Typically there is a single cropping season, although some parts of Ethiopia have a second, shorter season. There are major problems in the farming system: for instance, soil fertility is declining because of erosion and a shortage of biomass; and cereal production is suffering from a lack of inputs. There is, however, considerable potential for diversification into higher-value temperate crops.

Household vulnerability stems mainly from the risky climate: early and late frosts at high altitudes can severely reduce yields, and crop failures are not uncommon in cold and wet years. As with other food-crop based farming systems, a hungry season occurs from planting time until the main grain harvest. Poverty incidence is moderate to extensive – in comparison with other systems in Africa – except for the periodic droughts which afflict the Horn of Africa[12]. The potential for poverty reduction and for agricultural growth potential is only moderate.

[11] Ethiopian 'false banana'.

[12] Often, the impact of droughts on poverty is even greater in lowland agropastoral and pastoral areas.

Root Crop Farming System

This farming system is situated in, and extends from, Sierra Leone to Côte d'Ivoire, Ghana, Togo, Benin, Nigeria and Cameroon, typically in the moist subhumid and humid agro-ecological zones. The area is bounded by the Tree Crop and Forest Based Farming Systems on the southern, wetter side and by the Cereal-Root Crop Mixed Farming System on the northern, drier side. There is a similar strip in Central and Southern Africa, on the south side of the forest zone – in Angola, Zambia, Southern Tanzania and Northern Mozambique – and a small area in Southern Madagascar. The system accounts for 282 million ha (around 11 percent) of the land area of the region, 28 million ha (16 percent) of the cultivated area and 44 million (11 percent) of the agricultural population of the region. Rainfall is either bimodal or nearly continuous and risk of crop failure is low. The system contains around 17 million cattle.

The prevalence of poverty is limited to moderate. Agricultural growth potential and poverty reduction potential are moderate; technologies for this system are not yet fully developed. Nonetheless, market prospects for export of oil palm products are attractive, urban demand for root crops is growing, and linkages between agriculture and off-farm activities are relatively better than elsewhere.

Cereal-Root Crop Mixed Farming System

This farming system extends from Guinea through Northern Côte d'Ivoire to Ghana, Togo, Benin and the mid-belt states of Nigeria to Northern Cameroon; and there is a similar zone in Central and Southern Africa. It accounts for 312 million ha (13 percent) of the land area of the region – predominantly in the dry subhumid zone – 31 million ha (18 percent) of the cultivated area and supports an agricultural population of 59 million (15 percent of the region). Cattle are numerous – some 42 million head. Although the system shares a number of climatic characteristics with the Maize Mixed System, other characteristics set it apart, namely; lower altitude, higher temperatures, lower population density, abundant cultivated land, higher livestock numbers per household, and poorer transport and communications infrastructure. Although cereals such as maize, sorghum and millet are widespread, wherever animal traction is absent root crops such as yams and cassava are more important than cereals. Intercropping is common, and a wide range of crops is grown and marketed.

The main source of vulnerability is drought. Poverty incidence is limited, numbers of poor people are modest and the potential for poverty reduction is moderate. Agricultural growth prospects are excellent and, as described in the relevant section below, this system could become the bread basket of Africa and an important source of export earnings.

Maize Mixed Farming System

This farming system is the most important food production system in East and Southern Africa, extending across plateau and highland areas at altitudes of

800 to 1500 metres, from Kenya and Tanzania to Zambia, Malawi, Zimbabwe, South Africa, Swaziland and Lesotho[13]. It accounts for 246 million ha (10 percent) of the land area, 32 million ha (19 percent) of the cultivated area and an agricultural population of 60 million (15 percent of the regional total). Climate varies from dry subhumid to moist subhumid. The most typical areas have monomodal rainfall, but some areas experience bimodal rainfall.

Population density is moderately high and average farm sizes are rather modest – often less than two ha. The farming system also contains scattered irrigation schemes, but these are mostly small-scale and amount to only six percent of the irrigated area in the region. Where a bimodal rainfall pattern occurs farmers have two cropping seasons, but in drier areas they usually harvest only once a year from a given field. The main staple is maize and the main cash sources are migrant remittances, cattle, small ruminants, tobacco, coffee and cotton, plus the sale of food crops such as maize and pulses. About 36 million cattle are kept for ploughing, breeding, milk, farm manure, bridewealth, savings and emergency sale. In spite of scattered settlement patterns, community institutions and market linkages in the maize belt are relatively better developed than in other farming systems.

Socio-economic differentiation is considerable, due mainly to migration, and the whole system is currently in crisis as input use has fallen sharply due to the shortage of seed, fertiliser and agro-chemicals, plus the high price of fertiliser relative to the maize price. As a result, yields have fallen and soil fertility is declining, while smallholders are reverting to extensive production practices. The main sources of vulnerability are drought and market volatility. There is a moderate incidence of chronic poverty, linked to small farm size and absence of draught oxen and migrant remittances. Recently transitory poverty has sharply increased as a result of retrenchment of off-farm workers coupled with policy reforms affecting maize. In spite of the current crisis, long term agricultural growth prospects are relatively good and the potential for reduction of poverty is high.

Large Commercial and Smallholder Farming System

This farming system extends across the northern part of the Republic of South Africa and the southern part of Namibia, mostly in semiarid and dry subhumid zones, and accounts for 123 million ha (5 percent) of the land in the region, 12 million ha (7 percent) of the cultivated land and 17 million (4 percent) of the agricultural population. It comprises two distinct types of farms: scattered smallholder farming in the homelands and large-scale commercialised farming. Both types are largely mixed cereal-livestock systems, with maize dominating in the north and east, and sorghum and millet in the west. Both cattle (an estimated 11 million head) and small ruminants are raised in this system, but the level of crop-livestock integration is only modest.

---

[13] There is some similarity in ecology to the Cereal-Root Crop Mixed Farming System.

Although the overall prevalence of poverty is moderate, it is often severe among smallholder families who often survive by means of off-farm income from employment, principally in other sectors outside the area. Vulnerability is high, since a considerable part of the farming system has poor soils and is drought-prone. Chronic and extensive poverty exists among smallholder families. Agricultural growth prospects are moderate, and there is a low-medium potential for poverty reduction.

Agro-Pastoral Millet/Sorghum Farming System

This farming system occupies 198 million ha (8 percent) of the land of the region, generally in the semiarid zone of West Africa from Senegal to Niger, and in substantial areas of East and Southern Africa from Somalia and Ethiopia to South Africa. It has an agricultural population of 33 million (8 percent) and their density is modest, but pressure on the limited amount of cultivated land is very high. Crops and livestock are of similar importance. Nearly 22 million ha are used for crops – 12 percent of the cultivated land in the region. Rainfed sorghum and pearl millet are the main sources of food and are rarely marketed, whereas sesame and pulses are sometimes sold. Land preparation is by oxen or camel, while hoe cultivation is common along riverbanks. The system contains nearly 25 million head of cattle as well as sheep and goats. Livestock are kept for subsistence (milk and milk products), offspring, transportation (camels, donkeys), land preparation (oxen, camels), sale or exchange, savings, bridewealth and insurance against crop failure. The population generally lives permanently in villages, although part of their herds may continue to migrate seasonally in the care of herdboys.

The main source of vulnerability is drought, leading to crop failure, weak animals and the distress sale of assets. Poverty is extensive, and often severe. The potential for poverty reduction is only moderate. Agricultural growth potential is also modest and presents important challenges.

Pastoral Farming System

This system is located in the arid and semiarid zones extending from Mauritania to the northern parts of Mali, Niger, Chad, Sudan, Ethiopia, Eritrea, Kenya and Uganda. There are also pastoral areas in the arid zones of Namibia and in parts of Botswana and Southern Angola. The system occupies 346 million ha (14 percent) of the regional land area, but accounts for only 27 million (7 percent) of the agricultural population and 21 million cattle, as well as sheep, goats and camels. During the driest period of the year, Sahelian pastoralists move south to the Cereal-Root Crop Mixed System areas and they return north during the rainy season.

The main source of vulnerability is the great climatic variability and consequently high incidence of drought. Socio-economic differentiation is considerable – many herders have lost most of their animals due to droughts or stock theft. Poverty incidence is extensive, but the potential for poverty reduction is low. Agricultural growth potential is also modest.

Sparse (Arid) Farming System

Despite covering some 429 million ha (17 percent) of the land area of the region, this system is found mainly in six countries: Sudan, Niger, Chad, Mauritania, Botswana and Namibia. It is of limited significance from the point of view of agriculture, and has a human population of around six million – 1.5 percent of the regional agricultural population – and a cattle population of eight million. Because the *wadis* and their surrounding areas are considered part of the Pastoral System, grazing within the actual Sparse (Arid) System is limited. There are some scattered irrigation settlements in these arid areas (and thus about 0.7 million ha of cultivation), in most cases used by pastoralists to supplement their livelihoods. [14]

Poverty is extensive and often severe, especially after droughts. The potential for both agricultural growth and poverty reduction is low.

Coastal Artisanal Fishing Farming System

In East Africa, the system stretches southward from Kenya to Mozambique and includes coastal areas of Zanzibar, Comoros and Madagascar. In West Africa it stretches southward from the Gambia and the Casamance region of Senegal, along the coast of Guinea Bissau, Sierra Leone, Liberia, Côte d'Ivoire and Ghana, to Nigeria, Cameroon and Gabon. The system occupies almost 38 million (two percent) of the land and accounts for 13 million (three percent) of the agricultural population in the region; with a fairly high average population density. Households that depend on lake and river fishing are not included in this system.

The livelihood system is based on artisanal fishing supplemented by crop production, sometimes in multi-storied tree crop gardens with root crops under coconuts, fruit trees and cashews, plus some animal production. Cultivated area amounts to five million ha (three percent of the regional total). Some four percent of cultivated land is irrigated. Artisanal fishing includes sea fishing from boats, seine net fishing from beaches, setting of nets and traps along estuaries and in shallow lagoons, and catching of crustaceans in mangrove swamps. Poultry and goats are the main domestic animals. Cattle keeping is rare, due to, *inter alia*, tsetse infestation, and land preparation is by hand. Off-farm opportunities are connected with tourist resorts along the beaches and with large tree crop estates. In West Africa, because of the humid climate, there is more swamp rice and little or no cashewnut.

Although socio-economic differentiation is considerable, the current prevalence of poverty is only moderate. The potential for poverty reduction is considered low, and agricultural growth potential is only modest.

Urban Based Farming System

Within the estimated total urban population of over 200 million in the region, there is a significant number of farmers in cities and large towns. In some cities it is estimated that 10 percent or more of the population are engaged in urban

---

[14] The larger schemes are, however, considered under the Irrigated System.

agriculture [15]. Overall, it is estimated that there are around 11 million agricultural producers in urban areas. This farming system is very heterogeneous; ranging from small-scale but capital-intensive market-oriented commercial vegetable growing, dairy farming and livestock fattening, and part-time farming by the urban poor to cover part of their subsistence requirements. The level of crop-livestock integration is often low, and there are some environmental and food quality concerns associated with urban farming.

The potential for poverty reduction is low, mainly because the absolute number of poor is low. Agricultural growth is likely to take place spontaneously, in response to urban market demand for fresh produce, even in the absence of public sector support. Unless curbed by concerns over negative environmental effects, rapid adoption of improved technologies can be expected. Overall, this is a very dynamic farming system that has considerable growth potential.

REGION-WIDE TRENDS IN SUB-SAHARAN AFRICA [16]

Building on the discussion in Chapter 1 of the global trends influencing farming system evolution, this section provides an overview of common trends affecting most farming systems in the region. These are discussed under the headings of population, hunger and poverty; natural resources and climate; science and technology; trade liberalisation and market development; policies, institutions and public goods; and information and human capital.

Population, hunger and poverty

The population of Sub-Saharan Africa is projected to increase by 78 percent in the coming three decades. This is considerably faster than the projected growth rate for developing countries as a whole. During this 30 year period, the rural population is projected to increase by 30 percent, and the agricultural component is expected to expand by a slightly lower proportion, moderated by growing urbanisation. Urban population – currently 33 percent – is expected to rise to 50 percent of the overall total by 2030. Sub-Saharan Africa is unique in that rapid urbanisation has been occurring during a period of economic contraction.

HIV/AIDS has already depressed population growth rates in many East and Southern African countries [17] and is causing immense suffering; infection rates are already rising in West Africa. If HIV spreads faster than expected, East and Southern Africa could experience an extremely sharp contraction of the labour force in the prime working age group (although with the exception of South Africa

---

[15] Urban and peri-urban agriculture are often referred to collectively. Whilst urban agriculture refers to production inside city (including suburban) limits, there are many definitions of the outer boundary of peri-urban agriculture. In this book, farmers outside the boundaries of cities and towns are included in the corresponding farming system.

[16] Except where indicated, these data are drawn from FAO (2000a).

[17] See United Nations Population Division (2000) for an analysis of the demographic impact of AIDS.

net populations growth will continue), a corresponding rise in dependency ratios, and an increase in the number of AIDS orphans requiring assistance. Already, traditional social safety nets are unable to cope with the existing orphans. The cost to the economy – in loss of productive labour, medical costs and orphan support – is likely to be overwhelming. Up to the present time, the farming systems most affected have been the Highland Perennial and the Maize Mixed Systems, but the Large-scale Commercial and Smallholder System has also lost much of its skilled supervisory labour force. Because labour requirements for cassava are more evenly spread throughout the year than they are for cereals, farmers try to cope by expanding the area under cassava and reducing the area under cereals. In the Highland Perennial System, neglect of coffee and bananas is partly due to AIDS-related labour shortages. Moreover, HIV/AIDS is adversely affecting government staff and private agricultural service providers. Staff turnover is so high that much of the investment in human capacity building by agricultural projects, including overseas training, may have been wasted.

During the past 30 years the number of undernourished people in the region has increased substantially, to an estimated 180 million people in 1995-1997. During 1995-1997, the average daily Sub-Saharan African diet contained 2 188 kcal/person/day compared with 2 626 in developing countries as a whole. It is estimated that 33 percent of the regional population was undernourished at this time, with a higher incidence of undernourishment found in rural areas than among urban dwellers. During the period until 2030, the average energy intake is projected to increase by 18 percent to 2 580 kcal/person/day. In spite of the increased calorie supply, it is estimated that around 15 percent of the population (about 165 million people) will still be undernourished – an increase in the absolute number – unless deliberate measures are taken to ensure better access to food.

The region has a higher proportion of people living in dollar poverty than any other region of the world. Across the whole region, rural poverty still accounts for 90 percent of total poverty and approximately 80 percent of the poor still depend on agriculture or farm labour for their livelihood. Of even more concern, the total number of poor people is increasing.

Natural resources and climate

Currently, forest covers approximately 400 million ha (almost 17 percent of land area). The current annual deforestation rate is 0.7 percent and the decline in forest area is expected to continue. The farming systems that are most closely linked with deforestation are: the Forest Based System; the Tree Crop System; the Root Crop System; and the Cereal-Root Crop Mixed System. Currently, the Maize Mixed, the Highland Perennial and the Highland Temperate Mixed Systems are experiencing particularly acute fuelwood shortages.

Cultivated area has expanded from 123 million ha in 1961-1963 to 173 million ha (including annually cultivated land and permanent crops) in 1999. This represents a slow annual expansion of 0.73 percent mostly through conversion of forest and grasslands and shortening of fallows. During the period until 2030, cultivated land is projected to expand even more slowly, but the actual rate of expansion will depend upon the future evolution of farming systems.

The area affected by land degradation is increasing and the causes are complex. There are many aspects of land degradation; including soil erosion, soil compaction, reduced soil organic matter, declining soil fertility and soil biodiversity. Although land degradation is evident in a majority of farming systems, it is particularly notable in those such as the Highland Perennial and the Highland Temperate Systems where – in the absence of policy incentives for good land management – high population density places excessive pressure on land.

The region has a moderate level of renewable water resources, but only two percent of the available resources are currently utilised for irrigation compared with 20 percent in the overall group of developing countries. Only 6.5 million ha are currently irrigated and during the period until 2030, projections suggest a slower expansion than the 2.1 percent per annum achieved during the past four decades.

As global warming accelerates the most affected farming systems are likely to be those in the arid, semiarid and dry subhumid areas[18]. The increasing frequency and severity of droughts are likely to cause: crop failure; high and rising cereal prices; low and falling livestock prices; distress sale of animals; decapitalisation, impoverishment, hunger, and eventually famine. Households will probably try to cope with their cash and food shortage by cutting and selling firewood – thereby exacerbating land degradation and accelerating the onset of desertification – and by moving temporarily or permanently to more favoured areas. Conflicts between sedentary farmers and pastoralists will become more common as a result.

The Forest Based System, on the other hand, might benefit from reduction of excess moisture, but it is likely to face a population influx from neighbouring areas. The new settlers will cut and clear the forest to plant their crops – which might reduce beneficial effects of carbon sequestration by tropical forests. With increased population pressure, fallow periods would decline, making it progressively more difficult for farmers to maintain soil fertility and to control noxious weeds. Not only could yields fall, but biodiversity could also suffer.

Science and technology

Total annual and permanent cropped area was about 173 million ha in 1999 and it is expected to expand substantially in the years up to 2030. Total production of all crops in 1995-1997 was just over 250 million tons and, if current farming trends continue, is forecast to more than double by 2030. FAO projections suggest that this increase would be associated with an average rise in crop yields of 60 percent[19]. The greater importance of productivity growth in future decades is in contrast to the

[18] See Fischer et al (2001) for recent assessments of the impact on agriculture under various scenarios.
[19] FAO 2000a.

nature of production growth in the past 30 years, during which time maize area expanded 1.5 percent per annum while yield increased only 1.2 percent per annum (see Table 2.2). Major increases are expected to come from expanded production on heavy lowland soils, humid and moist subhumid tropics, and on irrigated land in several farming systems – although most production in Sub-Saharan Africa will continue to come from rainfed farming.

Inorganic fertiliser consumption is very low despite the declining soil fertility noted above. Total regional consumption is only 1.3 million tons of nutrient – equivalent to an average of only 8 kg/ha of nutrient within the region compared with 107 kg/ha in all developing countries. During the period until 2030, total fertiliser consumption in the region is only expected to increase slowly[20]. Even if fertiliser use expands rapidly in Africa, average application rates will continue to be far lower than in other regions. The use of compost or other soil amendments does not compensate for these very low levels of fertiliser use.

Currently, the region has 219 million head of cattle, 19 million goats and 189 million sheep (see Table 2.3). Tsetse infestation is a major factor influencing the distribution of livestock between different farming systems. The tsetse challenge tends to be concentrated in the moist subhumid and humid lowlands, and in drier areas near game reserves. In spite of this, increasing numbers of cattle are raised in

Table 2.2 Trends in Crop Area, Yield and Output in Sub-Saharan Africa, 1970-2000

Crop	Harvested Area 2000 (m ha)	Yield 2000 (t/ha)	Production 2000 (m tons)	Average Annual Change 1970-2000 (%)		
				Area	Yield	Production
Rice	7	1.6	11	2.4	0.6	2.9
Maize	26	1.5	38	1.5	1.2	2.7
Millet	20	0.7	14	1.4	0.4	1.8
Sorghum	21	0.8	18	1.2	0.5	1.6
Oilcrops	24	0.3	6	0.9	0.7	1.6
Roots & Tubers	18	8.4	154	1.7	1.0	2.8
Pulses	16	0.4	7	1.6	0.2	1.9
Vegetables	3	6.6	22	1.9	0.8	2.6
Fruits	8	6.2	47	1.6	0.0	1.6

Source: FAOSTAT.

[20] Reasons include subsidy removal in recent years, high and rising fertiliser prices as a consequence of currency devaluation, high transport costs, continued poor input/output price ratios and high risks if crop failure occurs, and the breakdown of credit for smallholder seasonal production loans.

Table 2.3 Trends in Livestock Populations and Output in Sub-Saharan Africa, 1970-2000

Species	Million Head 2000	Ave Annual Change 1970-2000 (%)
Cattle	219	1.5
Sheep	189	1.4
Goats	194	2.3
Pigs	19	3.2
Poultry	809	2.9
Product	Output 2000 (million tons)	Ave Annual Change (%)
Total Meat	8	2.0
Total Milk	19	1.8
Total Eggs	1	3.7
Cattle Hides	0.5	1.7

Source: FAOSTAT.

areas that were originally tsetse infested in the moist subhumid and dry subhumid zones, e.g. in the Root Crop and Cereal-Root Crop Mixed Systems. This trend is likely to continue. Nevertheless, cattle numbers per household tend to be higher in the dry farming systems than in the moist systems. From 1970 to the present time, regional cattle, goat and sheep numbers grew moderately, but poultry and pig populations have grown faster, at around three percent per annum. Between 2000 and 2030, livestock and poultry numbers production are projected to grow at a moderate rate, due to expansion of urban consumer demand for meat, milk and eggs.

Trade liberalisation and market development

Since 1961, although the absolute value of agricultural exports has risen, the region's share of world agricultural trade has fallen. In absolute terms, the sharpest fall has been in Southern Africa, whose share of world agricultural trade fell from nine percent in 1961 to three percent in 1998. In proportional terms, however, the other sub-regions of Africa have done little better. There has been much more stability in Africa's share of world agricultural imports, which forms a smaller proportion of world trade than do exports – ranging from 0.2 percent in Central Africa to one percent in West Africa.

In 1998, agriculture still accounted for 47 percent of total exports from East Africa, whereas in West and Central Africa agriculture's share of total exports have dropped from over 70 percent in 1961 to only 9 to 10 percent in 1998, partly as a consequence of the development of petroleum exports. Over the same period, in

Southern Africa, agricultural exports declined from 59 percent to 14 percent of total exports due to expansion of non-agricultural sectors. The region's principal agricultural exports are cocoa, coffee and cotton. Cocoa accounted for 22 percent of total agricultural exports in Central Africa and 48 percent in West Africa. For coffee, the share varied between 12 and 25 percent (in West Africa and East Africa respectively). For cotton, the range was between five percent in East Africa and 26 percent in Central Africa. In Southern Africa, by contrast, the major exports were sugar, wine and fruits – mainly from the Republic of South Africa.

Over the past three decades, there has been a broad stability in the proportion of agricultural products in total imports to the region. This now ranges from a high of around of 20 percent in Central Africa, to 15 percent in East Africa and West Africa and a low of 8 to 12 percent in Southern Africa. The main agricultural imports consist of cereals (wheat, rice and maize). Over the past 30 years, these have risen from five percent of total cereal consumption to 14 percent. If these trends continue, in 2030 the region would need to import an estimated one-sixth of its total cereal requirements.

Most cereal imports have been made on a commercial basis, rather than as food aid. Except in a few years, food aid has represented less than half of cereal imports and the proportion for 1995-1978 (17 percent) was lower than in 1975-1978 (25 percent). Nonetheless, in 1998 per capita food aid flows were three times as large as food aid flows to Asia and Latin America.

Policies, institutions and public goods

Structural adjustment programmes have been implemented in many countries in the region. Whilst these programmes have conferred macroeconomic stability on many economies, farmers have faced declining terms of trade and poorer access to many agricultural inputs such as improved seed and agro-chemicals, as well as lower and more uncertain grain prices.

These effects are particularly evident in the Maize Mixed Farming System where, over the years, considerable public sector investment has been directed towards input distribution. The Farmers Marketing Board (FMB) in Malawi, for example, established high quality grain buying and marketing depots at all main centres throughout the late 1950s and 1960s. As diversification opportunities were recognised, it renamed itself and became involved with a number of quasi-commercial activities, including the production and processing of non-traditional crops, plantation crops, canning and similar specialised activities.

The effects of structural adjustment on cash crop producers have been more mixed and largely reflect movements in international commodity prices. Cashew in Tanzania, for example, has experienced a boom-bust cycle, as production grew rapidly in the face of high international prices in the 1990s and then crashed spectacularly at the beginning of the next decade when prices slumped.

As part of the structural adjustment process, governments have focused on the core facilitation roles of Ministries of Agriculture (MOA). Despite the simultaneous emphasis on decentralization in many countries, local government structures have suffered progressively reduced budgets, resulting in cuts of staff and service delivery capacity. In most cases the private sector has not yet filled the vacuum, and it is not clear how long this will take[21]. To improve this situation, external support has been channelled through public and civil society channels for small business development, including village entrepreneurs.

Rural areas in many African countries have benefited from a slow but steady increase in public goods during the past 30 years. However, the transition to private sector involvement and cost recovery for services have been difficult in many countries. In general, the immediate effect of reduced public expenditure has been a crisis in the maintenance of infrastructure (e.g. roads and health facilities) and a reduction in essential services to rural populations – including schooling and health clinics – which will have a substantial negative effect on human capital.

Information and human capital

The reduction in government expenditure on extension and agricultural training in many countries, during the past decade, has reduced the access of farmers to technology and market information. It is expected that existing alternative sources of information will expand and new channels for agricultural information flows to rural areas will emerge, including the Internet. Already farmers' organisations in a number of countries have increased their extension and training activities; and internet connectivity is being supported. In addition, the private sector's role in technical and market information provision is expected to expand greatly during the coming three decades.

Selection of farming systems for analysis

On the basis of their potentials for poverty reduction and agricultural growth[22], as well as their importance in demographic terms, five farming systems have been selected for analysis of strategic priorities, namely the:

- Maize Mixed System;

- Tree Crop System;

- Irrigated System;

- Cereal-Root Crop Mixed System; and

- Agro-Pastoral Millet/Sorghum System.

---

[21] The hesitation of private sector to invest in agricultural input supply and produce marketing has been aggravated by mixed signals from governments: for instance, the provision of Starter Kits in Malawi and the discussion of the reintroduction of subsidised fertilizer distribution through co-operatives in Zambia.

[22] Systems selected either have high poverty with moderate growth potential or high growth potential in spite of limited poverty.

The greatest overall agricultural growth potential in the immediate future is found in the Irrigated and Cereal-Root Crop Systems. The trends, issues and priorities for each of these five systems are considered in turn below. The development of the first two systems would be expected to lead directly to both agricultural growth and poverty reduction. The development of the third and fourth would have a greater impact on agricultural growth, and only indirectly alleviate poverty. The fifth system offers the possibility of modest poverty reduction, although the growth dividend would be limited.

MAIZE MIXED FARMING SYSTEM

CHARACTERISTICS OF THE SYSTEM

This farming system serves as the food basket of the East and Southern Africa region (see Box 2.1 for basic data on the system). Both local and hybrid maize are grown and the former is often preferred for home consumption because of its better taste – in spite of lower yields. Minor crops include pulses and oilseeds which, like maize, are grown as dual-purpose subsistence

Box 2.1 Basic Data: Maize Mixed Farming System	
Total population (m)	95
Agricultural population (m)	60
Total area (m ha)	246
Agro-ecological zone	Dry subhumid
Cultivated area (m ha)	32
Irrigated area (m ha)	0.4
Cattle population (m)	36

and cash crops. Cash crops include coffee, tobacco, groundnuts and sunflower. Cattle are the most important livestock species. Crop-livestock integration is strong; oxen often prepare land[23], dung is collected and used to manure the fields, and animals are increasingly stall-fed on crop residues supplemented by cut fodder from fodder trees, hedges or forage plots. Although livestock density is higher than in any other production system in the region, most farmers cannot afford to keep more than two oxen and one milking cow, plus one or two calves or heifers.

Although the maize belt suffers during major droughts, drought is not the main cause of poverty. In areas with low population density, the majority of households are able to produce enough grain to feed themselves, but households with less than 0.5 ha have a food deficit. Crop failure can occur in severe drought years. Livelihood diversification is a hedge against bad weather and marketing risks. The main causes of poverty are; very small farm size or landlessness, lack of oxen, low off-farm income and deteriorating terms of trade for maize producers. A typical household in the Maize Mixed System is briefly described in Box 2.2.

---

[23] Some is also prepared by hand hoe.

Box 2.2 A Typical Household of the Maize Mixed Farming System

A typical middle stratum household would include a husband, wife and four of their own children plus an older relative and several orphans left by one of the husband's deceased brothers. They would live directly on their farmland in a dispersed homestead. It would have a cropped area of 1.6 ha of which one ha would be planted to maize and some sorghum, 0.1 ha to cassava, 0.1 ha to cotton and the rest to a wide range of other crops. The family would own 2 or 3 cattle and use its oxen to plough the land. It would obtain average yields of 1.2 t/ha for maize and around 900 kg/ha for sorghum, 800 kg/ha for millet and 500 kg/ha for pulses. Maize and other cereals would account for 80 percent of total food production, pulses for nine percent, cassava for eight percent and oilseeds for the rest. The household would be food self-sufficient in average to good years and in deficit during drought years. One son works outside the farm and sends occasional remittances, used to pay for school fees and clothes. Home-grown maize is the main source of subsistence and, cash is obtained either from off-farm activities or from the sale of agricultural products, such as maize, tobacco or coffee and milk. Income would formerly have been above the poverty line.

A poor household in the same community would have less than 0.5 ha of land and its main source of livelihood would be casual labour for other farmers and beer brewing by the wife. It would have no cattle but might own a goat and a couple of chickens. Women, often widows of migrant workers who died of AIDS and left them with children to support, would head many such households.

Differences in wealth are partly explained by differences in off-farm earnings and their re-investment in farming or commercial enterprises, not by differences in farm income. Nonetheless, the upper stratum of farm families has more and better farmland, more crossbred dairy cattle and larger areas of cash crops. Irrigation is more likely to be found on medium and larger farms. They also use more fertiliser, agro-chemicals and hybrid seed, as well as taking more credit. Poor households consist of landless or marginal farmers, often with no cattle (40 percent of households), no regular off-farm earnings and no high value crops. They grow mostly local maize for home consumption and cannot afford to buy fertiliser or hybrid seeds.

TRENDS AND ISSUES IN MAIZE MIXED SYSTEM

It was formerly assumed that smallholder maize production in East and Southern Africa could be boosted by a combination of high doses of inorganic fertilisers and hybrid varieties; and indeed much of the extension effort over the past two decades in Kenya, Zambia, Tanzania and Malawi focused on promoting these technologies. Once subsidies on inputs and guaranteed product prices were removed, and the full brunt of devaluation came to be felt, use of high-cost inputs on maize became uneconomic. As a consequence, farmers have reverted to cultivating traditional varieties where available, and even to growing substitute crops such as sorghum and sweet potatoes. In former maize-exporting areas such as the Southern Highlands of Tanzania and Central Province in Zambia, use of purchased seed and fertiliser has fallen sharply. Thus, smallholder maize growers are adopting more extensive husbandry techniques by reverting to low-input/low-output strategies and poverty appears to be increasing. However, in the future, the effectiveness of agricultural support systems – notably marketing – may be restored, at which stage a shift to intensification and diversification is likely.

The input/output price ratio for maize has steadily deteriorated as a result of trade and price liberalisation. Following the removal of input subsidies, dismantling of price supports, withdrawal of the state from grain purchasing and abolition of pan-territorial pricing, most smallholders have been struggling to adjust to rising input prices and declining maize prices. Smallholder input supply, credit and marketing services have collapsed and the private sector response has been less than anticipated. In keeping with policy reforms, governments were advised to withdraw from seed production and leave it to private seed companies. However, the private companies were only interested in hybrid maize; they were not interested in open pollinated varieties because farmers can save their seed for up to three seasons before renewing it. Hence smallholder access to farm inputs, credit, markets and good quality open-pollinated seed remains a problem.

As a result of rapid population growth, average farm sizes have fallen to under 0.5 ha in several areas. This size is not viable under these conditions, without supplementary off-farm earnings. In some Communal Areas in Zimbabwe, there is no longer sufficient grazing land to support enough cattle to plough the land or manure the fields. There are signs of serious fertility decline and increasing soil acidity in some instances where there has been prolonged use of inorganic fertilisers. Key issues include the high cost of mineral fertiliser relative to the price of maize – given existing productivity levels – the difficulty of maintaining soil fertility, shortage of livestock to produce manure due to feed shortage and shortage of oxen for farm power. One well-known response to this situation is the Starter Pack Programme in Malawi, which distributed subsidised seed and fertiliser very widely and has successfully increased national maize production. Whilst the fiscal sustainability of such a programme is questionable, the initiative has eliminated maize imports and even led to a surplus of production.

Top-down, message-based, technician-driven extension systems that were designed for promotion of single component 'quick fix' technical packages – such as hybrid maize with mineral fertiliser – are ill-suited for addressing the current problems of this farming system. Even in the past, messages based on high external input use were often irrelevant to smallholders because the inputs were too costly and overlooked risk under rainfed conditions. In practice, farmer and other civil society organisations are now organising farmer-based seed multiplication and dissemination of technical information, and are beginning to fill the void left by government extension services.

In the short term, the major input supply and produce marketing issues are unlikely to be resolved. In the absence of targeted policies and programmes, land degradation is likely to spread and exert further downward pressure on crop yields. Through these processes the incidence and severity of chronic poverty are likely to increase, leading to the risk of disastrous famines when rains fail. The declining trend in maize surpluses marketed by farmers will threaten national food security in bad seasons and could force governments to import food to feed the cities.

There are signs of entrepreneurs establishing themselves in rural areas. Access to transport, a line of credit and a market in the neighbouring communities and towns have encouraged the initiation of small-scale processing, for example, for threshing, oil extraction, milling, cleaning, bagging and similar activities. For example, the Rwembo Multipurpose Women's Association of Kasese in Western Uganda (comprising just 20 families) established a maize mill in 2000. Just one year later the mill has a throughput of 800 t per annum and the Association is seeking to extend into food processing.

PRIORITIES FOR MAIZE MIXED SYSTEM

Whilst the Maize Mixed System is currently in crisis, its long-term prospects are positive. In some parts, household strategies for escape from poverty focus on area expansion. In other more densely populated areas with better services, intensification and especially diversification out of maize into higher value cash crops and livestock, along with increasing off-farm income, are more important strategies for poverty reduction. Implementation of these strategies depends on private sector investment for the development of viable input and output marketing. Productive and profitable technologies and practices for improved soil fertility management – and more generally, improved land management and diversification – are essential. Although significant diversification to non-food crops and livestock is expected in the medium term, this system will still continue to be the food basket of the sub-region and to underpin urban food security.

To address farmers' problems related to declining soil fertility, one main strategic option is to improve land husbandry, by implementing such approaches as conservation farming (see Box 2.3). This lowers cultivation costs, saves time in land preparation, makes the best use of rainfall and creates optimum growing conditions through timely planting. It also maximises *in situ* moisture retention by maintaining "open" soil surface conditions and a deep rooting zone – possibly using biological means of breaking dense soil layers such as plough pans. At the same time, it raises soil fertility through: (i) judicious use of legumes for biological nitrogen fixation, especially for fallow enrichment and in rotation, or as intercrops with cereals; (ii) integration of livestock in the farming system, maximising use of manure, e.g. through stall feeding; (iii) composting any available plant material; and (iv) woodlot planting to reduce use of dung and crop residues for fuel. Application of purchased phosphate or lime may also have to be part of the fertility management strategy.

To address pest problems without recourse to costly and environmentally damaging pesticides, the main option is to apply IPM or the recently-demonstrated push-pull methods[24], with a special emphasis on weed (especially *striga*) control – for which rotations and phosphate application are important ingredients – combined with use of disease-resistant varieties and improved crop storage (e.g. to control the large grain borer).

In areas with low population density and where there are no restrictive tenure practices in place, labour rather than land becomes the key constraint. This

---

Box 2.3 Conservation Agriculture

Conservation Agriculture is a farming approach which has the main aim of making more efficient use of the soil, water and biological resources and natural processes through improved soil-water-plant nutrient management. The Better Land Husbandry approach is fully in line with, and encompasses, the principles of Conservation Agriculture. It stems from the narrower technology set of 'conservation tillage', which has been widened to incorporate other aspects of land management. Conservation Agriculture contributes to environmental conservation as well as to enhanced and sustained agricultural productivity.

The key principles of Conservation Agriculture are ensuring the recycling and restoration of soil nutrients and organic matter and optimal use of rainfall through retention and better use of biomass, moisture and nutrients. One key aspect is retaining, where possible, a permanent soil cover which implies zero or minimum tillage and often entails the use of green manure crops. In extreme arid and semiarid environments this may be reduced to maintaining below-ground root systems, as the above-ground biomass may be totally desiccated and lost. As a result of soil cover by vegetation and residues, soil erosion and water loss through runoff are eliminated or greatly reduced, crop production is more reliable and less vulnerable to climatic vagaries and higher yields can be obtained. Conservation Agriculture requires systematic interplanting and cropping sequences. Not only does it improve and especially stabilise yields in risky environments, it also reduces production costs, including costs of farm labour and farm power, due to reduction or elimination of tillage and, once established, of weeding requirements.

Conservation Agriculture is extensively practised in Brazil through its spontaneous adoption and adaptation to suit different farm contexts and farming systems. Problems of soil erosion – and, in drier areas, vulnerability to drought – have decreased significantly and farm output has increased leading to improved farmers' welfare and security. It is also being developed in Africa, for example in Cameroon, Côte d'Ivoire, Ghana, Tanzania, Uganda, Zambia and Zimbabwe. The African Conservation Tillage Network is contributing to its development and expansion in different environments.

---

[24] These technologies use a combination of attractants (to draw or pull pests away from the crop) and repellents (to repel or push pests away from the crop). Small holders in Kenya are adopting this push-pull technology for maize stalk borer, which builds on farmers' indigenous knowledge.

situation strengthens interest in such technologies as zero tillage with draft animal power and conservation farming to allow dry season land preparation when labour demand is slack. There is also scope for integration of soybean into the rotation, and for promoting farmer-based multiplication of seeds and planting materials.

Ultimately, sustainable land management and soil nutrient capitalisation depend upon secure and equitable access to resources, and especially land and water. Various models to promote secure access to land by poor farmers have been promoted in the region, often with disappointing results. Among the novel tenure models being tested, one community-based model that is dependent upon customary tenure and community control is thought to hold particular promise (see Box 2.4).

Box 2.4 Community Based Land Tenure Reform[25]

Problems related to land rights and tenure are common across Sub-Saharan Africa. In addition to expanding access to credit and limiting existing disputes, developing effective tenure systems can have a profound impact on the ability of communities to enter into productive partnership arrangements and to intensify production. A programme initiated in the mid-1990s in Mozambique has developed new policy and legal measures for smallholders, under which existing land rights are secured and new investment into rural areas is promoted. The 1997 Land Law defines the new concept of 'local community' through which land use rights are acquired by the vast majority of people according to customary 'norms and practices'. These rights are identical to those which would be obtained by private investors seeking land through a formal request to the State (still the owner of all land under the present Constitution).

The use of the farming systems approach has been critical in developing a new legal framework that protects *all* resources and not just areas physically occupied and presently under cultivation. The new framework also offers a legal mechanism to support farm communities in reaching mutually advantageous joint-venture arrangements with agri-business investors. Considering the open nature of rural social and farm systems, an 'open border' model has been adopted by Mozambique which allows investors to gain access to land inside the delimited borders of a community. This access is achieved through consultation with local people and agreements over land use, joint ventures, employment and other concrete resources that bring benefits to both the community and the investor.

Although the new policies and legislation are recently established, there are already clear indications that local communities are gaining a clearer understanding of both their land rights and the real value and potential of their resources. Farming systems are not only strengthened, but are permitted to adapt to provide new incomes and employment sources for local people. This relatively low-cost approach could provide a key input to investment support programmes throughout the African continent where similar land and farming systems problems are found.

---

[25] Tanner 2001.

For areas of high density, the emphasis shifts towards maximising returns to land, particularly through converting amply available labour into increased output. In such areas, it is important to increase the amount of land available for cultivation each year (e.g. through fallow enrichment using *Tephrosia*)[26]. It is also important, to the extent that markets allow, to encourage a shift out of maize and other low-value crops towards high-value crops such as beans, sunflower, tobacco, vegetables, perennials and flowers. Diversification could also involve development of low-lying areas for irrigated or rainfed vegetable production, introduction of improved sunflower varieties and manual oilseed presses, promotion of intensive dairying and small-scale pig and poultry production, as well as aquaculture for urban markets.

Low maize prices can also be addressed by the promotion of off-farm activities with strong linkages to agriculture. Farmers' problems of inadequate access to input supply, credit and marketing services can be minimised by promoting group activities such as bulk buying, rotational savings or joint marketing, as well as through promotion of sustainable rural micro-finance institutions capable of meeting farmers' seasonal credit needs. Problems of access to good quality open-pollinated seeds can be addressed by promoting farmer-based seed multiplication (see Box 2.5).

Box 2.5 Community-Based Seed Supply Systems[27]

The seed sector in Zambia faces problems common to other countries in Sub-Saharan Africa. Firstly, the Ministry of Agriculture Food and Fisheries (MAFF), which develops the majority of new crop varieties, does not have adequate resources to meet the costs of bulking and distributing seeds of such varieties. Secondly, the private sector is not keen to invest in the types of crops preferred by smallholders, as most retain seed from season to season, limiting future sales.

The main agricultural activity of CARE's Livingstone Food Security Project has been the introduction of drought tolerant varieties of a number of crops – including varieties of maize, sorghum and cowpea – through a community-based seed bulking and distribution scheme. Related crops and soils agronomy information, seed handling and post harvest storage topics have been included in the extension messages shared with farmers. In the pilot phase 330 farmers participated, virtually on an individual basis. For the 1995-1996 season, a group approach was introduced and over 6 800 farmers participated. A further expansion of the scheme in 1996-1997 increased the number of participating farmers to 9 600, and over 12 000 by 1997-1998 season. The project has therefore allowed access to good quality seed of new, early maturing varieties to a fairly large number of farmers in a relatively short time.

The scheme's rapid expansion has been aided by two factors: (i) the high priority farmers place upon drought tolerant crop varieties, and (ii) the strategy of bulking and distributing seed through community-based organisations.

---

[26] Complementary technologies include the systematic transfer of biomass from uncultivated land to cropped land, in order to increase nutrient availability.

[27] Mitti 2001.

The availability of information to small farmers will be a critical factor in diversification. The adoption of conservation farming and IPM will require educational rather than prescriptive approaches to extension. Each farmer must be given the means to judge which avenues for livelihood improvement best match his or her resource endowment. Thus, investment in farmer training, including the revitalisation of farmer training institutes and complementary village and field level education, is indicated.

TREE CROP FARMING SYSTEM

CHARACTERISTICS OF THE SYSTEM

The backbone of this farming system is tree crop production, notably cocoa, *robusta* coffee, oil palm and rubber. Food crops are often interplanted between tree crops. Roots and tubers (cassava, yam and cocoyam) are the main staples; tree crops and off-farm activities are the main source of cash. Livestock keeping is limited by tsetse infestation in many areas and so land

Box 2.6 Basic Data: Tree Crop Farming System	
Total population (m)	50
Agricultural population (m)	25
Total area (m ha)	73
Agro-ecological zone	Humid
Cultivated area (m ha)	10
Irrigated area (m ha)	0.1
Cattle population (m)	2

preparation is by hand. The main animal species are pigs and poultry. Fish farming is popular in some areas. Off-farm activities are relatively well developed. A typical farm household within this system is outlined in Box 2.7.

Industrial tree crops were originally established by indigenous farmers through a process of annual clearance. Each year a household would clear from the forest as much land as it could manage with family labour (e.g. 0.5 to 1 ha), plant coffee or cocoa, and grow food crops (a mix of cassava, cocoyam, cereals, pulses) between the immature plants. However, after a year or two, family labour would not be sufficient to manage both the newly cleared land and the care of the plots established during previous years. Farmers addressed the problem by contracting the care of their second and third year coffee gardens to immigrant farmers from the savannah zone in exchange for the right to interplant food crops among the trees. Once the tree canopy closed and certain types of food crops could no longer be successfully grown underneath them, the tree crops began bearing enough coffee to pay for hired labour.

The current practices of commercial outgrower schemes are often in sharp contrast to the indigenous system. Commercial schemes usually set a minimum plot size (e.g. 5 ha per grower) and farmers are expected to establish the entire area in a single year; this situation forces some farmers into debt. The lack of staggered

> **Box 2.7 A Typical Household of the Tree Crop Farming System**
>
> A typical tree crop farming household has five ha of land, all of which is under coffee in various stages of maturity. Food crops such as cassava, cocoyam and cereals are interplanted between the immature trees. It has a multi-storied homestead garden with fruit trees and vegetables. The wife owns about 20 scavenging chickens. The young sons each own a goat or two and the wife raises a couple of her own. The husband might have a shop or business. An occasional farmer has a fishpond. The household is generally food self-sufficient and earns a per capita income well above the poverty line.
>
> A typical poor migrant worker in this farming system has a wife and family back in the savannah, who still work for the man's father. The family feeds itself for 4 to 6 months a year from their own production and addresses its food and income deficit by migration. The income from tending tree crops and growing food between the immature trees is insufficient to boost the household income above the poverty line.

planting also increases vulnerability to pest and disease attacks. It is a major reason why many farmers linked to estate schemes meet with difficulties.

TRENDS AND ISSUES IN TREE CROP SYSTEM

The main trends affecting the Tree Crop System relate to: population pressure on natural resources, declining terms of trade and market share, dismantling of parastatal input supply and marketing services, and withdrawal of the public sector from industrial crop research and extension. The result has been increasing poverty and growing social conflict between tree crop owners and migrant workers – especially in Côte d'Ivoire.

Strong international competition has led to depressed producer prices and a declining market share for most industrial tree crops grown in the region. The consequent low profitability has resulted in neglect of some tree crops, as well as decreased demand for hired labour on commercial estates. In some cases, low farmgate prices are also due to high taxation of export crops and the low share of export price accruing to farmers. Use of mineral fertiliser and agro-chemicals is declining due to high prices, low profitability and lack of credit.

Smallholder services have broken down as a consequence of: failure of private sector to provide input supply, credit, extension and crop buying services previously provided by the parastatals; and, the divestment of state-owned agro-processing and its take-over by large-scale private investors. The private sector has been reluctant to advance inputs to outgrowers on credit and to deduct their cost from the marketed product. With the dismantling of parastatal commodity boards, tree crop extension was handed over to public extension services. The latter have, however, been severely downsized due to inability of governments to sustain their cost. Public extension services are currently attempting to transfer industrial crop extension to private commodity producer groups.

As a result of policy reform, public sector agricultural research institutes are withdrawing from research on export crops and leaving this to the private sector. However, private commodity research focuses only on export commodities. It does not consider other parts of the tree crop based farming and livelihood systems; hence the current failure to address farmers' problems, concerned with food crops and soil fertility.

PRIORITIES FOR TREE CROP SYSTEM

The Tree Crop System was once a key source of agricultural exports for a number of countries in West and Central Africa. Despite the problems referred to above, it is a high potential system and its growth prospects in the medium term are sound. The main household strategies for reduction of poverty are intensification (of both tree crops and associated crops) and increase in off-farm income. Both diversification – including processing and grading – and increased farm size, will also contribute to better incomes. The strategic focus for development lies in the improvement of support services, particularly those related to farm inputs and export marketing. To be effective, such improvements will need to be tailored to the particular needs of different groups of farmers.

Options for dealing with deteriorating terms of trade for traditional export commodities include: upgrading product quality for traditional export crops (crop rehabilitation, replanting with higher-yielding clonal planting material, better processing, grading and packaging); processing into semi-finished and finished products; a search for niche markets (e.g. biologically grown cocoa); diversification into non-traditional export crops to reduce vulnerability to world price fluctuations; and, in cases where prices are still administered by parastatals and export crops are heavily taxed, increasing producers' share of the export price.

The breakdown of input supply, credit and marketing services can be addressed by assisting smallholder tree crop growers to form commodity producer groups and by building their capacity to assume responsibility for input supply and marketing services. Another complementary strategy is to create self-sustaining, savings-based micro-finance institutions capable of meeting the needs of tree crop growers for seasonal production loans. Care should be taken to involve women in these micro-finance groups. However, because micro-finance institutions cannot afford to lend for long-term uses, long-term credit or one-time matching grants for tree crop establishment and replanting may also be needed.

In order to underpin intensification, agricultural research needs to be more focused on priority production problems of smallholders, and to involve producers in all stages of research. In order to reduce hunger, technology development should embrace food crops production, as well as tree crops – and involve women in the technology design, testing and dissemination. Technologies for sustainable tree-crop-soil management, building on agro-forestry principles, should be developed. Extension services can be made more relevant by strengthening smallholder producer associations to enable them to articulate priority problems and, if external support were available, to provide advisory services directly by contracting NGOs.

The need to boost support services – including marketing – underlines the importance of price, product quality and other market-related information. These services could be organised through forming partnerships between private sector and farmers' organisations; the main challenge is to ensure the relevance and financial viability of the information services that are created.

IRRIGATED FARMING SYSTEM

CHARACTERISTICS OF THE SYSTEM

For the purposes of this analysis, the Irrigated Farming System includes large-scale schemes covering nearly 2 million ha of equipped area which supports an agricultural population of almost 7 million (see Box 2.8). These include centrally managed, and mechanised schemes such as the Gezira scheme, and the larger farmer-managed schemes such as traditional

Box 2.8 Basic Data: Irrigated Farming System	
Total population (m)	14
Agricultural population (m)	7
Total area (m ha)	35
Agro-ecological zone	Various
Cultivated area (m ha)	3
Irrigated area (m ha)	2
Cattle population (m)	3

riverine and flood-recession based cropping that is found in small pockets along major rivers, and dugwell-based irrigation in West African fadamas (wetlands). Sahelian oases, which individually tend to cover limited areas, are included under the Sparse (Arid) Farming System. Similarly, small-scale irrigation schemes and water harvesting are considered under other farming systems. Projections indicate that, in the next 30 years, production from irrigated land in the region could increase substantially, with most of the increase coming from yield increases on existing irrigated land.

TRENDS AND ISSUES IN IRRIGATED SYSTEM

In Sub-Saharan Africa, public sector irrigation schemes have generally been expensive to construct and maintain and their performance has been disappointing. Not only have production increases been lower than anticipated, but systems have often been unsustainable, due to low output prices and high operation and maintenance costs. Examples include the Gezira scheme in the Sudan (see Box 2.9), the Office du Niger in Mali, the Awash Valley scheme in Ethiopia and the Jahaly/Pacharr scheme in the Gambia.

Increasingly, economic liberalisation has led governments to attempt to restructure parastatal schemes on a commercial basis, or to hand over management to farmers in an effort to lower operation and maintenance costs. This strategy has met with success only in the case of the Office du Niger. In the Jahaly/Pacharr scheme, farmer management was tried, but proved to be beyond local management capacity. The remaining options are to redesign it as a series of smaller, more manageable schemes, or to find a private company willing to operate it on a commercial basis.

Box 2.9 Challenges of the Gezira Scheme in Sudan

The combined Gezira/Managil scheme, located between the Blue and the White Nile, constitutes one of the largest irrigation complexes in the world under single management (around 900 000 ha), with around 100 000 tenant farmers. Three main crops have traditionally been grown – sorghum, cotton and groundnuts. Cultivation was totally organised by the irrigation authority and the main responsibilities of the tenant farmers were to maintain bunds and control water distribution within their fields, while managing all aspects of groundnut production. As the introduction of mechanical cotton harvesting was not successful, farmers were also responsible for organising manual picking, which involves hiring labour. Production has increasingly suffered from water shortages due to: poor maintenance, inadequate and late inputs and supplies, declining efficiency of farm machinery services, lack of information and technical guidance for farmers, insufficient financial resources and low farmgate prices.

In 1992, scheme operation was profoundly affected by economic liberalisation, withdrawal of the public sector from direct financing of agriculture, elimination of subsidies on crop production inputs and devolution of support services to the private sector. The prices of inputs to farmers rose sharply, especially for imported chemicals, but without a corresponding increase in product prices. Moreover, the scheme was expected to be self-supporting and to operate on a commercial basis. These policy changes have not succeeded, because farmers were ill-prepared, the Corporations were not oriented to operating as independent businesses, and the schemes were generally dilapidated and required significant rehabilitation of irrigation works. As a result, cropping areas and general level of operations have declined and some of the smaller schemes have been abandoned. Substantial financial deficits have developed and the deterioration of operations has accelerated. Shortage of water and lack of financial resources have led to poor incentives for production and reduced farm and scheme efficiency. Sound production practices are being neglected and irrigation water is being wasted. The Government has, in 1999, embarked on a rehabilitation programme – which includes mechanisms to involve farmers in land and water management – intended to reverse the declining trends and restore production.

Small-scale Farmer-Managed Irrigation (SSFMI) has been more successful and holds the promise of being sustained by farmers (see Box 2.10). However, although the region has the lowest proportion of its cropped area under irrigation in the developing world, construction of new irrigation schemes is often more expensive than elsewhere and therefore difficult to justify. For new irrigation to be economically viable, farmers have to be able to grow and market high-value crops such as vegetables, and this is only feasible in proximity to markets. Hence, much of the effort in recent decades has concentrated on rehabilitation of existing schemes. In latter years, more attention has been given to ensuring sustainability through the organisation of farmer water users' groups for operation and maintenance. However, rehabilitation of existing schemes is often beyond farmers' economic means and even if farmers can meet recurrent operating costs, rehabilitation still depends heavily on donor financing.

Box 2.10 Importance of Capacity Building in Farmer-Managed Schemes

The Thematic Evaluation of the IFAD Special Programme for Africa concluded that the main problem in farmer-managed irrigation within the region is not the technologies employed but the lack of adequate social organization and cohesion. Units dealing with farmer participation and Water User Associations (WUAs) were under-funded and this held back the pace of development. At the project design stage, insufficient resources were allocated to institutions responsible for support to WUA formation, mobilising community participation, training farmers in on-farm water management and involving them in scheme Organisation and Management (O&M) and rehabilitation. Demand-led approaches based on farmers' initiative are better than top-down efforts to stimulate farmer participation in schemes designed by engineers, and may not need such heavy 'social' support.

Experience with traditional farmer-constructed and farmer-managed systems has been quite positive. For instance, recent experience in Mali indicates that, when an enabling environment for smallholder development is in place, spontaneous development will occur through reinvestment of farmers' savings. It is reported that over 10 000 ha were developed spontaneously outside the Office du Niger on farmers' initiative – largely financed by the savings of migrant workers. Spontaneous growth of small-scale irrigation is also reported in Guinea-Bissau (in the balanta wetland rice system in the coastal plain) and in central Tanzania (e.g. Dodoma). During coming decades, it is expected that most irrigation development will take the form of SSFMI or individual initiatives. The expansion of the latter depends critically on market-driven diversification of smallholder farming systems.

PRIORITIES FOR IRRIGATED SYSTEM

The Irrigated Farming System is a high potential system, with ample scope for expansion in the region. Whilst the principal contribution of large-scale schemes is to national food security and agricultural growth, smaller schemes confer the added benefit of livelihood security and poverty reduction. The main household strategies to escape poverty in this system are intensification of existing patterns of production, diversification to higher value products and expanded farm size. An important consideration is to reduce risks of drought-induced crop failure by promoting, where feasible and environmentally compatible, extension of the irrigated or water harvesting area through low-cost techniques – such as flood recession and run of river – that build on indigenous technical knowledge. Where markets exist, the reduction of risk often encourages higher input use and intensification.

Assisting farmers to diversify into higher-value crops and to establish market linkages for inputs and outputs can address the low profitability of existing schemes. The improvement of product grading and packaging is also needed, as is support for small-scale agro-processing of perishable products. It will also be important to identify niche markets – for instance those for biologically grown produce.

Farmer-managed schemes and traditional irrigation should have priority because of their greater sustainability. Policies that give priority to small-scale farmer-built and managed schemes – especially for high-value horticulture crops – should be encouraged. Support to small-scale irrigation under Community-Driven Development (CDD) funds will also be important[28]. The promotion of farmer-based seed multiplication should also be accorded high priority in connection with both intensification and diversification efforts. Further priority areas include: promotion of self-sustaining, rural micro-finance systems to cater for farmers' demand for short-term credit for seasonal inputs, hired labour, small-scale processing and produce trading; improving water use and productivity on existing schemes by building the capacity of water user groups for greater participation in scheme operation, maintenance and rehabilitation; strengthening the capacity of farmer associations to buy agricultural advice and market information; and, supporting farmers' field schools in connection with IPM for pest control in vegetables.

For large, centrally-managed schemes, interventions should be supported by a clear policy for sustainable agricultural production, free of controls over production choices. Improvement measures would include: a transparent pricing system; clear management and beneficiary obligations; modernisation and decentralisation of agricultural support services; delegation of responsibility for managing schemes to WUAs: and restructuring parastatal corporation along competitive commercial lines. In the short term, the priority is to rehabilitate,

---

[28] This strategic priority is also relevant to predominantly-rainfed farming systems in which small scale irrigation can be developed.

re-equip and modernise irrigation and drainage systems. In the long term, if technically feasible, priority should be given to sub-dividing larger schemes into smaller units, to make it easier for scheme farmers to take over their management.

CEREAL-ROOT CROP MIXED FARMING SYSTEM

CHARACTERISTICS OF THE SYSTEM

Although this system shares some characteristics with the Maize Mixed System (such as 120 to 180 growing days with, in some areas, mono-modal rainfall). It has, however, certain characteristics that set it apart: relatively low population density; abundant cultivated land; poor communications; lower altitude; higher temperatures; and the presence of a tsetse challenge that limits livestock numbers and prevents the use of animal traction in much of the area. Although cereals such as maize, sorghum and millet are important in the system, in the absence of animal traction, root crops such as yams and cassava are more important than cereals. A wider range of crops is grown and marketed, and intercropping is far more significant (see Box 2.11 for basic data, and Box 2.12 for a description of a typical farm household).

Box 2.11 Basic Data: Cereal-Root Crop Mixed Farming System	
Total population (m)	85
Agricultural population (m)	59
Total area (m)	312
Agro-ecological zone	Dry subhumid
Cultivated area (m ha)	31
Irrigated area (m)	0.4
Cattle population (m)	43

TRENDS AND ISSUES IN CEREAL-ROOT CROP MIXED SYSTEM

The Guinea savannah represents one of the major under-utilised resources in the region. Cultivated land is abundant and tends to be relatively under-utilised due to a combination of low population density, poor communications and labour shortages in the absence of animal traction. Although land is sufficiently abundant to permit substantial fallow periods in the crop rotation, there are already signs of fertility decline and an increasing acidity level in some soils; sometimes associated with prolonged use of inorganic fertilisers without attention to maintaining organic matter levels. As the application of mineral fertiliser to cereals has declined, due to deteriorating input/output price ratios, farmers are experiencing increasing difficulty in maintaining soil fertility, while weeds such as *striga* have become more difficult to control. In the northern part of the area, prolonged use of mechanisation for land preparation has resulted in loss of soil structure and organic matter.

Box 2.12 A Typical Household of the Cereal-Root Crop Mixed Farming System

A typical household would farm two ha by hand cultivation and would grow maize, sorghum, cassava, yams, cotton, and minor crops such as groundnuts, pigeon pea, cowpea, beans, sweet potato and squash, with use of organic manure (animal night corrals are periodically moved to selectively manure fields). A substantial part of the manure is provided by Fulani herd which pass through the area in order to graze on crop stubble. Often the farm household does not own cattle, but would keep a few chickens and goats. In cotton growing areas, minimal doses of purchased fertiliser and pesticides would be used, in spite of their high cost. But little or no mineral fertiliser would be used on maize or other food crops. Some hired labour might be used on cotton but none on food crops. The household would be food self-sufficient and have a surplus for sale – some of which would rot due to perishability and poor market access. The main sources of cash would be cotton, yams, cassava and vegetables.

A typical poor household would not grow cotton due to lack of cash for inputs and would meet its food deficit during the rainy (hungry) season by working for meals in other farmers' fields. During the dry season the husband would migrate to the forest zone to do casual labour for industrial tree crop farmers.

In the 1980s and early 1990s, smallholder maize and cotton expanded rapidly at the expense of sorghum and root crops – especially in the more northern, drier part of the Guinea savannah – as a result of the diffusion of improved early-maturing maize varieties. This expansion was facilitated by government policies aimed at promotion of national food self-sufficiency, with the support of fertiliser subsidies, seasonal production credit and parastatal marketing support. In the long run, these policies were unsustainable, because their cost to governments was high and their impact on production was disappointing.

As trade and price liberalisation led to further deterioration of fertiliser/maize price ratios and to lower profitability of maize production, smallholder maize lost much of its attraction as a cash crop. On the other hand, currency devaluation also reduced urban demand for imported cereals and increased demand for traditional foods such as yams and cassava. This factor led to reversal of the earlier cropping pattern changes, with an expansion of the area under root crops at the expense of maize. However, since root crop production was highly elastic, as supply increased producer prices levelled off. Hence the impact of devaluation on the incomes of food crop growers has been rather modest.

Smallholder cotton also lost some of its attraction with the dismantling of parastatal programmes that supplied small farmers with seeds, fertiliser and chemicals at the beginning of the season and then deducted their cost from the marketed product. Although private ginneries took over processing, most were reluctant to advance inputs to small farmers on credit and then try to recover the cost at the end of the season. In the absence of credit, and with sharply rising fertiliser prices and stagnant or falling cotton prices, farmers found it risky to buy fertiliser and agro-chemicals. Hence, productivity declined as a consequence of reduced fertiliser application, plus pest and disease flare-ups.

The success of the Onchocerciasis Control Programme (OCP) has opened up large areas of cultivated land to farmers. The coming three decades may well witness the development of infrastructure, access to markets and consequent intensification and diversification. Livestock populations are likely to expand, especially in the southern fringes of the farming system, as tsetse pressure is reduced. Whilst land has been plentiful up to the present time, local population growth and in-migration will increase future pressure on land resources. In the absence of corrective measures, soil fertility problems can be expected – as in other more densely settled farming systems.

PRIORITIES FOR CEREAL-ROOT CROP MIXED SYSTEM

This farming system – because of its relatively low population density and the abundance of cultivated land that could be brought under cultivation – is considered to be one with the highest agricultural growth potential in Africa. It has ample opportunity for growth through expansion of the cropped area as well as through higher yields per ha (see Box 2.13 for an overview of this potential in West Africa). In addition, there is potential for poverty reduction through – in order of importance – the following household strategies: (i) intensification of production; (ii) expansion of farm size; and (iii) diversification to high value products and processing. Some improvement in livelihoods will also be derived from off-farm income.

The exploitation of these opportunities involves three types of concerted action: (i) conservation farming; (ii) integrated pest management; and (iii) crop-livestock integration. In the long run, there could be scope for extension of the cropped area per household in connection with tsetse eradication and mechanisation (either through animal traction or small tractors), as well as through agricultural industrialisation. Conservation agriculture would involve the introduction of reduced tillage, and improved land husbandry[29], including the use of cover crops and mulching, as well as better soil management to address the soil fertility problem (see Box 2.3). As a condition for its success, the adoption of conservation agriculture also entails — confinement and stallfeeding of animals, which releases organic matter for surface mulching and composting. Integrated pest and plant management mainly involves biological control of plant pests and weeds (especially striga). Crop-livestock integration is based upon increased cultivation of fodder crops, with cut and carry feeding systems. In the long run, such integration might involve pushing the frontier of animal traction southward into the tsetse-prone zone using new technologies[30]. Introduction of animal traction could facilitate the

[29] Land husbandry is described in Box 2.18.
[30] Based upon FAO's successful experience with tsetse eradication.

Box 2.13 Exploiting the Productive Potential of the Cereal-Root Crop Mixed System in West Africa[31]

The Cereal-Root Crop Mixed Farming System is based in West Africa on the Northern and Southern Guinea savannahs which extend in a broad band through most West African countries (and similar agro-ecologies exist in Southern and Eastern Africa). The growing period ranges from about 150 days near the border with the Sahel to about 210 days in the southern part. Average annual rainfall in the area varies from 800 mm in the north to 1200 mm in the south. The farming system still has much land that is only used extensively, particularly at a distance from roads. The more easily accessible land is largely used for annual crops – generally with low external inputs – and produces low yields. Crops include maize and sorghum, millets in the northern part, cotton, cassava, soybean and cowpea; with yam near the southern border, and wetland rice in parts of the river plains and valley areas. Infrastructure is generally poorly developed and maintained. Historically, development in this area has suffered from two major health constraints: *onchocerciasis* and *trypanosomosis*. Control efforts related to the OCP have freed up an estimated 25 million ha of cultivated land for agricultural development. However, tsetse-transmitted African Animal Trypanosomosis is still a significant constraint to agricultural development.

Farm households in this system can achieve significant improvements in farm productivity, and in their economic and nutritional status, through modifying their soil, crop and livestock management. The availability of farm power, particularly during planting operations, would become critical to any attempt to intensify cropping. Initially, the utilisation of draft animal power is also a key factor in the integration of livestock and crop agriculture. Later, crop-livestock integration will evolve as mechanisation is introduced. The need for farm power depends on the degree of adoption of conservation agriculture. Major additional gains should be available from the implementation of simple, affordable systems for drip irrigation. The recent development of high-yielding, precocious oil palm clones adapted to certain environments outside their traditional range, has provided an opportunity for their introduction in parts of the Guinea savannah zone – specifically in valleys and river plains. The development of tropical soybean varieties has now made the commercial production of soybeans possible in such areas. In addition, some areas in West Africa with access to a low cost transportation may become competitive suppliers of cassava chips to European feed markets. In conclusion, there is a great potential for the intensification of this farming system, the realisation of which could be accelerated by, *inter alia,* investment in strengthening infrastructure and agricultural services.

replication of successful models for the expansion cotton production that were promoted by the former cotton parastatals.

Farmers have responded to declining maize prices by diversifying crop production – increasing production of traditional root crops, as well as vegetables

---

[31] Abstracted from Case Study 3, Annex 1.

for urban markets. However, when the quantity of food supplied to urban markets expanded, prices levelled off and income increases were limited. Some options for addressing the problem of low farmer incomes include: improved small-scale, rural-based cassava processing for human food and animal feed to allow smallholders to capture more of the value-added; and, upgrading of product packaging to increase their appeal to urban consumers. To address the problem of breakdown of input supply and marketing services for cotton, the best options will be to organise small farmers to reinforce input supply and marketing services, and to introduce IPM methods for improved pest control, thereby reducing the dependence on purchased inputs.

AGRO-PASTORAL MILLET/SORGHUM FARMING SYSTEM

CHARACTERISTICS OF THE SYSTEM

As mentioned in the first section of this Chapter, crops and livestock are of comparable importance in this farming system (see Box 2.14 for basic data on the system). Rainfed sorghum and pearl millet are the main sources of food and are rarely sold, whereas sesame and pulses are sometimes sold. Land preparation is by oxen, or by hoe

Box 2.14 Basic Data: Agro-Pastoral Millet/Sorghum Farming System	
Total population (m)	54
Agricultural population (m)	33
Total area (m ha)	198
Agro-ecological zone	Dry subhumid
Cultivated area (m ha)	22
Irrigated area (m ha)	0.6
Cattle population (m)	25

along river banks. Camels are sometimes used in the drier parts. Ethnic groups are often former livestock-keeping peoples who have become sedentary. Livestock are kept for subsistence (milk and milk products), offspring, transportation (camels, donkeys), land preparation (oxen, camels), sale or exchange, savings, bridewealth and insurance against crop failure. Rather than carts, pack animals or animal-drawn sledges are used to transport crops. Crop-livestock interaction is limited; animals are used for ploughing, crop residues are grazed in the fields after harvest (and sometimes cut), but fodder crops are not grown and *kraal* manure is rarely applied to fields. The population lives in villages the whole year round, although part of the herd may continue to migrate seasonally with herd boys. A typical household in the Agro-Pastoral Farming System is outlined in Box 2.15.

Food insecurity is basically caused by drought and aggravated by low levels of assets. Upper stratum households are food secure even in most bad years, because they have enough livestock to trade for the grain they lack. Households in the lower stratum are chronically food insecure – in both good and bad years – because they cannot grow enough grain to feed themselves and they have few livestock or other

---

Box 2.15   A Typical Household of the Agro-Pastoral Millet/Sorghum Farming System

A typical household would have around 1.5 ha of cultivated land, with a level of food production of only 93 kg/capita. Most households experience food deficits even in years when crops do not fail. The average household would have 1.1 ha of millet or sorghum and 0.2 ha of pulses, with the rest planted to minor crops such as vegetables, sesame or cotton. Yields are low, averaging only 400 kg/ha for sorghum, 350 kg/ha for millet and 230 kg/ha for pulses. The household would own a few chickens, plus 2 or 3 cattle or 5 to 10 sheep and goats. Millet and sorghum would be grown almost exclusively for subsistence (including beer brewing). The main cash sources would be livestock, cotton and seasonal migration to the forest zone.

Socio-economic differentiation is based on livestock ownership. About 40 percent of households have no large animals (apart from a donkey) and 60 percent are not self-sufficient in draught power (especially in Botswana where a span of eight oxen is needed for non-mechanised land preparation). In a typical poor household, domestic food production would only last for 2 to 6 months, depending on the rains. Casual labour on other farms, beer and firewood sales would account for 40 to 50 percent of household income, and probably more in years when crops fail due to drought.

---

assets to exchange for grain. The middle stratum is grain self-sufficient in good years and in deficit during bad years. They are food secure in average years because they have some animals to exchange for grain, but in bad years they are highly vulnerable. Coping mechanisms include: (i) growing early-maturing, drought-resistant millet and sorghum varieties; (ii) storing grain from one year to the next; (iii) selling or exchanging small ruminants to buy grain in the hungry season; and (iv) in years when crops fail and where off-farm work opportunities are available, earning off-farm income to buy grain in order to minimize distress sales of animals. The poorest, who no longer have any animals to sell, cope by reducing meals, collecting and eating wild foods, cutting and selling firewood and working for others in exchange for meals.

The main cause of poverty is successive droughts. These result in crop failure, food shortages, sharp increases in grain prices, collapse of livestock prices and weak animals whose condition leads to deaths and decapitalisation of herds through distress sales. Destitution occurs when households have eaten all their seed and lost all their breeding animals, so that they cannot plant or start reconstituting their herds after the drought ends. Apart from drought, typical household problems include: (i) acute dry season water shortage for people and animals; (ii) shortage of seasonal grazing; (iii) physical isolation, lack of roads and market access; (iv) disadvantageous terms of trade for both crops and livestock; and (v) lack of health facilities and schools. Specific problems of this farming system include bird and locust damage to crops, laborious grain dehulling, stock theft, encroachment of farming on riverine areas and, in Southern Africa, land shortage and overcrowding due to the legacy of colonial dualism.

TRENDS AND ISSUES IN AGRO-PASTORAL MILLET/SORGHUM SYSTEM

The farming system has suffered from a general reduction in rainfall during the past two decades. Insufficient and erratic rainfall has led to low crop yields and the abandonment of groundnuts and late-maturing sorghum. There is an acute shortage of drinking water and firewood in certain areas. Soil fertility problems are emerging in the plains due to shortened fallow intervals and long periods of continuous cultivation. Land shortage is also a problem in the more densely populated areas where soils are more fertile.

Pressure on resources is expected to intensify in coming decades with the growth of human and livestock populations in the system. In some cases, this may lead to spontaneous sustainable resource management and intensification such as in Machakos – albeit a slightly more favourable agro-ecology – but such successes are likely to be the exception rather than the rule. Soil fertility of the better, cropped land can be expected to decline in the absence of dramatic technological breakthroughs related to fertility. In the absence of sound grazing management by communities, grazing resources in many areas will also deteriorate. Under these circumstances, both chronic and transient poverty can be expected to increase.

Crop-related constraints include drought, declining soil fertility, weed infestation – mainly by *striga* – in cereals and cowpeas, pests and diseases in cowpeas and groundnuts, and the high cost and general lack of credit for cotton inputs. Past research recommendations were often inappropriate to poor smallholders because they focused on yield maximisation rather than yield stabilisation and risk reduction. Livestock-related constraints include shortage of dry-season grazing and the weak condition of draught animals at the time of greatest physical effort. Crop failure is exacerbated by the seasonal price 'scissors effect' between grain and livestock. In the hungry season it takes three times as many animals to buy a bag of grain than in the harvest season; while grain prices soar and livestock prices collapse when crops fail.

This farming system has not been much affected by the withdrawal of the public sector from seed and fertiliser supply and crop marketing, because it never did benefit much from these services. Public extension services were unresponsive to the needs of resource poor farmers and often promoted packages that were too costly and risky for crop growing under semiarid conditions. Good quality seeds of early-maturing, drought-tolerant varieties remain in short supply.

PRIORITIES FOR AGRO-PASTORAL MILLET/SORGHUM SYSTEM

In the difficult environment of the Agro-Pastoral Millet/Sorghum System, the household strategies for poverty reduction are diversified. Whilst the greatest source of poverty reduction is exit from agriculture, three other strategies are also of importance, namely: intensification; diversification; and increase in farm size. A key priority will be to reduce the likelihood of crop failure in drought years through improved land husbandry and water harvesting; plus multiplication of palatable, drought-resistant, early-maturing millet and sorghum varieties. Control of bird damage and the attacks of desert locusts should complement this strategy. To address problems of declining soil fertility, improved methods of maintaining fertility should be identified and applied on soils of different types. The savannah vegetation should be regenerated to provide strategic forage reserves and sustainable fuelwood supplies.

Specific interventions to address food and income insecurity include: maximisation of soil moisture retention and utilisation through land husbandry techniques; promotion of the diffusion of run-off water harvesting structures such as *demi-lunes* (half-moon-shaped bunds) and stone contour bunds based on successful experiences in Mali, Niger and Burkina Faso (see Box 2.16). They should also involve facilitation of farmer-based multiplication of early-maturing, drought-tolerant sorghum and millet varieties with desirable local characteristics – including acceptable taste and tolerance to *striga* and bird damage. Of equal importance is the development of integrated control methods for *striga* and other field and storage pests and diseases; plus improvement of grain storage methods. In the livestock subsector, animal productivity will be increased through better utilisation of crop residues and by-products, promoting the use of locally-adapted breeds, control of epizootic diseases and improving village poultry production. Forest regeneration is necessary for sustainable fuelwood supplies.

Interventions to increase income from livestock should include: (i) the organisation and implementation of disease monitoring; (ii) approved certification schemes for the export of live animals and animal products; (iii) greater integration with crop farming for fodder supplies and sale of feeder cattle in more favoured areas – such as the Cereal-Root Crop and the Maize Mixed Systems; and, (iv) support to small-scale private livestock trading. Hides and skins are products of agro-pastoral systems which are often undervalued[32]. To ensure a high quality product, extension services should place more emphasis on the veterinary care given to the live animal, as well as to the treatment of the skin immediately after slaughter.

Problems connected with input supply and marketing channels for cotton can be reduced by assisting smallholder producer groups to take over these functions. Shortage of credit for cotton inputs, lack of animal traction, and hungry season food deficits can be minimised by organising networks of self-sustaining, savings-based micro-finance institutions. Loss of animals can be addressed by improving access to animal health services through community-based animal health workers. Grazing pressure can be lowered by: (i) developing sound land use and water policies for the rangelands; (ii) negotiating recognition of pastoralists' customary

---

[32] During the 1990s 25 percent of hide and skins entering the tanneries in Addis Ababa were downgraded, resulting in a loss of export value estimated at US$6.9 million (Bayou 1998).

> **Box 2.16 Improving Local Soil and Water Conservation Practices in Semiarid Areas**[33]
>
> In common with many semiarid areas, Niger has suffered land degradation as a result of population pressure and drought. An IFAD-funded project tested a number of locally-based technologies to bring land back into production, reduce inter-annual variability of output and enhance the resilience of farming systems to climatic risk. One key success was the development of a modified form of the tassas practice. This continued to expand spontaneously to new plots after the project had closed.
>
> The tassa practice consists of digging holes some 200 to 300 mm in diameter and 150 to 200 mm deep and covering the hole bottoms with manure. This helps to promote termite activity during the dry season, thus improving water infiltration further. Farmers then plant millet or sorghum in them. Tassas have allowed the region to attain average millet yields of over 480kg/ha, in comparison with only 130 kg/ha without tassas. As a result, tassas have become an integral part of the local technology base. The technique is spreading at a surprising rate.
>
> Three main factors contributed to success: (i) an action-research approach that combines flexibility, openness to farmer initiatives, a forward-looking attitude and willingness to negotiate; (ii) a technology that yields quick and tangible benefits, yet is simple, easily replicable and fits well with existing farming systems, and (iii) a technology that can adjust to the changing local context. The tassa practice is based on a local practice that, although not high-performing, is effective.
>
> Tassas appeal to farmers because they yield quick and appreciable results, restoring productivity of land that was previously unfit for cultivation while mitigating agroclimatic risks and increasing food availability in participating households by 20 to 40 percent. They are easily replicable because they entail only minor adjustments to local hand tools and do not involve any additional work during the critical sowing and weeding periods. Because they can be constructed by individual farmers without external assistance, tassas are particularly interesting to youths, since they make it possible to cultivate plateau lands, which have become a valuable resource in the face of growing pressure on land.

rights to dry-season grazing areas – including those to adjacent zones that are more humid; and (iii) promoting mechanisms for community-based conflict resolution to deal with problems between pastoralists and sedentary farmers over access to land and water.

STRATEGIC PRIORITIES FOR SUB-SAHARAN AFRICA

This final section highlights some of the major challenges in the region and consolidates the priorities proposed for each system. Drawing on the preceding

---

[33] Mascaretti 2001.

Table 2.4 Potential and Relative Importance of Household Strategies for Poverty Reduction in Sub-Saharan Africa

Farming System	Potential for agricultural growth	Potential for poverty reduction	Strategies for poverty reduction				
			Intensi-fication	Diversi-fication	Increased Farm Size	Increased off-farm Income	Exit from Agriculture
Irrigated	High	Low	3.5	2	2.5	1.5	0.5
Tree Crop	Medium-high	Medium	4	1.5	1.5	2	1
Forest Based	Low-medium	Low	2.5	2	4	0	1.5
Rice-Tree Crop	Low	Low	1	3	2	2	2
Highland Perennial	Low	Low	1	2	1	2	4
Highland Temperate Mixed	Medium	Medium	1	3	2	1	3
Root Crop	Medium	Medium	2.5	3	2	1.5	1
Cereal-Root Crop Mixed	High	Medium	3.5	2	3	1	0.5
Maize Mixed	Medium-high	High	2	3	2	2	1
Large Commercial and Smallholder	Medium	Low-medium	2	2	3	1	2
Agro-Pastoral Millet/Sorghum	Low-medium	Medium	2	2	2	1	3
Pastoral	Low-medium	Low	1	1	1	2	5
Sparse Agriculture (Arid)	Low	Low	0	1	0	3	6
Coastal Artisanal Fishing	Low-medium	Low	1	3	0	4	2
Urban Based	Medium	Low	1	3	3	3	0
Average for Region			2.1	2.3	2.1	1.6	1.9

Source: Expert judgement.
Note: Total score for each farming system equals 10. Assessments refer to poor farmers only.
Agricultural population weightings by system are derived from Table 2.1.

analyses of farming systems, Table 2.4 ranks the potentials of each system for agricultural growth and for poverty reduction, and indicates the relative importance of five major household strategies for escaping poverty. This provides the frame for the consolidation of strategic priorities in respect of policies, markets, information, technology and natural resources, and the identification of a number of crosscutting strategic initiatives for the region.

Despite the fact that Sub-Saharan Africa is relatively well endowed with natural resources, the incidence of hunger and poverty is greater than in other developing regions, while the population growth rate is higher and the number of poor is increasing at an alarming rate. Rural poverty still accounts for 90 percent of total poverty and roughly 80 percent of the poor still depend on agriculture or farm labour for their main source or livelihood. Nevertheless, the policy, economic and institutional environment do not, in general, create the incentives for agricultural production – especially broad-based inclusive growth to benefit the poor. There is still an urban bias in development programmes and the supply of rural public goods is low. The performance of past investments in agricultural research and extension has been disappointing. Moreover, declining terms of trade, poor governance and civil strife, gender inequality, low levels of schooling and HIV/AIDS are all of deep concern.

The analysis of the selected farming systems indicates their different development prospects. Two systems have medium to high potential for both growth and poverty reduction: the Maize Mixed System in the medium to long term; and the Tree Crop System in the short to medium term. The Maize Mixed System is facing a crisis, but there are possible solutions through intensification and diversification. Agricultural growth potential depends to a large extent on the availability of under-utilised resources, intensification possibilities and market prospects. Two systems hold significant growth potential: the Irrigated and Cereal-Root Crop Mixed Systems – the latter in particular has enormous potential for integrated crop-livestock intensification if infrastructure and market access constraints could be overcome. The fifth farming system that was analysed in depth, the Agro-Pastoral Millet/Sorghum System, is considered to have only modest scope for agricultural growth and poverty reduction.

Other farming systems in the region also offer possibilities for agricultural growth and the reduction of hunger and poverty. There is potential for expansion of cultivated area in the Forest Based and the Root Crop Farming Systems, although in both cases there are significant soil and environmental constraints. In other systems, valley bottoms that usually have heavy soils are the main under-utilised resource. The Forest Based System has large under-utilised areas, but soils are fragile, market access is very poor and rainfall is often excessive. The Root Crop System has a moderate growth potential for supplying urban markets with root crops and for exporting oil palm.

In relation to the five pathways for households to escape poverty[34], massive efforts must be directed to support the intensification of productivity on the farms of poor households and the diversification of production towards high return activities, especially in the high potential areas where a majority of the poor are found. The development of alternative livelihoods – both local off-farm employment, and even exit from agriculture – will be an important component of

---

[34] See the discussion of the five household strategies to escape poverty in Chapter I.

poverty reduction programmes, especially in the low potential areas. Substantial effort should also be targeted towards expanding the productive asset base of poor farm households.

The following sub-sections of this Chapter outline the major strategic priorities and interventions needed to support the development of agriculture in the region. First, the priorities for national policy adjustments are identified. Next, the main thrusts for improved functioning of markets and for information availability, are considered. Key technology and natural resource management needs are then outlined.

TRADE LIBERALISATION AND MARKET DEVELOPMENT

Trade liberalisation is a double-edged sword for many farming systems. The expansion of export markets is crucial for the future of the Tree Crop System and for the long-term development prospects of other high potential farming systems. However, as a result of trade liberalisation, some preferential access to markets will be lost during the coming decades; and some domestic production will be threatened, and largely displaced, by lower cost imports. In these cases, governments may need to establish safety nets or other poverty reduction mechanisms.

In general terms, not only should non-traditional exports be promoted but there is also a need for a general focus on higher value products. This strategy responds to farmers' felt need to cope with the declining profitability of traditional export crops that is affecting Tree Crop systems, as well as savannah and semiarid cotton growers and highland *Arabica* coffee producers. Partial solutions include: diversification into non-traditional export crops; upgrading of existing export products to obtain the highest possible price (rehabilitation, improved processing); and a search for niche markets such as biologically produced items.

For pastoralists, agro-pastoralists and highland livestock keepers, the main thrust will be to devise and implement disease monitoring and approved certification schemes for the export of live animals and animal products. Since the region is one of the world's most open regions, in the sense that international trade is large relative to GDP, the effect of more rapid liberalisation might be less than in other regions. However, since the region already faces strong competition for world market share, and the traditional exports are already declining as a result, faster liberalisation might well accelerate this trend. It is unlikely that the region can produce as cheaply as some Asian countries because of higher labour and transaction costs. Even high-quality products for speciality markets (e.g. biologically grown *Arabica* coffee and cocoa) are likely to be affected, as competitors will tend to pursue the same market niches. The Tree Crop System would be the most affected by these changes. On the other hand, market niches for African ethnic foods could increase among immigrant communities in developed countries as a result of greater migratory flows from the region to developed countries, and these niches could widen further as others become familiar with these foods. Such opportunities would apply mainly to the Cereal-Root Crop Mixed and Root Crop Systems.

Ex-European colonies in the region could lose their preferential access to European Union (EU) markets and would face stiff competition from other developing regions. Access to developed country markets would continue to be limited by various types of health, veterinary and phyto-sanitary regulations. The recent changes in EU regulations regarding chocolate are likely to reduce cocoa imports from the region. The opening of EU markets to agricultural products may not be a panacea, since some competitors in North and South America may have rapid supply responses for cereals and livestock products.

POLICIES, INSTITUTIONS AND PUBLIC GOODS

The major distortions in many economies have now been removed during the implementation of Structural Adjustment Programmes. Whilst there is a need to continue with ongoing macro-economic adjustments, substantial benefits would be derived from a renewed focus on improved agricultural sector policies. Two major priority areas stand out in this respect: (i) resource user rights and (ii) long-term investments in public goods.

Despite the substantial land area of Africa and the favourable average farm size compared with several other regions, there are areas where, for reasons of history or of population pressure, small farm size is a production constraint. In order to secure equitable access to land and other resources, two main problems need to be solved: (i) how best to enable rural communities in areas with low population density to protect their customary land rights; and (ii) how to achieve more equitable access to land in dualistic countries in Southern Africa. The farming systems affected by the former issue are mainly the Forest Based System, the Coastal Artisanal Fishing System, and the Pastoral and Agro-Pastoral Millet/Sorghum Systems. On the other hand, the latter issue primarily affects the Maize Mixed System and adjacent Large Commercial and Smallholder Systems. The main strategic thrust for addressing the former problem should be some type of community-based land tenure reform[35]. Other possibilities include: promulgation of pastoral codes in arid and semiarid Sahelian countries and of a code of conduct for artisanal fisheries in West Africa; plus *gestion de terroir* approaches or conflict resolution in connection with community-based, natural resource management.

Because of the well-known shortcomings of private sector interventions there are a number of critical areas requiring the provision of public goods. In this context, it is extremely important to ensure a proper balance between short-term issues that interest smallholders and long-term investment in public goods of interest to

---

[35] Tanner 2001.

governments, or to humanity as a whole. Whilst the opportunities and strategic thrusts for each farming system are highly context specific, examples of the latter include: conservation of the resource base for future generations; good land husbandry; sustainable natural resource management; soil and water conservation; environmental protection; maintenance of biodiversity; tsetse eradication; and, carbon sequestration. Farming systems with high growth potential are strongly constrained by a lack of services, including transportation and education (see also below). The challenge is to provide such public goods in a sustainable fashion, by ensuring that local authorities and communities contribute to their maintenance.

INFORMATION AND HUMAN CAPITAL

The adoption of technology and the ability to exploit market opportunities, is closely related to the level of schooling of farm decision makers. A massive effort is needed in the education of farm women and men, and in the revitalisation of primary education services. The latter should not only prepare children to become modern farmers, but also equip them with the skills for gainful employment in non-agricultural areas.

The popular conception of the coming information age applies as fully to smallholder agriculture as it does to other industries. By 2030, knowledge-intensive farming will be the norm in high potential farming systems in the region, just as such agriculture is prevalent in OECD countries today. For example, the adoption of conservation farming and IPM will require an educational rather than a prescriptive approach to extension – each farmer must be given the means to judge which avenues for livelihood improvement best match his or her resource endowment. This implies not only wide availability of high quality technical and market information, but also requires massive investment in farmer training. Such training could be located in revitalised farmer training institutes, complemented by village and field level education. Not only should farmers be trained in agricultural production, but some should be trained as entrepreneurs and micro-traders.

HIV/AIDS is having a profound affect on farming communities in Africa. The most crucial short term action is to halt the spread of HIV/AIDS through appropriate information campaigns and a cheap supply of condoms. There is also a need for safety nets to reinforce the efforts of rural communities to support AIDS orphans and for land tenure reform to prevent widows from losing access to, and control over, land and household property when their husbands die.

In much of the region, medium to large farms have considerable scope for increasing agricultural productivity and for diversification. These farms tend to be more specialised, and accelerated development would require improved services. One means would be the privatisation of financial, input supply and advisory services, since commercial farms will be able to meet user charges. However, public support to research and dissemination is justified in order that natural resources are

75

protected for future generations. Equal access of farm women to these facilities and services is imperative for the future development of farming systems in the region.

SCIENCE AND TECHNOLOGY

Diversification from low value to higher value crops or livestock enterprises is a major strategic thrust for the Maize Mixed, the Cereal-Root Crop Mixed, the Highland Temperate and the Tree Crop Systems. In the Agro-Pastoral Millet/Sorghum and Pastoral Systems, the main strategic thrust is diversification into lower risk crops and activities in order to reduce vulnerability to drought. It provides a partial answer to farmers' problems related to: deteriorating input/output price ratios for maize and wheat; deteriorating terms of trade for traditional export crops; and, vulnerability to crop failure in arid and semiarid zones. Diversification, with a focus on added value, is equally applicable at farm or community level. Access to transport, a line of credit and a market in the neighbouring communities is often sufficient to encourage widespread small-scale processing, for example, for threshing, oil extraction, maize milling, cleaning, bagging and micro bakeries – and with good management such enterprises can expand rapidly and provide local jobs for farmers [36].

For households with insufficient land to depend upon farming alone, the main focus should be on diversification of income sources to evolve an optimal combination of crop, livestock and off-farm activities. Diversification is particularly beneficial to poor households because it increases the resilience of poor households in the face of both weather-related and market shocks.

Existing technologies for reducing vulnerability to drought need to be popularised. Drought risk affects Pastoral and Agro-Pastoral Millet/Sorghum Systems and – to a lesser extent – the Maize Mixed and Highland Temperate Mixed Systems. The main thrusts for addressing the problem on the crop side are: introduction of drought-tolerant, early-maturing crops and varieties; maximisation of soil moisture retention and utilisation through land husbandry; water harvesting; and, small-scale, farmer-managed irrigation.

Key technologies for livestock centre on vulnerability reduction through the development of sound rangeland and and water use policies implementing procedures for drought early warning, and drought mitigation and rehabilitation practices; control of epizootic diseases; development of conservation agriculture appropriate for arid and semiarid areas; and, development of viable non-pastoral alternatives for those that can no longer be sustained by the resource base.

Affordable and environmentally friendly pest and weed control technologies should be promoted. Pest and weed problems occur to some extent in all systems: crop damage by wild animals in the Forest Based System; locusts in the Sahel; *striga*

---

[36] Steele 2001, *pers. comm.*

weed in Cereal-Root Crop Mixed and Agro-Pastoral Millet/Sorghum systems. However, viable alternatives to costly pesticides are particularly important for cotton growers and irrigated vegetable producers, and will involve promotion and training in pro-active, IPM-based, farmer-centred pest and weed control management. Farmer-based multiplication can contribute to effective seed distribution at limited cost (see the Zambia case study).

It is necessary to develop productive partnerships between public, private sector and civil society organisation, notably farmers' organisations, to invest in technology development. However, the private sector lacks the incentive for research in important areas such as long term resource management. This may call for the introduction of innovative funding mechanisms.

NATURAL RESOURCES AND CLIMATE

The issue of land degradation and soil fertility cuts across all systems to a greater or lesser extent. However, a particularly acute crisis is currently being experienced in the Maize Mixed and Highland Temperate Mixed Systems. The causes of declining fertility are complex but attempts to recapitalise soil fertility (see Box 2.17) solely

Box 2.17 Soil Nutrient Recapitalisation

Declining soil fertility is an important element in the land degradation suffered by many regional farming systems in recent years, and includes the breakdown of soil structure, a reduction in organic matter and nutrient content, as well as reduced rainwater infiltration and moisture storage capacity. While soil nutrients must be recapitalised whenever intensive agricultural production is occurring, inorganic fertilisers have too often been seen as a solution in themselves, rather than as an element in a range of land management practices. Experience has shown that a sole reliance on fertilisers for crop intensification has often yielded disappointing results.

While fertilisers may produce significantly increased yields within high potential systems when used in conjunction with improved seeds, their use may not be financially viable for smaller producers growing food crops – particularly maize and sorghum – or in remote areas where input prices are significantly increased by transport costs. Even where fertiliser application is profitable, small farmers simply may not have the capital at the start of the planting season to afford fertilisers, or be able to accept the risk that the capital outlay implies.

However, in the absence of nutrient recapitalisation, soil productivity is likely to degrade, even under good land husbandry practices, resulting in further poverty and increased food security problems. Thus, there is an urgent need to develop alternative approaches to soil recapitalisation for resource-poor farmers. These may include a greater reliance on green manures, mulches, and animal faeces, plus the increased use of nitrogen-fixing crops in the rotational cycle – including as intercrops, and enriched fallows.

through the use of inorganic fertilizers have produced only short-term responses, and in many cases appear to have had little impact on overall yields – at least in the crops for which they were intended. Furthermore, economic liberalisation and the removal of subsidies has led to sharp reduction in fertiliser application on maize and wheat in the high potential farming systems as input supply chains have broken down and the fertiliser:grain price ratio increased. Some areas – such as the Southern Highlands of Tanzania in the Maize Mixed System – that once specialised in smallholder maize, are reverting to extensive cultivation of traditional varieties without fertiliser, and poverty is increasing.

One well-proven solution to the problem of land degradation in general is the adoption of improved land management practices. This is best described as a set of principles rather than a package of technologies (see Box 2.18). The

---

Box 2.18 Principles of Good Land Management

Good land management requires an *integrated and synergistic resource management approach* embracing locally-appropriate combinations of the following technical options:

- build-up of soil organic matter and related biological activity to optimum sustainable levels (for improved moisture, infiltration and storage, nutrient supply, and soil structure) through the use of compost, farmyard manure, green manures, surface mulch, enriched fallows, agroforestry, cover crops and crop residue management;

- integrated plant nutrition management with locally appropriate and cost effective combinations of organic/inorganic and on/off-farm sources of plant nutrients (e.g. organic manures, crop residues, rhizobial N-fixation, transfer of nutrients released by weathering in the deeper soil layers to the surface via tree roots and leaf litter, use of rock phosphate, lime and mineral fertiliser);

- better crop management using improved seeds of appropriate varieties, improved crop establishment at the beginning of the rains (to increase protective ground cover, thereby reducing water loss and soil erosion), effective weed control and integrated pest management;

- better rainwater management to increase infiltration and eliminate or reduce runoff so as to improve soil moisture conditions within the rooting zone, thereby lessening the risk of moisture stress during dry spells, while reducing erosion;

- improvement of soil rooting depth and permeability through breaking of cultivation-induced compacted soil layers (hoe/plough pan) through conservation tillage practices by means of tractor drawn subsoilers, ox drawn chisel ploughs, or hand hoe planting pits/ double dug beds, or interplanting of deep rooted perennial crops/trees and shrubs); and

- reclamation, where appropriate (i.e. if technically feasible and cost effective), of cultivated land that has been severely degraded by such processes as gullying, loss of topsoil from sheet erosion, soil compaction, acidification or salinisation.

---

implementation of these principles can take place within a number of technological practices, including conservation tillage and related conservation agriculture (see Box 2.3 above).

Projections indicate a slow expansion of irrigation during the coming 30 years, in the context of large reserves of land for the expansion of low cost rainfed agricultural production. Thus, unlike other regions where irrigated lands will generate a major part of the increases in food production, irrigation in Africa may play a very modest role during the coming three decades.

CONCLUSIONS

In Sub-Saharan Africa, hunger and poverty are extensive and increasing rapidly. Roughly 80 percent of the poor depend on farming for their main livelihood. The best available predictions suggest only a gradual decline in the prevalence of hunger and poverty in coming years[37]; and the levels of hunger and poverty implied under this 'business as usual' scenario fail to meet international development goals by a very substantial margin. Policy, economic and institutional environments within the region do not, in general, create the required incentives for agricultural production – especially broad-based inclusive growth to benefit the poor. There is still an urban bias in development programmes, agriculture is over-taxed and the supply of rural public goods is less than in other regions, while transaction costs remain high. The performance of past investments in agricultural research and extension has been disappointing, while terms of trade have been declining. Moreover, poor governance, civil strife, a degenerating law and order situation, gender inequality, low levels of schooling and HIV/AIDS are all of deep concern.

The abundance of natural resources in the region provides the basis for pro-poor agricultural development if the appropriate incentives are created by the adjustments in national policies, reorientation of institutions and provision of public goods and services. The analysis of major farming systems indicates the relative importance of household strategies to escape poverty – in order of importance: diversification; intensification; increase in farm size; exit from agriculture; and, increase in off-farm income. The overall strategic goal should be broad-based inclusive agricultural growth occurring in poorer communities and the poorer sections of each community. In order to halve hunger and poverty by the year 2015, massive efforts are required to stimulate such growth, which ultimately depends on the initiative and effort of individual farm families within each farming system. Although it is impossible, based on the foregoing regional analysis, to prescribe specific national actions, the overall challenge of reducing hunger and poverty in the region demands five strategic, inter-linked, initiatives:

[37] FAO 2000a.

Sustainable resource management. Sustainable resource management must address widespread land degradation, declining soil fertility and low crop yields resulting from inadequate rainfall; it should result in soil recapitalisation and improved productivity. Components include farmer-centred agricultural knowledge and information systems to document and share successes; resource enhancements such as small-scale irrigation and water harvesting; participatory applied research focused on integrated technologies blending indigenous and scientists' knowledge, related to conservation agriculture, agroforestry, IPM and crop-livestock integration; and strengthening resource user groups.

Improved resource access. Access to agricultural resources by poor farmers is intended to create a viable resource base for small family farms. Components include: market-based land reform; adjustment of legislation; strengthened public land administration; and functional community land tenure.

Increased small farm competitiveness. Increasing competitiveness of small and poor farmers will build capacity to exploit market opportunities. Components include: improved production technology; diversification; processing; upgrading product quality; linking production to niche markets; and strengthening support services, including market institutions based on public-private partnerships.

Reduced household vulnerability. Household risk management will reduce the vulnerability of farm households to natural and economic shocks, both of which are prevalent in African agriculture. Components include: drought-resistant and early varieties and hardy breeds; improved production practices for moisture retention; insurance mechanisms; and strengthening traditional and other risk spreading mechanisms.

Responding to HIV/AIDS. Immediate action is required to halt the spread and impact of HIV/AIDS. Components include: information campaigns; a cheap supply of condoms; affordable treatment; land tenure reform to prevent widows losing access to, and control over, land and household property when their husbands die; agricultural training for AIDS orphans; and safety nets to reinforce the efforts of rural communities to support AIDS orphans.

MIDDLE EAST
AND NORTH AFRICA

•••

REGIONAL SETTING

CHARACTERISTICS OF THE REGION

The Middle East and North Africa region[1] comprises 14 low and middle-income countries or territories stretching from Iran to Morocco (see Map). The region supports a population of 296 million people, over 120 million of whom live in rural areas. Of these, about 84 million are dependent on agriculture – including fishing and livestock. The region has ancient historical settlements, but there is also a long history of immigration from other areas. The Middle East is an important site of early settled agriculture, and the centre of origin and diversity of several major cereal and legume crops, and of the early domestication of sheep and goats. The region was also a major area of innovation in agriculture between the 4th and 11th Century AD, when many new crops and technologies were introduced from the Far East.

Settlement patterns vary, depending on historical forces and political changes, but populations are increasing in major cities and concentrating in larger villages in rural areas. The region contains a significant number of pastoralists who move seasonally between low and high altitudes in mountainous regions and between wetter zones and the dry *steppe*. The long history of human settlement, unequal access to land and increasing urbanisation have led to serious degradation of land and forest resources in much of the region.

The region covers an area of 1100 million ha and includes a diversity of environments. However, arid and semiarid areas with low and variable rainfall predominate. The more humid areas have a Mediterranean climate, characterised by long, dry summers and mild, wet winters. These moderately humid zones account for less than 10 percent of the land area but nearly half of the agricultural

---

[1] See Annex 3 for a list of countries in the region. Turkey is not considered to be part of this system, being included within the Eastern Europe and Central Asian region.

population, while the drier areas account for nearly 90 percent of the land area but less than 30 percent of the population. These aggregates include centres of population, often located in dispersed, intensively irrigated areas within arid and semiarid zones. In addition, the large-scale irrigated areas – which cover only 2 percent of total land area – include a further 17 percent of the agricultural population.

Rainfed crops are grown during the wetter winter period, while irrigated areas are cultivated year round. The main rainfed crops are wheat, barley, legumes, olives, grapes, fruit and vegetables. A wide range of subtropical crops, including fruit and vegetables, is also grown under irrigation in the summer months. Livestock, mainly sheep and goats, are an important feature of many farming systems and provide key linkages between and within the different systems – from extensive pastoralism to feedlots in peri-urban agriculture.

In comparison with other developing areas of the world, the Middle East and North Africa is not a particularly impoverished zone. The early development of irrigation-based civilisations in much of the area laid the foundation for intensive agricultural systems still in use today. Furthermore, historical evidence indicates that, in Roman times, much of North Africa enjoyed sufficient rainfall to support widespread rainfed cultivation of cereals and other crops. Climatic conditions and vegetative cover appear to have deteriorated since then.

Historically, irrigation practices, coupled with effective indigenous technologies for managing the limited resources available, have meant that any outright malnutrition in rural areas has been associated mainly with crop failures resulting from droughts, pests, or the failure of the annual flood in the Nile Valley. Rapid increases in population, arising from improved child survival rates and lower mortality in general, now threaten this historical equilibrium. Although the growing cities have proved to be a magnet for many young people, unemployment rates in urban areas are high. While only around two percent of the total population fall below the international poverty line of US$1 per day an estimated nine percent (or 33 million people)[2] – mostly living in rural areas – are undernourished.

In rural areas poverty is much more widespread than in urban areas. A high proportion of poor households consist of farmers or pastoralists who depend on agriculture as a primary food and livelihood source. Poverty is conditioned primarily by lack of access to the limited soil and water resources and by low productivity, and it is aggravated by highly unpredictable rainfall, relatively few crop and livestock options, and continuing natural resource degradation. Access to sufficient land to support growing families is already a major problem in many countries. Land ownership is highly skewed, with a small number of farmers owning large areas of the better quality land. In addition, the highly fragmented nature of many holdings leads to inefficient land management practices. Markets

---

[2] FAO 2000a.

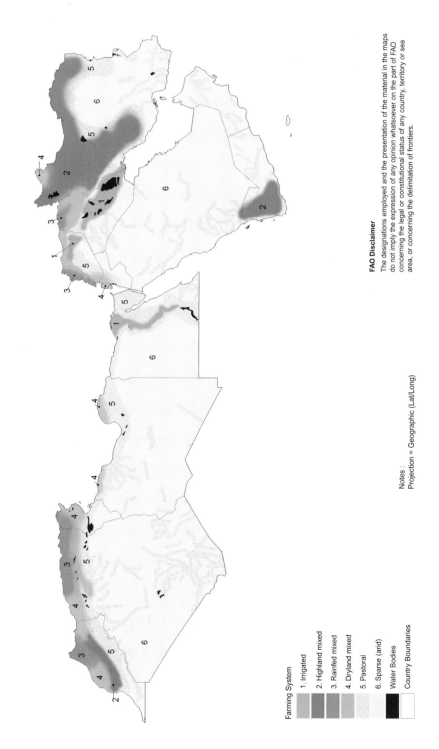

Major Farming Systems
MIDDLE EAST AND NORTH AFRICA

Farming System

1. Irrigated
2. Highland mixed
3. Rainfed mixed
4. Dryland mixed
5. Pastoral
6. Sparse (arid)
Water Bodies
Country Boundaries

FAO Disclaimer

The designations employed and the presentation of the material in the maps do not imply the expression of any opinion whatsoever on the part of FAO concerning the legal or constitutional status of any country, territory or sea area, or concerning the delimitation of frontiers.

Notes :
Projection = Geographic (Lat/Long)

are generally weak and many policies are geared toward urban needs – for the most part the provision of cheap food. Cereal farmers and pastoralists are particularly vulnerable to the impacts of subsidies on imported grains.

Historically, agriculture has played a key role in the development of many economies of the Middle East and North Africa; initially in the production of cereals and livestock and later in the development of fruits, vegetables and cash crops from irrigated or partially irrigated land. In 1997, agriculture contributed 13 percent to regional GDP and accounted for 19 percent of exports and 50 percent of employment in the region. However, there are large variations across countries depending on the relative importance of non-agricultural income in the economy. Access to water, both in terms of quantity and quality, remains a key issue in the both agricultural and national economies. The relatively low potential for increasing output without irrigation has meant that many economies have had to rely on alternative engines for economic growth, including petroleum extraction, mining, manufacturing, trading and other commercial activities.

MAJOR FARMING SYSTEMS IN MIDDLE EAST AND NORTH AFRICA

Eight major farming systems have been identified and broadly delimited, based on a range of criteria discussed in the first Chapter. They are listed in Table 3.1 and their geographical location is indicated in the accompanying Map.

Irrigated Farming System

Given the arid and semiarid nature of much of North Africa and the Middle East, the Irrigated Farming System has always been of crucial importance in generating much of the region's agricultural output. The system contains both large and small-scale irrigation schemes. The large-scale system consists of 8.1 million ha of irrigated cropland and an agricultural population of nearly 16 million[3]; resulting in high population densities and generally very small farm sizes. The prevalence of poverty within both sub-systems is moderate.

Traditionally, areas within the **Large-scale Irrigation Sub-System** have been linked primarily to perennial surface water resources, such as the Nile and Euphrates valleys, but the intensification of traditional *karez* or *qanat* systems has also led to the evolution of large-scale irrigated areas wherever sub-surface water is abundant. More recently, the availability of deep drilling and pumping technologies has permitted the development of new areas drawing entirely on subterranean aquifers. Large-scale schemes are found across all zones and include high-value cash and export cropping and intensive vegetable and fruit cropping. Patterns of water use vary greatly but, throughout the region, inappropriate policies on water

[3]
Land area and population estimates are for the large-scale system. Area and population for the scattered small-scale irrigated system are included in the totals for the other farming systems.

pricing and centralised management systems have meant that water is seldom used efficiently. Significant economic and environmental externalities have arisen through excessive utilisation of non-recharged aquifers while, in a number of cases, the excessive application of irrigation water has resulted in rising groundwater tables, soil salinisation and sodisation problems.

The **Small-scale Irrigated Sub-System** also occurs widely across the region and although not as important as the larger schemes in terms of numbers of people involved, or in the amount of food and other crops produced, it is a significant element in the survival of many people in arid and remote mountain areas. This sub-system, which may be of considerable antiquity, typically develops along small perennial streams and at oases, or where flood and spate irrigation is feasible. It sometimes also draws on shallow aquifers and boreholes, although these rarely penetrate to the depths seen in the large schemes. The major crops grown within small-scale irrigation areas are mixed cereals, fodder and vegetables. These areas also provide important focal points for socio-economic activity, but intense local competition for limited water resources between small rural farmers and other users is becoming increasingly evident. The Small-scale Irrigation Sub-System is not mapped due to its highly dispersed nature, but areas of substantial small-scale irrigation within other systems are indicated on the regional Map by hatching.

Highland Mixed Farming System

The Highland Mixed Farming System is the most important system in the region in terms of population – with 27 million people engaged in agriculture – but contains only 74 million ha (7 percent) of the land area, thus leading to moderately high population densities. The cultivated area is 22 million ha, of which nearly five million ha are irrigated. It covers two, sometimes overlapping, sub-systems. The first is dominated by rainfed cereal and legume cropping, with tree crops, fruits and olives on terraces, together with vines. In Yemen, this sub-system includes *qat* and coffee, which are traditionally the most important tree crops in mountain regions. The second sub-system is based primarily on the raising of livestock (mostly sheep) on communally managed lands. In some cases, both the livestock and the people who control them are transhumant, migrating seasonally between lowland *steppe* in the more humid winter season and upland areas in the dry season. This type of livestock keeping is still important in Iran and Morocco. Poverty within this system is extensive, as markets are often distant, infrastructure is poorly developed and the degradation of natural resources is a serious problem.

Rainfed Mixed Farming System

The Rainfed Mixed Farming System contains almost 18 percent of the agricultural population but occupies only two percent of the land area, resulting in high population densities. Cultivated area is 14 million ha, including tree crops and

Table 3.1 Major Farming Systems of Middle East and North Africa

Farming Systems	Land Area (% of region)	Agric. Popn. (% of region)	Principal Livelihoods	Prevalence of Poverty
Irrigated	2	17	Fruits, vegetables, cash crops	Moderate
Highland Mixed	7	30	Cereals, legumes, sheep, off-farm work	Extensive
Rainfed Mixed	2	18	Tree crops, cereals, legumes, off-farm work	Moderate (for small farmers)
Dryland Mixed	4	14	Cereals, sheep, off-farm work	Extensive (for small farmers)
Pastoral	23	9	Sheep, goats, barley, off-farm work	Extensive (for small herders)
Sparse (Arid)	62	5	Camels, sheep, off-farm work	Limited
Coastal Artisanal Fishing	1	1	Fishing, off-farm work	Moderate
Urban Based	<1	6	Horticulture, poultry, off-farm work	Limited

Source: FAO data and expert knowledge.
Note: Prevalence of poverty refers to number in poverty, not depth of poverty, and is a relative assessment for this region.

vines; and there are about eight million cattle. Although the system is by definition principally rainfed, an increasing area (presently about 0.6 million ha) is now benefiting from the availability of new drilling and pumping technologies, which have made it possible to use supplementary winter irrigation on wheat and full irrigation on summer cash crops[4]. There is some dry-season grazing of sheep migrating from the *steppe* areas. The more humid areas (600 to 1 000 mm annual rainfall) are characterised by tree crops (olives and fruit), melons and grapes. There is also some protected cropping[5] with supplementary irrigation, for potatoes, vegetables and flowers. Common crops are wheat, barley, chickpeas, lentils, and the fodder crops – vetches and medics. Poverty is moderate, but would be higher without extensive off-farm income from seasonal labour migration.

Dryland Mixed Farming System

The Dryland Mixed Farming System is found in dry subhumid areas which receive an annual rainfall of between 150 to 300 mm. The system contains an agricultural population of 13 million people and includes 17 million ha of cultivated land. Population density tends to be lower than in the other main arable systems and average farm sizes are larger. The main rainfed cereals are barley and wheat grown in a rotation that includes an annual or two-year fallow, but the risk of drought is

[4] Rodriguez *et al* 1999.
[5] Mainly using polythene tunnels.

high and considerable food insecurity exists. The livestock, including six million cattle and a greater number of small ruminants, interact strongly with the cropping and fodder system. In good years, rainfed barley is grown for grain, but when there is insufficient rainfall for adequate maturation, it is common for it to be fed as fodder to livestock. Local barley varieties are particularly well adapted to this system. The development of higher value crops, such as fruits and vegetables, has been constrained not only by low rainfall, but also by relatively poor market linkages. Poverty is extensive among small farmers.

Pastoral Farming System

The Pastoral Farming System, mainly involving sheep and goats but also with some cattle and camels, is found across almost a quarter of the land area of the region – equivalent to around 250 million ha. It includes large areas of semiarid *steppe* lands, and is characterised by low population densities, with more densely populated areas around irrigated settlements. There are some 2.9 million ha of irrigated cropland scattered throughout the system, thus boosting the agricultural population – which is around eight million people – and helping to support a cattle population of 2.5 million. Strong linkages exist to other farming systems through the movement of stock, both through seasonal grazing of herds in more humid areas and through the sale of animals to large feedlots located in urban areas. Seasonal migration, which is particularly important as a risk minimisation measure, depends on the availability of grass, water and crop residues in neighbouring arable systems. Nowadays, pastoral herds are often partially controlled and financed by urban capital. Where water is available, small areas of crop production have been developed to supplement the diets and income of pastoral families. However, such sites are few and poverty within the system is extensive.

Sparse (Arid) Farming System

The Sparse (Arid) Farming System covers more than 60 percent of the region and includes vast desert zones. Approximately four million people (about five percent of the region's agricultural population) live within the system, and are concentrated in oases and a number of irrigation schemes (notably in Tunisia, Algeria, Morocco and Libya). About 1.2 million ha of irrigated cropland are utilised for the production of dates, other palms, fodder and vegetables. In addition, an estimated 2.7 million cattle, pastoralists within this system also raise camels, sheep and goats. The system provides opportunistic grazing for the herds of pastoralists, following scattered storms and in good seasons. The boundary between pastoral grazing and sparse agriculture systems is indistinct and depends on climatic conditions. Poverty within this system is generally low as population pressure is limited.

Coastal Artisanal Fishing System

Small-scale artisanal fishermen have lived along the coasts of the Mediterranean and the Atlantic Ocean for thousands of years, supplementing income from the sale of fish with small-scale crop and livestock production. There are an estimated one million people living in this system, which has an area of around 11 million ha. As modern technology and capital have been injected into the offshore fishing industry, the artisanal fishing system has contracted.

Urban Based Farming System

Throughout the region a small population of urban residents, estimated to be less than 6 million people, engage in small-scale production of horticultural and livestock products – notably fruit, vegetables and poultry. The contribution of this system to GADP is small at present, but the growth in livestock feedlots, fruit, and intensive vegetable production in urban areas may become increasingly important in the coming decades. This system sometimes has important linkages with peri-urban and rural production systems.

REGION-WIDE TRENDS IN MIDDLE EAST AND NORTH AFRICA

This section describes the most important region-wide trends in terms of: population, hunger and poverty; natural resources and climate; science and technology; trade liberalisation and market development; policies, institutions and public goods; and information and human capital. At the end of the section, four of the regional farming systems described in the previous section of the Chapter are selected for further description and analysis.

Population, hunger and poverty

During the period 2000-2030, the population of the region is projected to almost double from its present 296 million[6]. This could have a considerable negative impact in areas with fragile or vulnerable soils and sloping land, and will certainly be of importance for water resources everywhere. The areas around major centres of population are particularly likely to suffer from various forms of environmental degradation and water shortage.

Although there has been some reduction of hunger since 1970, it is estimated that 33 million people within the region were still undernourished in 1995-1997[7]. This number is not expected to change much during the period to 2030, although the percentage of the population that is undernourished will decline. Currently, the average daily calorie intake is 2 980 kcal – 13 percent higher than the average for all developing countries and the highest among the six regions in this study. The overall calorie intake reflects high levels of consumption of cereals (20 percent higher than the developing world average) and meat, and is also influenced by the

---

[6] FAO (2000a) reports regional population growth estimates of 1.9 and 1.4 percent per annum for the periods 1995/1997-2015 and 2015-2030 respectively, compared with 1.4 and 1.0 percent per annum for all developing countries.

[7] FAO 2000a.

above-average access to food in the oil-rich countries of the region. However, this average masks the existence of vulnerable groups within some countries, as well as hiding the differences between oil-exporting and the non-exporting countries.

The overall total of 6 percent projected growth in calorie consumption is low, but the region will still achieve an average daily intake of 3170 kcal by 2030, comfortably exceeding the developing world average of 3020 kcal. The increase is expected to derive mainly from the continued growth in consumption of meat (60 percent), as well as milk and dairy products (23 percent). In many rural areas the quality of nutrition is not good, particularly for poorer people in drier and more isolated systems. Although meat and cereals may be reasonably accessible, vegetables and fruits are relatively scarce and expensive. As shown in Figure 1.3 of the first Chapter, there has been some reduction in dollar poverty within the region during the past decade.

Natural resources and climate

Since 1961, cultivated land has expanded by 14 percent, while cropping intensity has increased by over 15 percent within the same period. Currently, cultivated land in the region is 65 million ha, accounting for 76 percent of the estimated total potential. These figures indicate that most cultivable land is already being exploited and that there is limited scope for further expansion. Nevertheless, during 2000-2030, cultivated land use is still expected to expand, reaching a figure of 82 percent of the total potential. However, the newly cultivated land will often be seriously constrained by climate, slope or poor soils. Access to land will become increasingly difficult over the coming years – particularly for poorer people – and the expected increase in the cultivation of marginal land will lead to significant environmental degradation.

Currently, more than 20 million ha of land are irrigated – representing 32 percent of the total cultivated land in use and 60 percent of the land with irrigation potential. The average irrigation efficiency is about 50 percent, somewhat higher than the average of 43 percent in all developing countries. The exploited hydrological resources of the region account for only 1.4 percent of the total annual renewable water resources in the developing world. The aridity of the region means that irrigation is the principal means of agricultural intensification and diversification. Away from large perennial waterways, agricultural requirements for water have traditionally been met through the exploitation of shallow groundwater and seepage and small-scale impoundment. The 20th Century saw the construction of several large dams to provide storage for large-scale perennial irrigation schemes covering many square kilometres. More significantly, groundwater has been progressively used as a principal buffer for the reduction of hydrological risk. This insurance function has now turned into dependency in many countries, as demand has outstripped the capacity of other sources.

Based on irrigated area and efficiency, it is calculated that as much as 58 percent of available water in the region is being used for irrigation. However, four countries – Jordan, Libya, Saudi Arabia and Yemen – are already withdrawing volumes that exceed their annual water resource recharge; due to increasing demands for water both from their cities and from intensive agricultural systems. Depletion of water resources is likely to become an acute problem in many more places. During 2000-2030, the total irrigated area within the region is forecast to grow by 20 percent. This will bring total irrigated area to a level equal to 77 percent of all land with irrigation potential. Overall irrigation water requirements are expected to grow by 14 percent and efficiency of water use is estimated to reach 65 percent.

Taking into account the expected expansion of the irrigated area, it is projected that water use for irrigation will account for 67 percent of the total renewable water resources in the region. These average figures hide far more serious situations in a number of locations, where abstraction of groundwater is exceeding recharge and thus depleting strategic reserves. Economic competition for the limited renewable water resource base of the region is intensifying. Disputes over water use rights and resource allocation between sectors and across international borders are also becoming more evident, as limits to economic capture are reached. Under these circumstances, irrigation development is becoming increasingly conditioned by socio-economic and environmental realities to the extent that management of demand for both water and irrigation services is now an imperative.

Science and technology

Crop production growth to 2030 is projected at 1.7 percent per annum (compared with 1.6 percent per annum in all developing countries). During 1961-1997, crop production increased as a result of both harvested land expansion (29 percent), and yield increase (71 percent). Wheat dominates cereal production. In 2000, the region produced 23 million tons of wheat with an average yield of 1.4 t/ha – representing an annual increase in yield of 1.8 percent since 1970 (see Table 3.2). Although barley is second in importance in terms of area, it is exceeded by both maize and rice in terms of output. Olive production, which is a substantial export earner, was 2.8 million tons with an average yield of 2 t/ha. During the last decade, the region experienced rapid growth of olive production in terms of both area (2.1 percent per annum) and yield (5.5 percent per annum) – and further substantial yield increases are expected during the coming three decades.

Current fertiliser consumption represents only 7.2 percent of the total in all developing countries. The was no increase in fertiliser consumption in the region during the past decade, in contrast to the 3.5 percent annual increase for the developing world as a whole. However, projections suggest a gradual rise in consumption in the coming three decades.

The region has 197 million head of sheep and goats (see Table 3.3), accounting for about one-seventh of the total population of these animals in developing countries. There is a great variety of production systems for sheep and goats. These include: extensive pastoral systems; seasonal exploitation of crop residues in arable systems; and feedlots in major urban areas. Important linkages exist between many

Table 3.2 Trends in Crop Area, Yield and Output in Middle East and
North Africa, 1970-2000

Crop	Harvested Area 2000 (m ha)	Yield 2000 (t/ha)	Production 2000 (m tons)	Average Annual Change 1970-2000 (%)		
				Area	Yield	Production
Rice	1	6.2	9	1.3	1.3	2.6
Wheat	16	1.4	23	0.4	1.8	2.2
Maize	1	6.1	8	0.3	3.3	3.6
Barley	7	0.6	4	0.0	-0.7	-0.7
Pulses	2	0.8	2	0.8	0.0	0.8
Oilcrops	4	0.3	1	0.8	1.8	2.7
Vegetables	3	17.9	44	2.3	1.7	4.0
Fruits	3	9.3	30	3.0	1.0	4.1

Source: FAOSTAT.

of these systems. In recent decades, poultry numbers (900 million in 2000) have increased very rapidly – at a rate of almost 6 percent per annum, nearly double that for developing countries as a whole. This growth rate is forecast to decelerate during the period 2000-2030[8].

In many countries, a few very large production units now dominate the industry, limiting the opportunity for small-scale producers to enter into the market. During the last decade, cattle and buffalo numbers increased at 0.8 percent per annum and continued expansion is projected until 2030; despite the fact that the region is not well-suited to cattle production. The current total annual production of meat is nearly 6 million tons and it is projected to continue to grow until 2030. Milk production is currently 17 million tons, following a growth rate of 3.4 percent per annum since 1970. However, the projected rate of growth during 2000-2030 is lower[9].

Trade liberalisation and market development
Trade liberalisation has favoured the larger producers in the region, as many smaller operators have moved out of farming and trading altogether. Smaller businesses which deal in agricultural products have also found it increasingly difficult to compete and there are few areas in which they have any comparative advantage. There is minimal development of small-scale agro-processing industries in all but a few countries. Any growth of small-scale enterprises has usually been

[8] FAO 2000a.
[9] FAO 2000a.

Table 3.3 Trends in Livestock Populations and Output in Middle East and North Africa, 1970-2000

Species	Million Head 2000	Ave Annual Change 1970-2000 (%)
Cattle	21	0.8
Sheep	143	1.6
Goats	54	1.5
Camels	1	0.3
Poultry	905	5.8
Product	Output 2000 (million tons)	Ave Annual Change (%)
Total Meat	6	4.5
Total Milk	17	3.4
Total Eggs	2	5.4

Source: FAOSTAT.

through individual, or close family efforts and not through co-operative movements or producer organisations. The absence of credit for small producers and lack of market intelligence concerning overseas markets has also acted as a constraint to any significant development at this level.

However, many small farm households have diversified their livelihoods by developing off-farm activities such as tourism, catering and other service activities – often through family linkages. This trend is expected to continue in the coming 30 years and off-farm income will progressively grow in importance, especially for poor households.

Market development over the coming decades will depend closely upon the relationship between the region and the European Union (EU). Growing incomes in the Mediterranean countries of the EU will increase demand for North African and Middle Eastern products, and will likely attract European investment. Nevertheless, the policies of national governments concerning private enterprise development will strongly affect the speed of response to these opportunities.

Policies, institutions and public goods
Both development policies and investments in public goods have had a strong urban bias for many decades. Many public institutions in the recent past have been extremely centralised and development policies have tended to favour cheap food for urban populations. Infrastructural investments have also favoured major centres of population; primarily in the provision of water, basic services and communications links. The development of road systems has generally served

national security or urban objectives, rather than rural development; indeed, their construction has sometimes been in conflict with agricultural needs. Similarly, a great deal of high quality land has been lost close to cities, as a result of weak planning regulations and lack of forward thinking. Conflicts over rates of water extraction are already becoming a major issue in and around centres of population, and these conflicts are expected to intensify in the future.

The land reform issue remains one of the most intractable, as many people hold onto their fragmented holdings without any rationalisation or consolidation process in place; even where countries are officially undertaking land reform. Migration of young people to the cities means that the will to change the current system of land allocation and inheritance is weak. The only places where there have been major change are where larger operators have been able to buy-out smaller farmers. It is widely recognised that the reorganisation of land holdings is a prerequisite for the introduction of technologies that will conserve soil and water resources in the long run.

National livestock policies have tended to aggravate problems of overstocking, and therefore overgrazing, through the encouragement of the importation of cheap feed grains and the lack of regulation of numbers. Technology advances in the transport of livestock and water, and the role of private capital, have continued to place exceptional stress on natural rangeland resources. The lack of regulation has undermined the strength of older institutions and the system of communal range management which were designed to manage resources in a sustainable manner.

The high degree of centralisation of planning systems, and the rigid imposition of a target approach to production, has stifled innovation and diversification in many areas – particularly in the major irrigation schemes. Research has rarely been focused on applied problems of producers in risk-prone areas, or on the more efficient use of water. Market research for small producers has been minimal. Extension systems have often been very top down in design and delivery, leaving little scope for farmer-driven initiatives and partnerships.

Information and human capital

For many years, the capitals of the region had relatively good communication connections with Europe, although some countries adopted a policy of strict control over the use of the facilities. However, the contrast with farming – and especially pastoral areas – could not have been greater; and this relative neglect has hindered the responsiveness of farmers in many countries to new international market opportunities. This situation may be set to change with recent advances in information technology, including satellites and cell phones, which open up new possibilities for communication.

Until recently, government agricultural extension services were strong in several countries of the region; albeit with an emphasis on high potential areas, and on the regulation and control of land use and production practices. However, both cultivated and pastoral areas with low population densities have always lacked an adequate flow of technical and market information. In recent years, however, some countries have piloted computer-linked dissemination of farm management information. Farmer training has lagged behind other regions and this is holding back technology adoption and farming efficiency, as well as failing to build the skills of household members related to employment opportunities in the off-farm and urban economies.

Tertiary agricultural education reached a world class level during the third quarter of the last century, with a number of globally recognised universities situated throughout the region. In recent years, agricultural education institutions have generally not adopted new approaches to their curricula, nor have they employed innovative systems of delivery, such as distance learning. However, many universities have the capacity to improve quite rapidly, and it is expected that most will modernise these aspects during the coming decades.

Selection of farming systems

Of the eight farming systems described above the following have been chosen for further analysis, on the basis of their potentials for poverty reduction or agricultural growth, as well as their demographic and economic importance:

- Irrigated Farming System;
- Highland Mixed Farming System;
- Rainfed Mixed Farming System; and
- Dryland Mixed Farming System.

The Pastoral Farming System has also been included because of its relevance to other farming systems across the region. While it is neither demographically important nor offers a significant opportunity for poverty reduction, the role of the system in providing a reservoir of livestock which feed through into other systems – either seasonally or in the form of animals for fattening – makes it important in regional terms.

IRRIGATED FARMING SYSTEM

The Irrigated Farming System is found throughout the region. It encompasses two quite distinct sub-systems: the Large-scale Irrigated Farming Sub-System, common in a number of countries within the region, including Iraq, Syria, Morocco and Egypt, and the Small-scale Irrigation Sub-System, found scattered in small areas throughout such countries as Egypt, Yemen, Oman, Syria and the Maghreb. Each of these sub-systems is discussed separately below.

LARGE-SCALE IRRIGATED SUB-SYSTEM

CHARACTERISTICS OF THE SUB-SYSTEM

The Large-scale Sub-System is usually found along the major river systems downstream from dams and most large-scale schemes have an ancient history of development. It contains an estimated agricultural population of 16 million, and. covers an area of 19 million ha, of which approximately 8 million ha are equipped for irrigation (see Box 3.1). This system is dominated

Box 3.1 Basic Data: Large-scale Irrigated Farming Sub-System

Total population (m)	80
Agricultural population (m)	16
Total area (m ha)	19
Agro-ecological zone	Arid semiarid
Cultivated area (m ha)	8
Irrigated area (m ha)	8
Cattle population (m)	2

by intensive year-round cropping, by both owner-occupiers and tenants. Many areas suffer from recurrent problems of water misuse and mismanagement, salinity, sodicity, and gypsum soil problems (Euphrates). In several cases, large-scale irrigation represents significant areas within the overall cropped area of the country (e.g. the Nile delta) and feature ancient and highly sophisticated water management techniques. Cash crops (e.g. cotton and sugarbeet), vegetables and other high-value crops and fodder are all common. Cropping intensity ranges between 120 and 160 percent. Some areas support significant numbers of livestock (cattle, buffalo, sheep and goats).

Many schemes have combinations of State and private land ownership. Conflicting management objectives and weak institutions appear to be common problems. Typically, these schemes are characterised by large-scale centralised management of water access and distribution, and may be managed in large blocks with mechanised inputs. In other schemes water access and distribution is also managed centrally, but the land has been allocated to large numbers of tenants or owners who individually manage small plots – from 0.5 to 5 ha – and share other inputs and marketing facilities. Water User Associations (WUAs) are becoming more common in these situations, dealing with ongoing operation and maintenance and ensuring better water sharing procedures.

Other large-scale fully irrigated individual schemes have emerged in recent years that are privately financed and operated. Water is extracted using tubewells and distributed through sprinkler or trickle systems to farmers growing mainly high-value crops for export. These schemes not only present a challenge to older irrigated areas in the market place, but are also a threat to nearby small-scale systems that rely on simpler water lifting devices, as the high volume of water extraction from deep aquifers is contributing to declining water tables as the rate of extraction exceeds the rate of recharge (e.g. the Sana'a Basin in Yemen, the Souss Plain in Morocco, the

Bekaa Valley in Lebanon). Box 3.2 contains a brief description of a typical sub-system household.

Box 3.2 A Typical Household of the Large-scale Irrigated Farming Sub-System

A household in this system might have access to 2.5 ha of land and grows a range of crops throughout the year, including; cereals, pulses, fodder, fruit crops and cash crops such as cotton and sugarbeet. The management of the irrigated land is often affected negatively by physical problems – soil and water quality, and problems of conflicting objectives between the State and individual owners and tenants. In addition, the household manages small numbers of cattle, goats and sheep, which are fed from a combination of limited common grazing land, crop residues and cultivated fodder crops.

TRENDS AND ISSUES IN LARGE-SCALE IRRIGATED SUB-SYSTEM

The history of the larger, centrally-managed schemes is not very encouraging. Many have been plagued with problems of poor water management, disputes over water access, and quality and quantity issues. The primary technical issues are: surface schemes working below design capacities and at low efficiencies; rapid depletion of aquifers; poor water delivery scheduling; rising groundwater tables; continued soil degradation; salinity and sodicity; declining soil organic matter levels; and low crop yields. Energy and machinery costs are also very high in some places. In addition to this, there are institutional and financial issues related to the responsibility of users for organisation and management of the systems and for cost recovery.

In view of the poor record of sustainability of state-managed irrigation schemes, the present trend is towards greater involvement of the water users in management. However, the participation of users in decision making concerning water management faces legal and institutional constraints to the transfer of management responsibility and to the legal basis for devolution of authority.

Measures aimed at reducing crop demand for water through rationing or switching to crops with a lower water requirement are now being promoted in the region. However, given the present weak water pricing policies, water and irrigation services costs may not be significant in relation to other costs such as seed, fertiliser, pesticide and energy. This situation does not encourage the efficient use of water and a far-reaching restructuring of water pricing and subsidy policies is required. A clear range of economic incentives to encourage the adoption and extension of innovative technologies is also necessary. If subsidies are provided, they should be focused on boosting on-farm investment in modern technology and equipment that will facilitate the re-allocation of water from low to high value uses.

PRIORITIES FOR LARGE-SCALE IRRIGATED SUB-SYSTEM

In order to underpin both the intensification and diversification of production, both of which are judged to be important strategies for poverty reduction, the most important priority is the introduction of water demand management, using a range of economic, regulatory and advocacy instruments. These initiatives have to be locally tailored, but must also be embedded in national agriculture and water management policies. In addition, irrigation will need to become more flexible to accommodate the perennial hydrological risk in the region. Conjunctive use [10] and aquifer storage and recovery will become important tools in managing this risk.

The overall management of these large schemes is in need of major overhaul if poverty reduction is to accelerate. Interventions need to include: (i) identification and implementation of economic incentives to reduce water demand; (ii) promotion of water user institutions that can ensure equitable sharing among all legitimate users, (iii) increased efficiency of water use; (iv) restoration of soil fertility by raising organic matter levels and improving soil and water management; (v) development of farmer-participatory irrigation management systems in which growers play a much more active role in research, development and management; (vi) provision of a legal framework for farmers' associations, co-operatives and companies; (vii) facilitation of rural savings and loan initiatives; (viii) development of innovative technologies, credit, training and education for the small farm sector; and (ix) introduction of irrigation scheduling strategies that will provide a major opportunity for water savings.

In view of the emerging emphasis on water quality, it is expected that institutional factors such as regulations on levels of use of pesticides or nutrients will be a major consideration influencing future irrigation research programs. Rising demand by non-agricultural users will lead to increasingly intense competition for water over time – making it a relatively more costly input. This will tend to shift water supplies towards higher-value crops requiring more sophisticated management and equipment.

SMALL-SCALE IRRIGATED SUB-SYSTEM

CHARACTERISTICS OF THE SUB-SYSTEM

In this sub-system, owner-occupiers or tenants typically farm very small units (0.02 to 1 ha) often within the boundaries of larger, rainfed systems. Thus, these small-scale irrigated schemes are considered as part of the relevant rainfed

[10] Combined use of surface and underground water.

farming system. The holding usually contains fruit trees and intensively grown vegetables. Small-scale irrigation schemes are often found in isolated areas and provide food and other products primarily for local markets. Some of these involve traditional irrigation practices, water rights and scheme organisation.

This sub-system is characterised by limited water supplies, which reduce production opportunities, and often lead to opportunist planting following flooding or exceptional run-off. The cropping pattern and the type of crop developed are adapted to the water supplies and regime experienced over the years. This type of farming occurs throughout the plains areas of the region, as well as on terraced hillsides where it may be derived from an ancient system.

TRENDS AND ISSUES IN SMALL-SCALE IRRIGATED SUB-SYSTEM

Water shortages and food deficits are among the crucial issues facing small-scale irrigation farmers in the region and should be given priority. A participatory process of introducing technological packages that provide improvements to local practices has proven to be effective in tackling the issue of water shortage in a number of cases. With extremely limited possibilities for the expansion of available water resources except at prohibitive costs, the only solution left is to optimise the output from existing resources. Box 3.3 illustrates a case from the Yemen where a participatory approach to water management has successfully reduced the mining of groundwater.

PRIORITIES FOR SMALL-SCALE IRRIGATED SUB-SYSTEM

The top priority is to address the lack of equitable access to water resources. It is evident in some areas that a number of powerful individuals are controlling and capturing the bulk of available resources, using modern drilling and pumping equipment. Where this is happening, policy initiatives to promote more equitable access will be essential. Small-scale schemes, which offer important niches for local economies and the potential for higher value crops, are threatened by the depletion of water resources and the degradation of the environment.

Small irrigated schemes in ecological niches offer opportunities for testing and introduction of new varieties of major crops and trees. Stress tolerance, and the ability to grow in soils of low fertility, are important required characteristics and more adaptive research on these attributes is needed. There is a strong and growing demand in Northern Europe for organic foods and other agricultural products grown without chemical inputs, and this has created an opportunity to grow crops that are suited to specific niche situations. The key to this process would be to support small producers with access to these markets, through region-branded marketing groups and introductory preferential access.

> **Box 3.3 Improved on-farm Participatory Water Management to Reduce Mining of Groundwater in Yemen** [11]
>
> Water shortage is the most crucial issue Yemen is currently facing and there is little chance that its importance will diminish in future unless appropriate measures are taken. The immediate consequence of the continuous decline in water resources has been household food insecurity, especially for poor families in vulnerable rural areas. As most renewable water resources have already been harnessed for use, the only viable option left is to improve the management of available resources, through the introduction of appropriate technologies and management tools.
>
> Conscious of these issues, the Government of Yemen launched a wide-scale programme to improve the general efficiency of irrigation from groundwater resources in 1995. The programme included the World Bank financed Land and Water Conservation Project which is based on cost-sharing, farmers' participation and modern irrigation technologies.
>
> Water savings achieved at the farm level have varied from 10 to over 50 percent. At the regional level, the mean savings in water use were at least 20 percent and have reached as high as 35 percent, particularly in the northwest of the country where most of the farms were equipped with bubbler irrigation systems. Considering the current operational costs that farmers have to pay for pumping water (even with relatively low energy costs), the cost of investment in modern irrigation equipment is recovered within two to four years from water savings alone. In addition, however, the new technology offers benefits beyond water savings, including significant improvements in yield and product quality, and added value resulting from changes in cropping patterns or increase in the irrigated area.

HIGHLAND MIXED FARMING SYSTEM

CHARACTERISTICS OF THE SYSTEM

This system has an estimated total population of 65 million people, of which 27 million are engaged in agriculture (see Box 3.4), making it the most important within the region in terms of population. However, it covers an area of 74 million ha, so population densities are lower than in the irrigated and rainfed-mixed systems. Annual rainfall is between 200 and 800mm.

Box 3.4 Basic Data: Highland Mixed Farming System	
Total population (m)	65
Agricultural population (m)	27
Total area (m ha)	74
Agro-ecological zone	Semiarid – subhumid
Cultivated area (m ha)	22
Irrigated area (m ha)	5
Cattle population (m)	2

[11] Bazza 2001.

The system depends upon the exploitation of high altitude arable and common grazing lands where cold winters lead to dormancy or very slow growth of crops and fodder species.

The cereals that form part of the system are adapted to survive under snow and extended cold periods. Wheat and barley dominate the cropping pattern, which comprises primarily of monocultures with occasional fallows. Common grazing lands usually surround these cropped areas, and may be used by owners from the same region or by pastoralists migrating to the plains for the winter season. Box 3.5 contains a brief description of a typical farm household.

As a sub-set of this system, on high-altitude sloping lands in several countries, (e.g. in Yemen) level terraces created several thousand years ago have been planted with fruit trees, coffee, *qat*, olives and vegetable crops – sometimes with supplementary irrigation in the summer months for crops such as melons or high-value fruits.

Box 3.5 A Typical Household of the Highland Mixed Farming System

A typical farm household within this system may have a small area of cropped land (four ha), typically on old terraces. The cultivated land is primarily used for cereal production (about three ha) and also for fruit trees, coffee, qat, olives and vegetables in some areas. Most farms have access to common grazing land for sheep and goats (four per family). The family may also have a cow that is used for milk production.

TRENDS AND ISSUES IN HIGHLAND MIXED SYSTEM

Within the Highland Mixed System, inadequate maintenance of terraces in recent years has led to a decline in the quality of the natural resource base, and to increasing water erosion that has reduced productivity. To some extent, this neglect of terrace maintenance has been caused by reduced labour availability, as a result of substantial levels of emigration to urban and plains areas. A decline in soil fertility, resulting from continuous cropping and low nutrient return, is also an issue in some plateau areas. Where livestock are present, overgrazing close to settlements and water points has further contributed to soil degradation. Increased competition from subsidised imports of meat and dairy products for urban consumers continues to impoverish small producers by pushing down prices.

PRIORITIES FOR HIGHLAND MIXED SYSTEM

There is limited scope for poverty reduction within the Highland Mixed Farming System through intensification or diversification of production. Nevertheless, in

Box 3.6 Participatory Watershed Management and Poverty Reduction[12]

The Highland Mixed Farming System is particularly prone to soil degradation and erosion. A pilot project undertaken over an area of 70 000 ha in the Atlas Hills of Tunisia has demonstrated the feasibility of combining improved watershed management with improved income opportunities for participants. The area is dominated by smallholders with fragmented holdings on slope land with extensive erosion, and has many landless families. Average family incomes are estimated at US$110 per month, of which seasonal migration and other off-farm labour account for about half. Degradation of vegetative cover and soil erosion is extensive in the zone, and conflicts over resource access were increasing, while technologies offered by public extension services were often inappropriate.

Project activities included forestry, agro-forestry, tree platforms (micro-terraces), small-scale earth bunds, small checkdams consolidated with fodder species, hill reservoirs and small irrigation schemes. Consultative processes aimed at resolving conflicts between farmers and the Government over access to, and use of, national forest areas resulted in changes in tree species used, the opening of access paths, and the contracting of local labour for many forest activities. Large water retention schemes, which mostly benefited downstream landowners, were replaced with farmer-selected technology options implementable on individual farms. Support was provided for tree crop establishment (olive, almond, and fruit trees) combined with contoured intercropping of legumes. The process of changing farmer organisation into user and special-interest groups, and the strengthening of locally active NGOs, have been critical to the success of the whole programme.

As the project is still underway, sustainability cannot be readily assessed, but an estimated 75 percent of the families have participated in one or more activities, while Government support systems have been restructured to provide options based on appropriate technologies and cost sharing with farmers. The combination of participatory approaches, conservation measures and income creation will offer considerable potential for development elsewhere in the region.

order to protect existing levels of productivity and downstream rural and urban water users, the primary need is for the development of more sustainable watershed planning and management systems, plus the introduction of conservation tillage systems, and better integration of crops and livestock. The effectiveness of these technical changes depends upon the participation of the agricultural population in the planning and management process; and on the establishment of appropriate local institutions that can ensure equitable benefits to all producers. Box 3.6 presents an example of an approach to effective watershed management that contributed to poverty reduction in Tunisia.

Similarly, there is a need for more equitable regulation and control of common grazing resources, that can only take place effectively with full participation of all

[12] Fe' D'Ostiani 2001.

stakeholders. Older systems of management may need additional measures and a modern legal basis to take account of new capital financing of livestock. Scarcity of drinking water, for both humans and animals, in the mountain areas is one of the most serious problems and large number of new water points are needed.

Finally, there is a need for an end to policies of import subsidies on animal feed grains that depress local prices and make it difficult for local producers to compete. Although a substantial proportion of households are likely to abandon farming and move to areas with better economic opportunities and services, it will also be important to foster land consolidation for the remaining small producers. Some poverty reduction can be achieved through increases in farm size. For similar reasons, linkages to the off-farm economy should be strengthened in order to promote, *inter alia*, off-farm employment.

RAINFED MIXED FARMING SYSTEM

CHARACTERISTICS OF THE SYSTEM

This system contains an estimated total population of 40 million people, and an agricultural population of 16 million (see Box 3.7). Despite supporting one fifth of all farm households within the region, it covers an area of only 17 million ha, giving rise to population densities similar to those of the irrigated system. Producers are typically owner-occupiers or tenants. Annual rainfall is between 300 and 1000 mm and the

Box 3.7 Basic Data: Rainfed Mixed Farming System	
Total population (m)	40
Agricultural population (m)	16
Total area (m)	17
Agro-ecological zone	Dry-moist subhumid
Cultivated area (m ha)	14
Irrigated area (m ha)	0.6
Cattle population (m)	8

growing period ranges from 180 to 365 days. A wide diversity of crops and trees are grown in well-established patterns around settlements.

In the more humid areas, tree crops (olives, fruits and nuts) are an important component and may dominate the system. They may be intercropped with cereals and vegetables while the trees are immature, but when mature they may become a monoculture. Wheat, barley, lentils, chickpeas, potatoes, sugarbeet and faba beans are the main annual crops. Summer crops are grown following a winter fallow. Vegetables, oil crops and flowers may also be grown, often with protection (polythene tunnels) in order to access specialised markets in Northern Europe and elsewhere.

Many farms are intensively capitalised with a high level of inputs, and farmers are very sensitive to market opportunities. There are a number of specialised dairy and

105

poultry enterprises within the system. In the drier areas, cereals become more dominant and there is often a greater interdependence among farming families who frequently share resources and equipment. Farm systems are diversified and there is a seasonal interaction with livestock (mainly sheep and goat) owners in the use of crop residues and other fodder. Box 3.8 contains a brief description of a typical farm system household.

Box 3.8 Typical Household of the Rainfed Mixed Farming System

A typical system farm manages about five ha in several parcels of land of different quality around the village. Cereals (about three ha) and legumes are managed collectively in blocks to aid mechanisation of operations and post-harvest grazing management. The farm has small areas of olives, fruits and vines. A cow and a few sheep are kept around the village. Off-farm income is substantial, mostly from seasonal employment in the city.

TRENDS AND ISSUES IN RAINFED MIXED SYSTEM

The principal trends and issues concern the poor access to quality land faced by increasing numbers of small farmers; soil erosion on slopes during rainstorms and erosion by wind on light, over-cultivated, exposed soils; and increasing attempts by farmers to diversify crops. Strategies and policies of research and extension institutions are not addressing the main needs of small farmers. Other trends include the decreasing proportion of wheat and the greater use of legumes in the rotation, increasing farm size and mechanisation (including the rapidly rising use of supplementary irrigation), migration to urban areas and growing dependence on off-farm income to secure food and livelihood security. Women are becoming increasingly marginalised in the production process and their labour is being progressively displaced, as men dominate the mechanisation processes for all the main crops.

Population density continues to rise and there is also a growing global influence on the system, both from imports of subsidised cereals and from the problems of access to markets. Subsistence farming is declining in these areas, while large-scale commercial interests are involved in high-input farming of export crops and livestock. At the same time there appears to be little commitment by many governments to supporting the sector – particularly the smaller farmers – through regulation of imports and specific support to poor farmers. Near the coast, the system is under considerable pressure in some areas by demand for land for urban settlement, tourism and other forms of economic speculation (e.g. Lebanon, Maghreb). This could also represent an opportunity for those farmers who wish to become more involved in the tourism sector.

PRIORITIES FOR RAINFED MIXED SYSTEM

This system appears to have potential for reduced poverty through intensification of production based, *inter alia*, on more effective management of natural resources and improved access to markets. Interventions and developments that could have a significant impact are: integrated water resources management; conservation agriculture on slopes and vulnerable soils; and the introduction of new crops and varieties to cope with short growing periods and droughts. The following improvement measures are of particular importance to small farming systems: (i) terrace restoration and soil contouring; (ii) cover cropping under trees; and (iii) watershed management by local communities or associations. In order to ensure the success of these changes, the following principal areas of action are suggested.

Land reform programmes, which were begun years ago, should be continued, focusing on farm amalgamation, more equitable distribution of land and water resources and better access to services. In conjunction with this, and with the active participation of small farmer groups, continuing research is needed on systems of land and water management including traditional techniques used in the region. In combination with these actions, there is a need to identify economic incentives for improved water resource management and to develop communally based initiatives for the long-term management of water catchments – including the rehabilitation of terrace systems and the reintroduction of intercropping systems. The success of these measures will depend to a large extent upon strengthening the role of women in watershed resource management and restoration.

There would appear to be a place for the development of niche (e.g. ethnic) and organic food production for international markets, e.g. olives, vines, pistachio, fruits, raisins, dates, spices, herbs and vegetables. Assistance with market entry is needed for small farmer groups. Connected with this, there is a place for the development of simple processing methods, direct marketing by producers, and storage facilities at strategic points.

Reforms are urgently needed in the institutions that are designed to serve farmers, and in the development of social infrastructure that will encourage young people to remain in rural areas. Restructuring and retraining of farmer-sensitive research systems and farmer-driven extension systems with farmer-researcher partnerships is one way forward. Particular focus is needed on technologies for small-scale women farmers and women's labour. Much can be adapted from widespread experiences elsewhere in Asia and Africa. Farmer study tours and interregional workshops for farmers, researchers and extensionists could be valuable. More adaptive, systemic research is required, both agricultural and socio-economic, on crop-livestock integration and risk reduction, and the stability and sustainability of farming systems. There is a need to address the dearth of recent case studies on farming systems in this region. The development of effective farmer-participatory research methods and support to farmer-driven research activity, also merit a high priority.

Policies are required to control a range of actions and practices with major negative environmental impacts; these include frequent, deep ploughing, excessive use of pesticides and excessive water extraction for irrigation. Improved natural resource management, enterprise diversification and off-farm income opportunities should also be promoted.

DRYLAND MIXED FARMING SYSTEM

CHARACTERISTICS OF THE SYSTEM

The Dryland Mixed Farming System covers an area of 42 million ha and contains an estimated total population of 50 million, with an agricultural population of 13 million (see Box 3.9). Annual rainfall is between 300 and 150 mm. The cultivated area is 17 million ha and cropping is dominated by cereals (mainly barley and wheat), grown in alternation with single or double season fallows. Occasionally, and especially in higher-rainfall areas, legumes (lentils and chickpeas) may be grown.

Box 3.9 Basic Data: Dryland Mixed Farming System	
Total population (m)	50
Agricultural population (m)	13
Total area (m ha)	42
Agro-ecological zone	Semiarid – subhumid
Cultivated area (m ha)	17
Irrigated area (m ha)	3
Cattle population (m)	6

Interactions with pastoral systems are potentially strong as sheep may graze green barley in a dry year and the stubble of the harvested crop in average or wetter years. Small areas of irrigated vegetables may be grown in association with these systems. Box 3.10 contains a brief description of a typical farm system household.

Box 3.10 A Typical Household of the Dryland Mixed Farming System

A typical household in this system has about seven ha of cultivated land located in small parcels on different types of land around the village. The household grows wheat and barley and a small area of legumes. The family has a few cows and small numbers of sheep (nine on average), which are grazed around the village and for part of the year in the *steppe*. Poorer families have some members who work for larger farmers or have temporary or more permanent work in urban areas.

TRENDS AND ISSUES IN DRYLAND MIXED SYSTEM

This system is primarily dependent on wheat and barley production, together with a strong interaction with small livestock (primarily sheep). The reliability of cropping is highly dependent on rainfall and the whole system is vulnerable to inter-annual and seasonal variation – both temporal and spatial – in rainfall. In the recent past, there has been a decline in wheat area and renewed use of indigenous barley varieties. The most critical issue concerns the limited access to new crops and varieties by most farmers.

A further issue has been the failure to fully integrate cropping and livestock systems, because policies and price ratios have worked against this potentially stabilising feature. Human nutrition in these systems is also an issue, as diets tend to lack variety and quality. Under these circumstances, farmers progressively rely more on livestock systems for subsistence and cash income. Migration to urban areas has been increasing and remittances to families remaining in these areas play a significant role in food security. Some of the more arid areas with lighter soils experience severe wind erosion problems during the dry season.

PRIORITIES FOR DRYLAND MIXED SYSTEM

Notwithstanding substantial emigration from this system, there is judged to be some scope for poverty reduction through production intensification and growth in off-farm income – the latter largely through seasonal migration. Priorities should be focused on regulatory measures for access and use of land and water resources, as well as on technology development and dissemination with a focus on the poor.

In this context, the importance of land consolidation and technologies for conservation is paramount: including development and adaptation of appropriate and financially accessible technologies for conservation agriculture on slopes and vulnerable soils. In many areas, this can only be achieved following a significant change in land ownership and distribution patterns through land consolidation. Interventions requiring collective action by resource user groups include the development of conservation methods, such as wind erosion control through windbreaks; water harvesting methods; stubble mulch or minimum or zero tillage methods that are feasible for all farmers, and shrubs that can also be used as fodder.

While irrigated systems remain a high political priority, there is a need to recognise that a shift in resource allocation from irrigated agriculture to rainfed farming is essential if there is to be a realistic regional focus on poverty alleviation. Irrigated and rainfed systems interact strongly and it is not efficient to strengthen one without addressing the problems of the other. A systems perspective on land and water resource management planning activities should be encouraged and ultimately adopted by the provincial and district planning bodies. Such bodies would benefit by extending their representative membership to include all stakeholders who can participate in decision making.

Interventions through extension and distribution outlets that are likely to have some impact on the poor include: (i) the generation and distribution of a wide range of new varieties of major crops; (ii) water conservation training; (iii) exploration and re-development of traditional water management techniques; (iv) increased emphasis on intercropping; (v) the application of appropriate technologies; and (vi) O&M training for those technologies.

A new approach to research is called for in order to develop crop varieties with a shorter growing period, drought resistance, and improved grain and straw quality. Pilot studies should consider the socio-economic and cultural impact of the characteristics of the new crops, to ascertain whether they meet the needs of the society in which they will be used. A new approach is also required in the way in which research is organised and managed to better serve these systems. There needs to be more proactive research with the active participation of smaller farmers – particularly women – on the development of these interventions. Participative, on-farm research related to crop-livestock integration, and to resource conservation with a focus on risk reduction and sustainability of systems, is likely to produce long-term benefits for the poor in these systems.

PASTORAL FARMING SYSTEM

CHARACTERISTICS OF THE SYSTEM

This system is found in most countries of the region. It contains an estimated total population of 30 million and an agricultural population of eight million (see Box 3.11). It covers an area of 250 million ha, or approximately a quarter of the regional land area. Some pastoralists also cultivate small areas of crops, where water is available. However, annual rainfall in this system

Box 3.11 Basic Data: Pastoral Farming System	
Total population (m)	30
Agricultural population (m)	8
Total area (m ha)	250
Agro-ecological zone	Arid – semiarid
Cultivated area (m ha)	3
Irrigated area (m ha)	3
Cattle population (m)	3

is less than 150 mm so opportunities are limited. Pastoralists keep mainly sheep in their herds and flocks, but many also have goats, donkeys and camels. There are an estimated 60 million sheep and goats and three million cattle in this system.

The system is based on the mobility of herds and flocks, which move with the availability of grazing – related to seasonal rainfall distribution – and the availability of water. This movement may be between more humid and drier lowland areas, or between the plains and highland areas. In the past, water was only obtainable from fixed water storage systems, but the use of mobile water tankers has enabled livestock owners to travel larger distances seasonally. Crop residues, subsidised grains and purchased fodder make up the remainder of feed requirements. Pastoralists are often partially funded by urban capital, or else they manage stock owned by urban dwellers. The technology associated with the management of modern pastoral systems has resulted in great pressure on *steppe* grazing land. Box 3.12 contains a brief description of a typical farm system household.

Box 3.12 A Typical Household of the Pastoral Farming System

A typical pastoral household has access to a very small area of cultivated land (1 to 2 ha), often cropped on an opportunistic basis. The family generally has access to about 100 ha of grazing land, and sometimes to larger areas through customary or rental arrangements, to support varying numbers of sheep, goats, and cattle. The household may manage a number of animals for urban based capitalists, either seasonally or in a long term arrangement.

TRENDS AND ISSUES IN PASTORAL SYSTEM

Pastoralists remain an important linking group across the major farming systems in the region. Because of the continually rising demand for meat, primarily from urban areas, pastoral systems will remain important, even with the rise in importance of urban-based livestock feedlots.

The principal long-term problem for pastoralists throughout the region is desertification. Resource degradation is the reason for the steady decline in pastoral incomes, resulting in complex demographic, economic and social changes. Total rainfall is the dominant limiting factor in the dry rangelands. Drought diminishes rangeland productivity, but also adversely affects feed quality and species diversity. Drought also causes changes in the composition and size of the herd. If drought continues to the extent of rangeland desiccation, pastoralists abandon the area.

However, heavy grazing of the rangelands by livestock is believed to be the most widespread cause of vegetation and land degradation throughout the region. In the hyper-arid zones, the livestock survive for a period on xerophytic shrubs and ephemeral grasses, and once these plants are grazed livestock have to be moved elsewhere. For this reason, there appears to be a balance between carrying capacity and livestock in the hyper-arid zones. In the arid and semiarid zones, livestock density is above the potential carrying capacity most of the year, and these are the areas where most of the desertification takes place.

Intensive grazing around settlements is often related to the sedentarisation of nomadic herders. The settlement of former nomads entails concentration of their herds on grazing land around their new homes. Under drought conditions, these herders are forced to graze their animals in areas where most drinking water is available. This eventually leads to the complete disappearance of the most palatable herbaceous cover, particularly around boreholes that provide drinking water for humans and animals all year round.

The availability of more secure watering points also induces pastoralists to change their herd composition in favour of sheep, which further increases grazing pressure around the watering points. While increased water supplies are necessary in the drylands for a proper use of natural resources and to alleviate adverse living conditions, the almost inevitable result is the concentration of population and livestock around these watering points, which disturbs the fragile ecosystem.

One of the most important recommendations approved by the 1977 United Nations Conference on Desertification dealt with land degradation in rainfed farming areas. The recommendation called for the establishment of legal limits to cultivation by tractor ploughing in marginal drylands, which are more suited for grazing. It was based on the fact that these areas are particularly vulnerable to extensive clearing and excessive mechanical cultivation. However, the recommendation has not been implemented in the region. Opportunistic ploughing of rainfed marginal areas may produce a few good harvests in the short term, but will, in the longer term, lead to erosion. The natural vegetation on such land often constitutes the better quality rangeland available to the pastoralists. As a result of erosion, the land is lost to both agriculture and pastoralism. The animals are thereby pushed to less productive rangeland, which becomes further impoverished as a result. Implementation of this recommendation would lead to important ecological benefits.

Centrally planned economies continue to marginalise and exclude pastoralists from most forms of support. This is unfortunate as pastoral systems with well-balanced grazing management are the most sustainable way in which natural resources in low-rainfall areas can be managed and conserved.

PRIORITIES FOR PASTORAL SYSTEM

Reduced poverty is expected to result from four main sources: intensification of livestock productivity; diversification; increased off-farm income; and exit from agriculture. The highest priority for this system is greater flexibility and integration in agropastoral systems. Increased capitalisation and specialisation has led to the marginalisation and neglect of many pastoral groups and without some attention, protection and support, many are likely to disappear. The long-term maintenance of the resource base in semiarid areas can only be assured by strong collective responsibility. This will probably require formal contractual arrangements – between pastoralists and cultivators – concerning the kinds of interaction that are desirable from the perspectives of equity and environmental management.

Pastoral (*steppe*) areas could be managed sustainably through the revival of, and support for, older institutions for control of communal grazing areas by pastoralists themselves (the Hema system). However, this would be only a partial solution as urban-based owners who frequently have different priorities to those of pastoralists, now finance many herds. Intervention is needed in order to monitor management systems – including both urban-based and pastoral stakeholder groups – and to establish codes of conduct and management that ensure the long-term sustainability of natural resources on the range. This will require training programmes for both urban and pastoral participants in monitoring and management of herds and range condition. Box 3.13 contains a brief description of a case from Syria in which an area of degraded *steppe* has been rehabilitated through the introduction of native plant and animal species together with the revival of older community based management systems.

In addition to the revival and development of local institutions, there is a need for new legislation that will protect the *steppe* environment and ensure sound long-term management of soil and pasture resources. Such legislation is critical to the sustainability of the farming system. It should reinforce or create conditions to ensure that the long-term interests of groups dependent on the rangelands for

---

Box 3.13 Range Rehabilitation in Pastoral Farming Systems [13]

The Al Badia *steppe* area of Syria receives less than 200 mm per annum of rainfall and has been subject to widespread deterioration of the rangelands and loss of wildlife habitats (and consequently of wildlife). An FAO project has been active in the area since 1996, covering 108 000 ha of rangeland and 22 000 ha of wildlife reserve. Its main focus has been on reversing the degradation of the rangelands, rehabilitating areas with the participation of the local Bedouin population and re-introducing oryx (*Oryx leucoryx*) and sand gazelle (*Gazella subgutturosa marica*) to the Talila wildlife reserve. In addition to the rehabilitation of nearly 10 000 ha using seed of native species (*Salsola vermiculata* and *Atriplex leucoclada*) and innovative and cost-effective direct seeding technologies, the project has: initiated grazing management strategies; introduced an environmental monitoring system; collected data on livestock production; identified and implemented options for income generation and employment for local community members, particularly women; improved the technical skills and capacities of national project staff, training technicians, extension officers and Bedouin promoters; and sensitised the Bedouin community.

Major impacts and lessons learned include the feasibility of range rehabilitation by reseeding native species, the importance of community participation, project implementation flexibility, longer-term assistance for sustainability, the need for both local and national drought strategies and the need to focus on land tenure issues.

---

[13] Batello 2001.

their livelihood, prevail over the short-term interests of individuals or groups external to the range.

There should also be a higher level of support given to research institutions engaged in the introduction of bushes and fodder intercrops adapted to local rangeland conditions (e.g. International Center for Agricultural Research in the Dry Areas [ICARDA] and its collaborating national research and extension partners). Several improved techniques and approaches are known, but not widely available. Local adaptive research with farmer and pastoralists – if encouraged and supported – will spread their application.

STRATEGIC PRIORITIES FOR MIDDLE EAST AND NORTH AFRICA

The review of the characteristics, trends and potentials of the main farming systems in the Middle East and North Africa clearly indicates the close interdependence of people, water and land-based resources. There are also important linkages between different farming systems, particularly between livestock and cropping systems. Investment in the agricultural and rural development sectors, apart from irrigation, has been relatively modest. Two groups that have been excluded from most development initiatives have been; (i) poorer farmers living in dryland areas; and (ii) the pastoralists who occupy a unique role in the rural economy and in the long-term maintenance of a stable environment in dry areas. In view of the interdependency of resource management systems, the neglect of one farming system could have a major impact on people dependent on other systems.

The most significant trend over the past 30 years has been accelerating urbanisation and the consequent growth of cities. This trend is likely to continue, resulting in rapidly rising demands for water and food – particularly cereals and livestock products. In the rural areas, the growth in the proportion of income earned from non-agricultural activities is likely to continue and this has to be considered when strategic options for potential investment are being reviewed. The prospects for reducing agricultural poverty in the region are fairly good. In the context of halving hunger and poverty and based on the above analysis of farming systems, the relative importance of five household strategies for escaping poverty are shown in Table 3.4. The table indicates that, for the region as a whole, exit from agriculture is the most important of these strategies, followed by increased off-farm income. Among on-farm household improvement strategies, diversification and intensification are of equal importance, following closely behind off-farm income in the overall ranking. Increased farm size appears to be of minor importance overall.

The key strategic priorities for the region are grouped below under five major themes that are considered to be essential elements in any overall support

Table 3.4 Potential and Relative Importance of Household Strategies for Poverty Poverty Reduction in the Middle East and North Africa

Farming System	Potential for agricultural growth	Potential for poverty reduction	Strategies for poverty reduction				
			Intensi-fication	Diversi-fication	Increased Farm Size	Increased off-farm Income	Exit from Agriculture
Irrigated	High	High	3	4	0	2	1
Highland Mixed	High	Moderate	1	1	2	2	4
Rainfed Mixed	High	High	3	2	1	2	2
Dryland Mixed	Moderate	Moderate	2	1	1	2	4
Pastoral	Low	Moderate	2	2	0	3	3
Sparse (Arid)	Low	Low	1	2	0	3	4
Coastal Artisanal Fishing	Low	Low	2.5	1.5	0	3	3
Urban Based	Low	Low	2	3	0	4	1
Average for Region			2.0	2.0	0.9	2.3	2.8

Source: Expert judgement.
Note: Total score for each farming system equals 10. Assessments refer to poor farmers only. Average for region weighted by agricultural populations of systems derived from Table 3.1.

programme for the revitalisation of farming systems and rural livelihoods in the region, namely: Policies, Markets, Information, Technologies and Natural Resources. They are all, to a large extent, interdependent and they cut across farming systems.

POLICIES, INSTITUTIONS AND PUBLIC GOODS

The priority roles of the State are to support the development of vital infrastructure (roads, water supplies, services, power systems) and to regulate resource use and pricing for increasingly scarce resources – notably water. The region has suffered in the past from excessively centralised planning and programme implementation, particularly in agriculture, and from a policy bias against agriculture in favour of urban populations. Such policies have been counterproductive and have acted as a significant disincentive for many smaller farmers, artisans and entrepreneurs. Greater devolution and subregional disbursement of resources appear to be essential if agriculture is to develop in a dynamic manner. As part of this strategy, there needs to be greater participation in the development of collective stakeholder responsibility for management and protection of land, water and grazing resources.

Such participation requires the strengthening of local institutions and community empowerment.

There are many private sector investments in agriculture and agriculture related industries. The region is also influenced by multinational companies, many of which have agendas that are not always sympathetic to the needs of poorer farmers. It should be possible to develop more constructive partnerships between the private sector, major donors and the State in order to address the most urgent needs of the poor in rural areas. It is possible that the private sector could play a more active role in contributing to infrastructural needs, notably through the provision of water supply systems, roads and other types of infrastructure.

One crucial area for improvement will be the regulation and management of livestock, both in the towns and in the countryside. This can only be done through extensive partnerships of stakeholders. As part of a new approach to research and development, national research and extension systems need to be integrated and both need profound changes in training content and methods in order to become more effective in addressing the needs of poorer farmers. The private sector could also play a much more active role in this area, as has occurred in Latin America. In addition, modern scientific approaches should be used in mapping and monitoring changes in natural resource distribution and use – particularly water.

In many areas of the region, land holding patterns have remained little changed for many years and restructuring has been discouraged by weak policy strategies and frameworks. Remnants of older systems of community land management persist, but these have been overlain by the impact of modernisation in agriculture which has encouraged individualisation of land holdings and the breakdown of once vital linkages. Currently, the cultivated plots that are managed in these systems are fragmented, have low productivity and suffer from lack of investment. They are also affected by the steady decline in labour as young men and women migrate to urban areas. There is a general lack of dynamism and innovative drive in agriculture, due in part to uncertain land tenure arrangements; a lack of effective local institutions; and unchanged soil and water management practices.

There are ongoing attempts to consolidate holdings through land reform but this is a slow and difficult process. The key policy and institutional reforms in this process will include consolidation and rationalisation of land holdings with a focus on the common, long-term interest and survival of the communities occupying a given water catchment area. The development of collective forms of land management, that will allow the introduction of more rational and efficient soil cultivation and management technologies, is also of great importance. This could be facilitated by the establishment of community resource management and livelihood groups.

Legislation and regulation, taking into account local practices, is needed to control the grazing pressure on drylands and uplands – one good example is the planned action in eastern pastoral region in Morocco. These actions should be linked to: (i) eliminating subsidies (direct and indirect) on the importation of grains used for intensive livestock production; (ii) the establishment of livestock producer marketing groups with a wide membership, i.e. not only pastoralists but also urban-based entrepreneurs who are involved in financing the industry; and (iii) the initiation of action research groups responding to the different management needs of different types of livestock owners and managers. These initiatives need to consider the wider aspects of livestock systems management, including the seasonal availability of feed, fodder and water and their distribution in space; both across systems in the plains and between these and highland systems. Integrated action research of this nature will benefit both livestock and arable producers. Special support is needed for the owners of small numbers of livestock who constitute the majority of livestock owners. This support could take several forms, including new modalities for access to supplementary feeds, planting materials and seeds, marketing arrangements and transport.

The regulation of water use and water rights – particularly those related to the use of non-renewable groundwater –– is urgently required in many areas. This is perhaps one of the most sensitive issues that will affect both the course of agriculture and the future of urban areas in the next 30 years (e.g. Sana'a basin in Yemen). There is a need for better monitoring methods and techniques for managing water, that involve all stakeholders in an impartial and participatory manner. Legislation to ensure equitable sharing of water resources needs to be supported through national and international agreements. This will inevitably involve the introduction of more effective systems of charging for water use, particularly in intensively irrigated areas. In addition, democratic local institutions should be established; including various forms of water users groups that control, regulate and manage water efficiently and equitably. Without these in place, technical improvements will not be sustainable or effective.

Decentralisation of power structures relating to rural development and livelihoods is an essential first step. The creation of new forms of integrated agricultural and natural resource research and extension systems is also needed. New policies and interventions are required to encourage better partnerships between public and private sector stakeholders in management of scarce resources. Policies are also necessary to ensure: greater access to information concerning new soil and crop technologies; integrated pest and soil management techniques; access to credit for production; the removal of trading and price distortions (e.g. on grains) that affect the poor more than the well off; and processing and marketing needs.

TRADE LIBERALISATION AND MARKET DEVELOPMENT

The rapid development of highly competitive, global markets has resulted in great pressures on existing production and marketing systems, with many smaller producers being squeezed out. Support is needed for medium-sized and smaller businesses to adapt to these changing conditions. The trends in farming in the region over the past thirty years indicate a steady out-migration from farming by younger people, particularly men, to local towns and cities – and even out of the region altogether. Farm amalgamations and take-overs are occurring, but many millions of small farms remain, often managed by women and older men. Some important areas of potential development follow.

Full trade liberalisation would level the playing field for agricultural production throughout the region. Because the region does not have a comparative advantage in many traditional farm products, this would force adjustment, particularly in Rainfed and Highland Mixed Farming Systems – possibly involving a move towards high-value products for niche markets. Examples could be olives and olive oil, primary and processed fruits and vegetables, such as citrus, grapes, raisins and tomatoes. In the Large-scale Irrigated System that is well served by markets, horticultural production and food grains such as wheat and rice, could be competitive and thus be in a position to expand. Similarly, the Pastoral System and associated feedlot chains would change, following expected increases in the prices of feed grains as current price distortions are removed.

Off-farm income generation has become an important way in which many small farming families secure their food and other needs in the face of a shrinking land resource base. These trends are likely to continue and any new initiatives and investments designed to alleviate poverty must take account of this. Strategies that offer opportunities to enhance existing enterprises and also create new options will include: (i) the encouragement of small enterprises for the processing and marketing of regional crops and livestock products, through the elimination of barriers to business establishment and the creation of business-oriented technical advisory services; (ii) savings clubs or organisations of small producers that will develop reinvestment funds for land and water improvement and small enterprise development; (iii) credit schemes that facilitate the purchase of processing and packaging equipment irrigation, cultivation or harvesting equipment that could be owned collectively and hired out; (iv) improving the knowledge of small entrepreneurs related to consumer requirements in destination markets, whether regional cities or in Europe; and (v) the identification and exploitation of markets for niche products (e.g. organic foods, herbs, medicines).

INFORMATION AND HUMAN CAPITAL

Investment in greater access to local and international information systems must be a key element in the development of agriculture in the region, and would include the improvement of access to market information – generally on a joint private-public sector basis. Improvements are particularly needed in access to knowledge of local and international markets for small producers, as well as access to relevant information for women farmers and rural workers.

Farmers can capitalise on the availability of better information only if they understand how to use such knowledge. Thus, governments and civil society should support and expand farmer training; both at schools and through farmer training centres. There is a need for restructuring and re-organisation of higher agricultural education systems, such that the focus is on rural and rural-urban livelihood systems rather than simply on production agriculture. Curricula should be redesigned to give greater emphasis to more systemic, interdisciplinary approaches to learning (i.e. not only on disciplines and commodities). A higher priority should also be given to the provision of information and training of young, rural people with respect to vocational skills, as well as in relation to opportunities for development of agro-industries and tourism.

SCIENCE AND TECHNOLOGY

National research and extension systems have been notably weak and unproductive for many years and there has been a serious lack of systemic thinking about the nature of natural resources and how they might be managed more sustainably in order to reduce poverty. Science and technology policies should be reviewed, with a clear focus on the needs of the majority of rural and urban people – particularly the poor. A fundamental re-orientation of research and extension systems is needed in order to bring them more in line with recent participatory approaches to research and development, involving producers as partners in the development of research and extension programmes. This would include support for collective action among producers in all aspects of the crop and livestock research and multiplication process. These measures could include seed selection, testing and multiplication; water and soil management technology development; design, testing and construction of land management; and harvesting equipment for small producers. Greater support is needed to develop technologies that specifically address the needs of women – both as farmers and as people who have untapped skills in food and fibre processing, manufacturing and marketing.

In order to support diversification, which is an important source of poverty reduction, research on minor crops and on livestock should be expanded. There is an urgent need for technologies that enable small farmers to respond to emerging niche markets in Europe for quality horticultural produce or for organic produce, but the introduction of such technologies is often best achieved through those firms buying the output. Often the key appears to lie not only in the nature and practice of science and technology, but in training and in institutional arrangements. Although ICARDA has been playing an active role in carrying out a large programme of strategic and applied commodity and natural resource based research for the past 25 years, there is now a requirement for a consolidation of effort and a more proactive role in supporting the national institutions of the region. This initiative requires investment in training for dynamic and learning research and extension systems. The professionals within these systems should build on existing research into technology design and maintenance from within the region (e.g. the Nile delta) and from other parts of the world. Farmers should be part of this process and contribute their particular knowledge on seeds, drought and salinity tolerance and the collection, storage and re-use of water.

Research and extension support for these systems needs to be much more imaginative and interdisciplinary than at present. Researchers and extension workers need to work more on strategic and systemic research and development goals and mechanisms for accountability should be agreed on. Among key interventions needed, a high priority should be given to research on the development of more sustainable and integrated farming and livelihood systems through: (i) greater diversification; (ii) IPM and integrated soil and water management; (iii) the incorporation of farmers, both men and women, into the research and dissemination process; (iv) development of salinity tolerant crop and fodder varieties; and (v) design and planning for better on-farm water management efficiency, conjunctive use and water re-use.

It will be logical to continue to invest national and international resources to increase the technical efficiency of irrigation systems of all kinds, as these can give farmers greater choice in enterprise and production practice. Irrigated systems, unlike many others, offer the possibility for greater diversification, intercropping and tree or crop intensification. A further area for investment is the diversification and shift to water-saving cropping patterns. This requires rapid development and accessibility by farmers to micro-water distribution systems that are currently used only by a relatively small group of commercial farmers. There is also a continuing need to develop these relatively new technologies in a sensitive manner and to involve women in this work. New systems of cropping sequences, inter-cropping and in-season management need to be explored by proactive farmer-researcher groups. These priorities apply not only to irrigated systems, but also to areas of higher rainfall and to areas where management of rainfall in a particular season can determine whether a crop is harvested or not.

The introduction of conservation agriculture techniques, equipment and strategies that make better use of labour, soil and water resources is of the highest importance in the region. The need to increase labour productivity implies that forms of mechanisation are required, which may well entail more sharing of equipment and labour. This could be facilitated through local institutional mechanisms, which oversee the strategic needs for sustainable land and water management in a district or sub-region. The kinds of techniques which could have application in the region have been in place for many years in other dry areas of the world and involve: (i) zero or minimum soil disturbance; (ii) careful monitoring of soil and water relationships; (iii) the development of rational options for long-term cropping choices and patterns; (iv) the involvement of farmers' groups in the decision-making process; and (v) the development of technologies that are geared specifically to women producers and processors.

NATURAL RESOURCES AND CLIMATE

The issues related to natural resource management arise partly from the continuing deterioration in quality of both water and soil resources. In addition, non-renewable water resources are under increasing threat from excessive extraction in several areas. Soil erosion by wind and water continues be a fundamental problem in the region, often as a consequence of inappropriate cultivation methods and heavy grazing pressure in specific areas. Climatic changes are likely to result in greater extremes of drought conditions, which may well affect the low-rainfall areas more severely than those that currently have moderate rainfall.

Steadily rising demands for livestock products in urban areas, and unregulated growth of urban- and rural-based industrial forms of livestock management, are resulting in unprecedented pressures on the landscapes of the *steppe* and highlands, as well as on the people who manage these livestock. The whole industry needs to be analysed and understood in a systemic way in order to regulate it in a rational manner in order to ensure the long-term sustainability of rural livelihoods.

Priority attention should be given to the following areas: (i) the revival and adaptation of older systems of rational, rotational grazing and land management that involve all stakeholders in planning and monitoring resource changes; (ii) watershed-based (rather than individual farm) soil and water management systems; (iii) the development of sustainable groundwater management systems; (iv) the introduction of realistic and equitable water charges; (v) long-term, sustainable soil and water management techniques for annual and perennial cropping; and (vi) the conservation and development of the unique flora and fauna of the region.

For many years there has also been a debate about the value and returns from low and high potential areas and whether there is more to be gained from investment in one or the other. It has often been noted that low potential areas will not yield satisfactory returns on investment. However, in the Middle East and North Africa, livestock play such an important linking role that these simplistic comparisons between low and high potential lands may not be very useful.

A great deal of attention will continue to be paid to high potential areas as these represent the most valuable lands for the production of cereals, fruits, legumes and cash crops. It is from these areas that governments will expect to extract the maximum contribution to national food security in grains and basic foods. There is a need to pay much greater attention to water management and to its interaction with soil and external inputs. There is a case for much greater control and regulation of the use of agrochemicals – particularly those used on vegetables and fruits close to urban markets – and for the serious consideration of lower external input and organic systems which will yield crops that are safer for humans and soil that is healthier in the longer term.

Areas of low resource potential do not only support crops which are key elements in rainfed systems, such as barley, but they also support large numbers of livestock (sheep and goats) that utilise the *steppe* and mountain regions very intensively during the wet season and then return to the wetter, high potential areas after the main crops have been harvested. The net productivity of livestock across all the systems that are utilised can be quite high. However, unless farmers and herders have access to both livestock and barley growing land, their options may be quite limited and poverty and migration are now very common. The forces of modernisation, such as the financing of large numbers of livestock from urban bases and the provision of transport for animals and water, mean that many areas are placed under constant grazing pressure and have little opportunity to recover. Forms of communal resource management – of land, forest, shrubs, animals and water – may make these areas more stable and their use more sustainable. Such areas would need to be protected through regulation and support under appropriate enabling policies. Protection and conservation of the low potential, sometimes arid, land of the region is a vital task for governments, local authorities and external agencies, as these areas contain some rare plants and fauna and provide seasonal grazing resources for many millions of livestock.

Both high and low potential areas and low and high altitude zones contain large and small farms. Farm lands, even smallholdings, are often fragmented in rainfed farming systems. In several countries, the lands around nuclear village settlements are managed in blocks, which facilitates mechanised management of land preparation and harvesting. It also eases the management of sheep grazing in the post-harvest period. There is a need for the older systems of co-operation between smallholders to be studied in order to evaluate their advantages and deficiencies, particularly with respect to input management, quality control and marketing of produce. The owners of large farms are usually relatively wealthy and may often be based in town, and the daily operation of such holdings is often left to foremen who lack incentives for good management. There is often much scope for improved soil and water management on these holdings, which could result in improved productivity.

CONCLUSIONS

Despite the oil-based wealth of some countries of the region, agricultural production and water resources are still vital to the livelihoods of many farming families. Prospects for reducing agricultural poverty and adhering to the current international goals in this respect, are fairly good. For the region as a whole, exit from agriculture is the most important of the available household strategies for reducing poverty and food insecurity, followed by increased off-farm income. Among on-farm household improvement strategies, diversification and intensification are of equal importance, following closely behind off-farm income in the overall ranking. Increased farm size appears to be of minor importance overall.

Two major groups continue to be excluded from most development initiatives: poorer farmers in dryland areas and pastoralists. There are many threats to the stability and sustainability of natural resource based systems and additional pressure has resulted from weak or inappropriate food policies, which have supported low urban prices at the expense of poorer farmers and livestock herders. Nonetheless, lessons have been learned and there has been a gradual acceptance of the need to re-orientate development towards the elimination of poverty, based upon sustainable resource use. Five broad strategic, inter-linked, initiatives are proposed:

Sustainable resource management. Natural resources need to be conserved, through improved watershed management in hill and mountain areas, soil conservation in sloping lands and improved range management in pastoral areas. Components include: strengthening local resource-user groups; both for better management practices; and improved long-term policies.

Improved irrigation management. Increased efficiency in irrigation water management is essential to support the intensification and diversification of production and to reduce resource depletion. Components include: schemes based on both surface and underground water technology; and adjustments to water charges and other regulatory measures.

Re-oriented agricultural services. The re-orientation of agricultural research systems to fully involve farmers will underpin intensification in the Irrigated and Rainfed Mixed Systems and enterprise diversification in all systems. Components include: extension services based on a variety of public and private service providers; and greater support for rural agribusinesses to create off-farm employment for farmers.

Enhanced human resources. New approaches to science and higher education learning systems are particularly important in the training of agricultural students who will work in both the public and private sectors. Components include: the adoptation of the significant advances in interdisciplinary learning and systemic thinking which have played such an important role in agricultural education elsewhere in the world.

Rationalised agricultural policies. Policies need to re-orientate development towards the elimination of poverty based upon sustainable resource use. Components include: eliminating subsidies for the import of grains (widely used for intensive livestock production) as well as other forms of support for low urban prices at the expense of poorer farmers and pastoralists.

4

EASTERN EUROPE
AND CENTRAL ASIA

•••

REGIONAL SETTING

CHARACTERISTICS OF THE REGION

The Eastern Europe and Central Asia region encompasses 28 countries with widely divergent levels of economic development[1]. With between 10 and 55 percent of the population dependent on agriculture, the countries of the region are at an intermediate stage of economic development. On average, the agricultural sector contributed 12 percent of GDP in value added terms in 1998, but individual country figures range from 4 to 54 percent. The average contribution of agriculture to exports was 11 percent[2]. During the past 10 years, the number of poor people has substantially increased. In 1997, five percent of the total population were living on less than US$1 per day, and one quarter on less than US$2 per day[3].

Most countries within the region have experienced major economic reforms during the recent past. However, history, as well as proximity to the European Union (EU), has determined two sub-regions with significant differences in the progress and outcome of these reforms: (i) Central and Southeastern Europe; and (ii) the Commonwealth of Independent States.

Central and Southeastern Europe (CSEE)

This sub-region includes the Baltic States, Poland, Central and Southern European countries and Turkey. It covers a total area of about 210 million ha and has a rural population of 67 million, of which 38 million are economically active in agriculture. On average, population density is 90 inhabitants/km², but there is significant variation depending, *inter alia*, on latitude. The most productive

---

[1] See Annex 3 for a list of countries in the region which for the purpose of this analysis includes Turkey.
[2] World Bank 2000f.
[3] World Bank 2000f.

agricultural area lies in the moist subhumid agro-ecological zone. Mountain and hilly areas with more than 30 percent slope are widespread in the southern part of the sub-region.

On average, agriculture contributed 17 percent of GDP in value-added terms during 1998, but individual country figures range from around 5 percent for the Czech Republic and Poland to 54 percent for Albania. The Czech Republic and Albania represent the extremes in terms of the importance of agricultural labour; in 1990 agriculture accounted for 11 and 55 percent respectively of their national labour force. The average contribution of agriculture to exports was 11 percent. Besides the global trends that have influenced farming systems during the last decade, the countries of the CSEE sub-region have been passing through a complex transformation of their political and economic systems.

All faced similar underlying challenges and initially at least, espoused the same broad objectives. However, they embarked on the reform process with substantial differences in both the degree of prior market development and the level of political commitment to the transformation process itself. Consequently, the implementation of reforms has varied in pace and specific content. As a result, progress in achieving a market-based agriculture differs substantially from country to country. In broad terms, however, the change of political and economic systems during the last decade has led to a dramatic fall in output and a sharp rise in inequality, accompanied by a substantial increase in the number of people in poverty.

Commonwealth of Independent States (CIS)

This sub-region includes all former Soviet Union countries except the Baltic States, and covers a total land area of about 2 180 million ha. The population of this sub-region is 284 million, of which 33 percent are rural. Population density averages 13 inhabitants/km^2, but there is significant variation depending on the agro-ecological zone and latitude. Huge areas, covering more than half of the region, lie in the arid or dry subhumid north above 78° latitude, where permafrost and lack of moisture render them unsuitable for crop production, and where population density is less than three inhabitants/km^2. Almost all of the regional forest cover is in the territory of the Russian Federation; the largest part of it in the *taiga* zone. The sub-region's most productive farming systems lie in the moist subhumid agro-ecological zone, in the west. The major part of the sub-region lies in the arid and semiarid zone and has only limited production potential, unless irrigated. For similar reasons to the CSEE sub-region, the CIS sub-region has seen a dramatic fall in output, a rise in inequality and an increase in the number of people in poverty. On average, in 1998, agriculture contributed only 10 percent of GDP in value-added terms – ranging from 7 percent in the Russian Federation to 46 percent in Kyrgyzstan[4].

[4] World Bank 2000f.

Major Farming Systems
EASTERN EUROPE AND CENTRAL ASIA

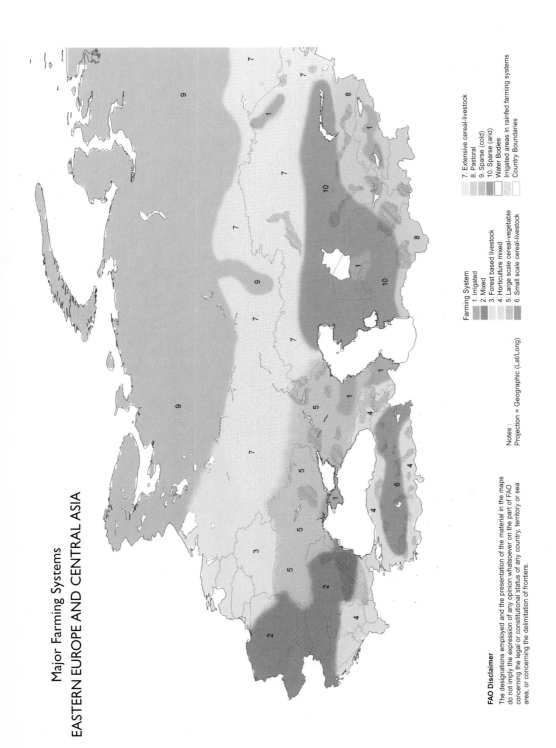

Farming System
1. Irrigated
2. Mixed
3. Forest based livestock
4. Horticulture mixed
5. Large scale cereal-vegetable
6. Small scale cereal-livestock

7. Extensive cereal-livestock
8. Pastoral
9. Sparse (cold)
10. Sparse (arid)
Water Bodies
Irrigated areas in rainfed farming systems
Country Boundaries

FAO Disclaimer

The designations employed and the presentation of the material in the maps do not imply the expression of any opinion whatsoever on the part of FAO concerning the legal or constitutional status of any country, territory or sea area, or concerning the delimitation of frontiers.

Notes :
Projection = Geographic (Lat/Long)

127

Major Farming Systems
EASTERN EUROPE AND CENTRAL ASIA

Farming System
1. Irrigated
2. Mixed
3. Forest based livestock
4. Horticulture mixed
5. Large scale cereal-vegetable
6. Small scale cereal-livestock

7. Extensive cereal-livestock
8. Pastoral
9. Sparse (cold)
10. Sparse (arid)
Water Bodies
Irrigated areas in rainfed farming systems
Country Boundaries

Notes :
Projection = Geographic (Lat/Long)

FAO Disclaimer

The designations employed and the presentation of the material in the maps do not imply the expression of any opinion whatsoever on the part of FAO concerning the legal or constitutional status of any country, territory or sea area, or concerning the delimitation of frontiers.

The countries of the CIS have all embarked on the complex processes of transforming their political and economic systems. They started at different levels of development, strategies have been diverse, and outcomes are also contrasting. In general, though, the results of the reforms have not yet met original expectations. In many countries, the major difficulty has been to create the basic ingredient of successful farming – the private farm. The reasons often relate to a reluctance to leave the protected environment of the former collective and state farms or co-operatives in order to face an unprotected world with no organised production, markets or rural services. To a large extent, the inherited large-scale collective farms have survived the transition, being reborn as production co-operatives or corporate holdings. The emergence of the family farm as a production unit has progressed only in countries where land has been distributed, but is still considered by many as too small to be efficient. Only rarely have truly commercially oriented family units been able to establish themselves.

For both sub-regions, the process of transforming underlying economic structures – particularly those relating to the rural sector – has proven to be a far more complex task than originally envisaged. Moreover, each farming system, with its distinctive natural resources, history, farm organisation and transition course, faces different challenges and prospects.

MAJOR FARMING SYSTEMS IN EASTERN EUROPE AND CENTRAL ASIA

There are significant differences in agro-ecological conditions among the farming systems in the region. The agro-ecologies vary from one of the world's most fertile regions in Southeast Europe, to poor, water-scarce regions of Central Asia. This agro-ecological diversity, plus the heterogeneity of political, economic and social conditions in the region, has resulted in the development of a wide variety of farming systems. Altogether eleven major farming systems, based on criteria outlined in Chapter 1, have been identified (see Table 4.1 and Map). The Urban Based system is dispersed throughout the region and is therefore not mapped. These farming systems are briefly described in the following paragraphs.

Irrigated Farming System[5]
This system occurs in scattered areas in the southern central and eastern areas of the region and covers an estimated 28 million ha, of which 10 million ha are cultivated and 8.6 million ha are irrigated, with an agricultural population of around 4 million. Medium to large irrigated farms, up to 500 ha in size, are found throughout the CIS countries and some areas of Romania. All have been severely

[5] The Irrigated Farming System refers to regions served by major irrigation systems and includes surrounding rainfed areas. It excludes smaller schemes and scattered irrigation associated with predominantly rainfed farming systems, which are discussed in relation to those rainfed systems. The more important concentrations of irrigation within rainfed areas are shown on the Map as hatched areas.

Table 4.1 Major Farming Systems in Eastern Europe and Central Asia Region

Farming Systems	Land Area (% of region)	Agric. Popn. (% of region)	Principal Livelihoods	Prevalence of Poverty
Irrigated	1	4	Cotton, rice, other cereals, tobacco, fruit, vegetables, off-farm	Moderate - extensive
Mixed	4	18	Wheat, maize, oilcrops, barley, livestock	Low - moderate
Forest Based Livestock	3	5	Fodder, hay, cereals, industrial crops, potatoes	Moderate
Horticulture Mixed	3	11	Wheat, maize, oilcrops, fruit, intensive vegetables, livestock, off-farm income	Moderate - extensive
Large-scale Cereal Vegetable	4	16	Wheat, barley, maize, sunflower, sugarbeet, vegetables	Moderate - extensive
Small-scale Cereal Livestock	1	4	Wheat, barley, sheep and goats	Moderate
Extensive Cereal-Livestock	18	15	Wheat, hay, fodder, cattle, sheep	Moderate - extensive
Pastoral	3	10	Sheep, cattle, cereals, fodder crops, potatoes	Moderate - extensive
Sparse (Cold)	52	2	Rye, oats, reindeer, potatoes, pigs, forestry	Extensive
Sparse (Arid)	6	8	Barley, sheep	Extensive
Urban Based	<1	7	Vegetables, poultry, pigs	Moderate

Source: FAO data and expert knowledge.
Note: Prevalence of poverty refers to number in poverty, not depth of poverty, and is a relative assessment for this region. Water bodies account for 5 percent of the total regional land area.

affected by the increase in previously subsidised energy prices, as well as the loss of traditional markets for high value crops such as fruits and vegetables. In the warmer areas in Uzbekistan, Turkmenistan and Southwestern Kazakhstan, irrigation is largely used for cotton cultivation, with some rice being grown. With readily available markets, cotton-producing irrigation systems can be maintained and cotton exports provide capital to cash-strapped farming economies. However, overuse of water during Soviet times has caused extensive environmental degradation – including the drying out of the Aral Sea, desertification of the surrounding area and widespread salinisation.

Smaller-scale irrigated systems are typical of the Caucasus, Balkan countries and Turkey, but they are found in other countries as well. The average farm size is in the range of 2 to 10 ha, owned and operated by a single family and focused on the production of such crops as wheat, barley, cotton, tobacco, fruit and vegetables. Depending on family size and irrigated area, the farms can provide part or full-time employment, producing marketable surpluses which are a major source of cash income. Poverty is widespread where former markets for fruits and vegetables have been lost, particularly in the Caucasus. However, some farms are gradually recapitalising, in spite of their very limited size.

Mixed Farming System

This system is widespread in those Central European countries seeking accession to the EU and has a total estimated area of 85 million ha, principally within the moist subhumid agro-ecological zone. Rural populations are estimated to comprise between 25 and 35 percent of the total population, and are declining. It has an agricultural population of 16 million, and the conditions for agricultural production vary considerably. Most of the crop area of 35 million ha is located within intermontane lowland plains, and is largely dedicated to wheat, maize, oil crops and barley, combined with smaller areas of fruit and vegetables. Livestock production is dominated by dairy and beef cattle, plus pigs. Associated hill and mountain areas are used for grazing and forestry.

Many new family farms have emerged in the region, with the exception of Poland and the countries of former Yugoslavia where small family farms were already the most common farm type even before the transition period. A majority of these new farms originated from the privatisation and decollectivisation of large-scale state and collective agricultural units and a large variety of organisation and ownership types has emerged. In some countries the State still owns a significant part of the land, or continues to have a share in the capital stock of transformed farms. As a consequence, in terms of ownership and management, the system is characterised by two dominant subsystems: small to medium-scale private family farms and medium to large corporate or co-operative farms.

The incidence of poverty is low to moderate and is concentrated among the most vulnerable groups, such as ethnic minorities, unemployed and unskilled workers, and those farming in marginal areas.

Forest Based Livestock Farming System

This system is located in the northwest of the region in a moist subhumid agro-ecological zone and extends over an estimated 72 million ha, of which 25 million ha are cultivated, with an agricultural population of some 5 million.

Large farms, with holding sizes from 500 to 2 000 ha, are typical in Belarus and Northwest Russia. They are characterised by co-operative or corporate ownership, with production focused on fodder, hay, cereals, industrial crops and potatoes. In the prevailing macroeconomic situation, these farms generate little or no cash income. Co-operative members or farm labourers depend largely on barter to sustain their livelihoods. In all probability, as political and economic reforms continue, many of these large farms will gradually be replaced by individually owned holdings[6]. Smaller holdings predominate in Baltic States.

Horticulture Mixed Farming System

This system covers 79 million ha of which 24 million ha are cultivated, and is typical of the Southern Balkans, Northern Turkey and the Caucasus. The system has an agricultural population of nearly 10 million scattered primarily on sloping lands in the dry subhumid agro-ecological zone, characterised by a Mediterranean climate. Although rural populations have been declining sharply in the Balkans over the last decade, they have actually risen in the Caucasus countries. The average farm size is small and has a diversified production pattern, including wheat, maize, oil crops, fruit and vegetables, combined with cattle, sheep and goats. Cultivation of fruit, nuts and vegetables, partly irrigated or produced in greenhouses or other protective structures, contributes significantly to the value of crop production and household income – although such cultivation occupies only about 15 percent of the cultivated land. In the Southern Balkans and the Caucasus, the farms and household plots resulting from privatisation are family owned and frequently operated part-time, with off-farm employment being common. Production of cereals and oil crops is in many cases for subsistence, while marketable surpluses of fruits, vegetables and animal products are a major source of cash income. The extent of poverty – partly arising from armed conflicts – is high; it primarily affects minorities, the unemployed and landless people in rural and urban areas, marginal groups (e.g. women, old people) and populations in marginal areas.

Large-scale Cereal-Vegetable Farming System

This system is typical of Ukraine, the southwest part of the Russian Federation and the Republic of Moldova. Covering an estimated 100 million ha, principally in the moist subhumid agro-ecological zone, it has an estimated agricultural population of about 15 million. Approximately 38 million ha are cultivated. Although the process of land privatisation has started, most of the farms are still large, ranging from 500 to 4 000 ha. The dominant ownership is co-operative or corporate, although private ownership is gradually gaining in importance. Rural populations represent a relatively large proportion of total population in this system – probably about one-third – and are declining only slowly. As in the case of farms in Northwest Russia and Belarus, these farms generate little cash income and co-operative members or farm labourers largely depend on production from their household plot and barter to sustain their families.

Small-scale Cereal-Livestock Farming System

This system is located in the semiarid and dry subhumid and mountainous zones of Turkey with a growing period of less than 180 days. It contains an estimated agricultural population of 4 million and covers an area of 35 million ha, of which

---

[6] As mentioned elsewhere, there is resistance among some officials to the implementation of these reforms.

nearly 8 million ha are farmed by owner-managers or tenants. Private ownership has led to better farm management, intensification of labour use and diversification of production. However, many farms created by land distribution are very small and some are hardly viable. Tenancy arrangements foster neither short term productivity nor long-term resource management. The main cereals are wheat and barley. Unreliable precipitation means that yields, and hence production of these rainfed crops, vary considerably from year to year. Nevertheless, small or subsistence farmers within this system produce most of Turkey's grain. Farm households consume about half of the wheat crop; the other half is marketed through commercial channels. Barley is almost exclusively used for animal feed or for export. Sheep and goats are the main livestock and play an important role in the system; but some cattle are also raised. There is some crop-livestock integration arising from traditional practices. Animals forage on crop stubble, weeds, and grass on fallow land and uncultivable grazing areas. Overgrazing of grasslands, wasteland, forests and mountain meadows is common, with substantial environmental damage and low livestock productivity.

Although poverty is increasing, the declining rate of population growth has reduced the pressure for land reform, and industrialisation offers an alternative part-time or full-time livelihood for many farmers.

Extensive Cereal-Livestock Farming System

This system is found throughout the semiarid agro-ecological zone of the Russian Federation and Northern Kazakhstan, but also covers substantial areas in Southern Kazakhstan, Turkmenistan and Uzbekistan. This is the domain of the *steppe*, which traditionally was used by transhumant herders, until converted to cropping over the last few decades. The major outputs are wheat, hay and other fodder crops, combined with cattle and sheep. In the drier parts, with an annual rainfall of only 200 to 300 mm, the land is fallowed every two years. The system occupies a total of 425 million ha, of which about 107 million ha are cultivated. It contains an estimated human population of only 14 million people. Ownership patterns are in transition, from collective and state farms to co-operative or corporate ownership, with an increasing number of smaller family farms. Poverty is increasing among old people, young families and former co-operative members, as well as in urban areas.

Pastoral Farming System

This is a system which is typical of much of Southeastern Central Asia. It covers an estimated 82 million ha and has a sparse agricultural population of about 9 million people. Rural populations constitute a large proportion of the total population, reaching over 60 percent in Kyrgyzstan. Most of the pastures are in high mountainous areas or adjacent dry zones. Principal livestock species are sheep with some cattle. Although the dominant activity is pastoralism, about 14 million ha in mountain valleys with slightly more favourable conditions are used for cultivation of cereals, fodder crops and potatoes for subsistence. Herd management is based on spring and autumn grazing of communal pastures close to the villages. Summer grazing is on distant, often heavily overgrazed, mountain pastures, while in winter stall-feeding predominates. Due to excessive animal populations, poor pasture management and overgrazing, deterioration of natural vegetation and soil erosion are important issues. Wool production, which was a major output during the Soviet era, has fallen dramatically since the early 1990s, while meat output has increased as farmers have reverted to the sturdy traditional meat breeds. Poverty is particularly widespread in this system.

Sparse (Cold) Farming System

This system is found in Russia, north of the Extensive Cereal-Livestock System. With 1 260 million ha of land occupied by a small agricultural population of perhaps 2 million, only about 23 million ha have been cleared for cropping, interspersed in the *tundra* and the *taiga* forests – mainly in the European part. The *taiga* remains the world's largest timber reserve. Natural conditions allow only limited cultivation of rye and oats, as well as of potatoes and some vegetables, possibly supplemented by pig raising. Farming is constrained by the short growing season, very low temperatures and poor soils. The dominant soil type is the *podzol*, characterised by intense nutrient leaching and acidity. Various indigenous groups, including the Yakut and the Evenk, practise reindeer pastoralism. This system has very limited potential for agricultural development.

Sparse (Arid) Farming System

The system covers 143 million ha and has an agricultural population of about 7 million. It is found to the south of the Eurasian *steppe*, in the southern part of Central Asia, including most of Turkmenistan and Uzbekistan, as well as a large strip of Kazakhstan. The driest parts are only used by nomads. In somewhat more favourable areas, extensive cereal cultivation, complemented by sheep raising, is practised on about 8 million ha – typically with a harvest every two years followed by a cultivated fallow to conserve soil moisture. Large-scale farms are the dominant production structure. They are heavily indebted and, unless irrigated, not viable now that most subsidies have been withdrawn. Where bankruptcy is allowed, as in Kazakhstan, the farms that are liquidated tend to be bought for their movable assets, such as tractors and machinery, leaving workers with no choice but to migrate to the cities. There is limited potential for development except where irrigation can be used, but existing water resources are already over-exploited. In the most arid parts, reversion to some form of pastoralism is unavoidable.

Urban Based Farming System

This system occurs within and surrounding cities in the region[7]. Although there are

---

[7] There are certain similarities to the traditional *dacha* system.

no statistical data available on urban agriculture, it is clear that its importance has grown recently, as a result of rising unemployment and poverty. The land used for farming is mostly private residential land, but may also include publicly owned land allocated to certain categories of beneficiary. Urban farming produces mainly vegetables, in particular leafy vegetables, but small livestock are also an important component. Like the farmers on small household plots in rural areas, many of the urban plot farmers produce for their own consumption, with occasional surpluses sold in local markets. However, a number of urban farmers engage in commercial agriculture.

REGION-WIDE TRENDS IN EASTERN EUROPE AND CENTRAL ASIA

This section describes the most important region-wide trends in terms of: population, hunger and poverty; natural resources and climate; science and technology; trade liberalisation and market development; policies institutions and public goods; and information and human capital. At the end of the section, three of the regional farming systems described in the previous section of the Chapter are selected for further description and analysis.

Population, Hunger and Poverty

Unlike other low and middle-income regions, populations are stagnant at present. The total population of the region – 478 million – is projected to increase only marginally to 2015 and subsequently to decline again in the period to 2030.

In part, this lack of population growth may reflect the steep decline in living standards experienced within the region since the collapse of the centrally planned economic system in the late 1980s. Per capita calorie consumption, which in the mid-1980s was higher than in the industrialised countries, had fallen by nearly 15 percent a decade later. This is still well above the developing world average, but below both the industrialised world and the Middle East and North Africa region. Projections suggest a slow recovery over the next 30 years that will still leave average consumption levels marginally below those of the mid-1980s.

Poverty levels have increased even faster than hunger. A study of the impact of the transition, using household survey data, estimates that the total number of people in poverty in the region has climbed from 14 million in 1987-1988 to 147 million in 1993-1995[8]. While poverty levels have risen only moderately in the Baltic countries and Central Europe, they are significant in Poland and the Balkans, and severe in the remainder of the region. Poverty in the Russian Federation alone has risen from 2 percent to 50 percent over this period, signifying a shift from 2 million to over 74 million people in poverty within a decade. Similar results are visible in Ukraine, Moldova and Belarus, while the Central Asian states have

---

[8] Milanovich (1998) applies nationally defined poverty levels which are significantly higher than the commonly used international standard of US$1 per day.

reached poverty levels as high as 88 percent (in the case of the Kyrgyz Republic), although from a higher initial level.

Natural Resources and Climate

Compared to many other developing regions, there is a favourable relationship between the potential of the available natural resource base and expected population growth. Land area is about 2.3 billion ha[9], or 17 percent of the world's land, while the population of the region constitutes only 8 percent of the world total. However, there is very limited potential for expansion of agricultural area – although it is argued below that there is significant scope for increased production intensity. Even though some of the land is no longer cultivated, particularly in the Extensive Crop-Livestock System[10], most is not suitable for cultivation and should revert to grazing land.

The highest population pressures on natural resources will continue to be in the Balkans, Central Asia, Turkey and the Caucasus. This will threaten conservation efforts unless different practices are adopted – such as the improved watershed management approach that has been introduced on the Anatolian Plateau of Turkey. The outcome of ongoing land reform in areas where large-scale farms still prevail, will also influence the way in which natural resources are used and will determine the risk of environmental degradation. Climate change will exert additional pressure, as recent studies point to a decline of precipitation and crop yields in Central Asia[11] during this century.

Annual and permanent crops cover about 292 million ha, which includes some of the most fertile soils in the world – the *chernozems*. Past trends indicate a decrease in cultivated land use during the 1990s, with only 60 to 70 percent of potential land resources now being cultivated in areas such as the Extensive Crop-Livestock Farming System. The reasons for this include: (i) difficulties in access to machinery and inputs; (ii) marketing issues; and (iii) the loss of irrigation facilities due to lack of maintenance. However, this decline follows decades of large-scale expansion of ploughed land to the detriment of marshes, forests and *steppes*, often in areas unsuitable for sustainable agriculture. It is likely that cropping in some of the more marginal areas will be abandoned, even including irrigated land where this technique is not economically viable. In fact, in most of the region, land *per se* is not the limiting factor; the real issues are access to land, support services and farm management capacity. However, land is severely limited in some specific areas; for example in the Caucasus and in the narrow valleys of the Central Asia Mountains.

Irrigation covers almost 29 million ha in the region, of which almost 20 million ha are located in the CIS countries (Kazakhstan, Kyrgiz Republic, Tajikistan and

---

[9] This land area excludes the 0.1 billion ha of inland water bodies in the region.

[10] In Kazakhstan, cultivated area declined from 34.9 million ha in 1991 to 21.8 million in 1997, and it is estimated that 30 percent of the land under cereals reverted to pasture.

[11] Fischer *et al* 2001.

Uzbekistan). A further 5 million ha are found in Eastern Europe, notably Romania (2.8 million ha), and the rest are in Turkey (4.2 million ha), where surveys have indicated that an extension of irrigated area up to 8.7 million ha would be physically possible. Due to a policy of expansion to compensate for stagnating agricultural productivity, the irrigated area in the region grew at an average annual rate of 2.8 percent from 1961 to 1990. A large part of that area is located in the Central Asian countries [12], where 20 to 30 percent of the cultivated land is irrigated. Cotton has always been irrigated throughout the sub-region, but in recent years the technique has also been used more widely in grain production. The development of very large irrigation systems, combined with rapid population increases in the sub-region, has led to huge water withdrawals that have had widespread and negative environmental consequences (see Box 4.1).

Box 4.1 Unsustainable Irrigation Development

The Aral Sea Basin is the most dramatic case of environmental disaster arising from unsustainable irrigation. Over eight million ha were developed using rivers from the Tien Shan Range which drained into the Aral Sea. The sea itself was reduced in area by more than half. Soils have been contaminated by salt, while poor drainage in the irrigated zones combined with poor maintenance of the systems has led to widespread problems of waterlogging and salinity, affecting crop yields. With the lack of maintenance of irrigation systems and the need to use water in winter for hydropower, irrigated areas have significantly declined in the past 10 years, and it is unlikely that they will ever regain their original size.

In other sub-regions, particularly in the Caucasus, much of the irrigated land relied on a high pumping lift that is no longer economically viable. Everywhere, maintenance of irrigation and drainage infrastructure has become erratic and irrigated agriculture is decreasing, both in coverage and in reliability. This trend is likely to continue over a number of years. Both rehabilitating the systems and rebuilding the irrigation management institutions is a long process, and requires sizeable resources as well as political will. Many of the systems may need to be redesigned and reduced in size; some may even need to be abandoned altogether because they are too costly to operate.

Forest covers about 4 percent of the Central Asia part of the region, and other parts have more than 20 percent forest on the average. The Baltic States and the Russian Federation have the largest proportion of forest cover – 37 and 45 percent respectively. Most forest areas are still under state ownership but, in some CSEE countries, part of the forest resources are privatised. In most countries, the multiple benefits of forests are not recognised, leading to underinvestment in their protection and sustainable management.

---

[12] Kazakhstan, Kyrgyzstan, Tajikistan, Turkmenistan and Uzbekistan.

Science and technology

Technological change has been the major driving force for increasing agricultural productivity and promoting agriculture development in all countries in the region. In the past, technologies were selected and adopted mainly to increase production and productivity, and agricultural research was directed towards resolving the problems arising in large-scale farming. Thus, there is a dearth of technologies adapted to sustainable small-scale family farming in the region.

Trends in crop area, yield and output are presented in Table 4.2 below. Crop output has been stable since 1995, and is possibly increasing in a few places, but this is not yet a general trend. Cropping patterns have changed to accommodate an increased share of food crops (wheat, potatoes and some vegetables) at the expense of forage and industrial crops. Crop yields have fallen and the main reason for decreased productivity has been the reduced or discontinued use of fertilisers. However, late ploughing, lack of irrigation and low seed quality are also important factors; together with inexperienced farmers where land has been redistributed to individuals. Fertiliser use is now only about 25 kg per ha of cultivated land – less than a quarter of the level before reform.

Table 4.2 Trends in Crop Area, Yield and Output in Eastern Europe and Central Asia, 1970-2000

Crop	Harvested Area 2000 (m ha)	Yield 2000 (t/ha)	Production 2000 (m tons)	Average Annual Change 1970-2000 (%)		
				Area	Yield	Production
Wheat	58	1.9	111	-1.2	0.9	-0.4
Barley	24	1.7	40	-0.4	0.0	-0.3
Maize	10	2.8	27	-0.5	0.1	-0.5
Other Grains	19	1.6	31	-1.8	0.8	-0.9
Roots & Tubers	8	12.1	101	-1.2	-0.3	-1.5
Pulses	4	1.2	5	-2.5	0.3	-2.2
Oilcrops	18	0.4	7	0.8	0.3	1.0
Vegetables	5	15.8	71	-0.3	1.2	1.5
Fruits	6	5.2	30	-0.1	0.0	0.1

Source: FAOSTAT.
Note: Geographical coverage is comparable for 1970 and 2000. However, changes in statistical collection procedures may produce significant distortions (e.g. exclusion of private sector activity from statistics prior to 1990).

Changes in yields and cropping patterns occurred first in private farms, and these have proven their ability to adjust to changing market conditions. Large-scale farms, even after reorganisation, have tended to keep to a traditional crop mix and management style, and their yields are lagging behind those of private farmers. Yields are expected to increase in future, but only very slowly, catalysed by farm re-capitalisation, availability of improved technologies, and increasing experience in crop management in a non-subsidised low external input setting. Market-led changes in cropping pattern are expected, with a trend away from subsistence crops towards higher value crops. Where conditions are harsh, e.g. in the Siberian *steppe*, yields may not rise much above former levels – stabilisation of yields and reduction of production costs are the main areas for future improvement.

Fertiliser consumption has declined during the past decade: on average by 15.8 percent per annum in CIS countries and by 6.2 percent per annum in Central Europe. The main reasons for the sharp decline in nutrient applications were the loss of subsidised energy and the rising fertiliser prices that resulted; further worsened by the lack of operating capital and credit institutions. Low fertiliser application rates have led to decreased yields, particularly for crops sensitive to nutrient deficiencies, such as potatoes and sugarbeet. Yields have eventually stabilised at a low level in the CIS countries, while they are recovering slightly in Central Europe.

Trends in livestock populations and output are presented in Table 4.3 below. Livestock in the region include cattle (88 million); sheep and goats (117 million); pigs (78 million); and poultry (1 100 million). During the last 10 years, the number of animals and livestock production has been decreasing. Forecasts up to 2030 indicate slow recovery and growth of animal numbers. The expected increase in meat production will therefore be generated mainly through increased productivity per animal.

Table 4.3 Trends in Livestock Populations and Output in Eastern Europe and Central Asia, 1970-2000

Species	Million Head 2000	Ave Annual Change 1970-2000 (%)
Cattle	88	-1.5
Small Ruminants	117	-2.3
Pigs	78	-0.6
Poultry	1 111	0.5

Product	Output 2000 (million tons)	Ave Annual Change (%)
Total Meat	18	-0.2
Total Milk	103	-0.5
Total Wool	0.2	-3.1
Total Eggs	5	1.1

Source: FAOSTAT.
Note: See note for Table 4.2.

The fall in livestock numbers has occurred across all farming systems, but possibly for different reasons. In the colder zones for example, cattle raising relied extensively on imported grain and is currently unprofitable. In the Caucasus, and even more in Southern Central Asia which have extensive grasslands and are better suited to low-cost livestock production, individual farmers were at first unable to keep all the animals released through the liquidation of the *sovkhozes* and *kolkhoses*. However, they are now keen to build up numbers again. Nonetheless, even with the renewed inclusion of fodder crops into the rotation, the finite range resources available in the vicinity of villages will limit the potential for livestock expansion in these areas. Overall, the scope for returning to former stocking rates is unclear, although there is potential for increased productivity through better health and feed management; specialisation is expected to become more widespread.

Trade liberalisation and market development

Due to the ending of economic ties within the former Soviet block, as well as to armed conflicts in some areas, many countries have lost their traditional markets. With the liberalisation of trade, domestic markets have been affected by rapidly increasing imports with which producers could not compete, even on the domestic market. This has particularly affected countries that were traditional exporters of horticultural produce (Bulgaria, Georgia, Moldova, Armenia, Macedonia). Reorientation to new regional and global markets has been constrained by the limited progress of economic reforms, as well as by the need for adoption and compliance with internationally recognised food quality and safety standards.

The dismantling of huge agro-food complexes has resulted in the breakdown of traditional marketing channels. In the absence of effective institutional and economic frameworks for agriculture and agro-processing, as well as of market support services, farmers are unable to sell their produce on local and regional markets. Marketing is sometimes constrained by local monopolies that are often the only available option for farmers to purchase inputs and sell their produce.

Low productivity and quality, as well as the absence of competition, were common features of agricultural systems in the region, thus restricting competitiveness in world export markets. With terms of trade for basic foodstuffs expected to decline over the next 30 years, the competitiveness of export commodities – especially those produced in irrigated areas – will remain a key problem. However, should major advances be made in farm reorganisation and management, the region in general, and in particular the Large-scale Cereal-Vegetable Farming System, offers potential for a substantial contribution to world cereal markets. Suitable agricultural policy measures in the Russian Federation, Ukraine and Moldova could transform world cereal markets by improving the competitive position of these countries with respect to the currently highly subsidised production in the EU.

Policies, institutions and public goods

All countries of the region have had to adapt in order to meet the requirements of the market economy. This has required change in all formal and informal institutions, and in the governmental, political, and organisational framework. Central European countries have advanced furthest and, with the prospect of joining the EU in sight, they are working towards completion of institutional and policy reforms within the framework of the EU accession process.

Although significant progress has been made in these countries, mostly in the areas of macroeconomic and trade policies, some areas of adjustment of farm structures, land policies and markets still require further deregulation and appropriate institutional arrangements. In the early years of transition, agricultural support fell substantially and policy instruments changed, as the role of central planning declined and trade barriers were reduced. However, in Central European countries, support for agriculture was gradually increased after the mid-1990s. In other countries of the region reforms began later and they are still engaged in land privatisation and establishment of property rights, restructuring of agricultural enterprises, and deregulation of markets. Some new policy instruments have been introduced, but the policy framework and institutional arrangements still need to be adapted to new market economy concepts.

Except in Poland and the countries of former Yugoslavia, where small family farms have always been the most common farm type, large collective and state farms have dominated agriculture during the past half century. These units, covering thousands to tens of thousands of hectares, employed hundreds to thousands of workers and were responsible for organising most of the life of these families – including primary production, marketing of products, and the provision of economic and social services. Moving from communism has often depended upon political willingness to dismantle these units[13]. The extent to which intent was translated into actual land reform – and the pace and procedures of this restructuration – varied considerably from one country to another. However, a common feature of these countries is the unforeseen complexity of this transformation process, linked to the extraordinary difficulty of 're-inventing' farming systems based on individual property and management.

Besides some resistance from the defenders of the previous system, the reasons for these difficulties mostly relate to the fear of many rural households of moving from a previously protected environment to a world full of uncertainties and risks, in which many institutions and support services have not yet been established. As a consequence, even though land is officially privatised in many countries, the new systems are far from being established on the ground. Whereas farm restructuring has hardly started in most of Russia and Ukraine, most other countries are at different intermediate stages of organisational change. This has

[13] This policy faces resistance in a number of countries (e.g. Russia, Ukraine, etc.).

led to the co-existence of a large variety of organisations and ownership forms such as: (i) joint stock companies; (ii) limited liability companies (these two types are in many cases managed as former collective farms); (iii) co-operatives (often involved in primary production); (iv) farm associations; (v) peasant farms (newly formed small groups of individual households); (vi) family farms; and (vii) household plots. In some countries the State still owns a significant part of the land, or has a share in the capital stock of transformed farms.

Land tenure is still a major issue, and in most countries, land titling is lagging behind schedule and property rights remain unclear. As a consequence, farmers are not able to use land as collateral. In other cases, although titles have been allocated, plots of land have not been distributed. So called 'absentee ownership' is rather common. These absentees include those who are reluctant to leave the collective and an important proportion of retirees who have received land shares but do not wish to embark on production. In many cases, land markets are not operational due to legal constraints or titling issues. In some countries, the existence of efficient land markets is inhibited by legal restrictions on land transfers, as well as by government interference in the valuation of land and determination of land prices. Often, informal renting arrangements are found, but these are not transparent, and therefore do not favour long-term management of land resources nor investment in improvements.

Box 4.2 Fragmentation and Consolidation of Land Holdings in the Mixed Farming System in Bulgaria[14]

Once restitution and distribution of property started in Bulgaria, the structure of land ownership changed radically and different types of farming emerged. The private sector became dominant, with around 1.75 million small landowners. However, 95 percent of these individual farmers operate an area of two ha or less. Land fragmentation is extreme and considered as an obstacle for the development of a healthy agricultural sector. As an outcome of land reform and structural reform, three main groups of operating structures emerged in agriculture: individual private farms, co-operatives and state farms. All of them are affected by land fragmentation.

In the existing economic and institutional environment, the most common approach to increasing farm size is that of short-term, informal consolidation. In the Dobjudja region of Bulgaria, land consolidation is often arranged on the basis of mutual and informal agreement among farmers within the territory belonging to a settlement. The practices observed include: leasing of land from the State Land Fund for a period of 10 years; purchase of agricultural land from the fund using compensatory bonds; exchange of scattered plots of private agricultural land for consolidated state land from the fund; interchange of private land plots between individual producers, owners of the land; and purchase and sale of agricultural land.

[14] Kopeva 2001.

One of the consequences of the land distribution process is the fragmentation of land (see Box 4.2). Individual recipients have received their land in the form of numerous plots which comprise various qualities of soils, as well as various perennial crops. The resultant production constraints mainly relate to use of farm machinery on small fields and increased transportation costs to scattered parcels. Over time, two types of land consolidation will occur: (i) producers will swap or exchange land either formally or informally; and (ii) the most active ones will concentrate larger quantities of land through renting or land purchase. These phenomena should be favoured through information campaigns, concerning the appropriate legal framework of these exchanges; but in no way should land consolidation be forced.

Another issue associated with farm restructuring is the distribution of farm assets, including farm machinery, buildings, stores, vehicles, and even processing equipment. In theory, farmers had the right to a certain share of these assets. However, they have largely been deprived of this right for a number of reasons including: (i) looted equipment; (ii) the difficulty of distributing large pieces of equipment or buildings to individuals; (iii) poor level of information concerning farmers' rights; and (iv) obsolete assets.

Finally, most of the large farms in the region have huge debts. The accumulation of these debts was in part due to a policy of write-offs, which came to be expected and which reduced farmers' interest in controlling their debts. In turn, these large debts have become a serious obstacle to restructuring collective agricultural enterprises in the region through bankruptcy[15]. Indebtedness has also inhibited the adoption of better technologies.

Information and human capital

Although initial steps have been taken towards more demand-driven agricultural knowledge support services, problems associated with the transformation of agricultural knowledge systems and their refocusing on the needs of market oriented farming are still widespread[16]. Severe budget cuts have weakened the existing, oversized research systems. Further developments will largely depend upon institutional reforms, as well as upon building a consensus among stakeholders concerning the basic principles that underlie demand-driven and cost-effective agricultural research and extension systems.

Following the end of central planning, it rapidly became clear that farmers needed access to information about technologies, farm management, business planning, markets and, in particular, prices. To address these needs, many countries have now established Market Information Services (MIS), usually with financial and technical assistance from outside donors. Several MIS are now

---

[15] The issue of accumulated debts is also one of the factors behind tax evasion. Situations when companies did not have sufficient funds to pay taxes were sometimes used by local authorities as an excuse to resist restructuring initiatives.

[16] See Rolls (2001) for a comprehensive review of advisory services in Eastern Europe.

finding that they lack the resources to continue a comprehensive service once donor funds have dried up. It is expected that various private channels of information and advice will develop but, unless a role for public support of extension is recognised, these will mostly target the better-off farmers, leaving the majority without proper information and advice.

Despite the deterioration of agricultural knowledge systems, there is still substantial human potential, particularly in technology-related fields, that can be used to develop and disseminate economically efficient and environmentally sustainable technologies. Further reforms and changes to agricultural research and extension systems – combining both public and private sectors – will be beneficial for expansion of technology options. These reforms, plus more participatory adaptation of new technologies and management practices by farmers, could decrease the cost of access to technology.

Rapid urban development during the last few decades, combined with the ending of formal restrictions on movement and settlement, has resulted in the wholesale migration of younger educated and skilled people from rural areas to cities, resulting in the ageing of the rural population. Due to the poor economic situation during the transition period, combined with restructuring of state and collective farms which included layoffs of surplus labour and the absence of employment opportunities in rural areas, these migration and ageing trends are continuing and even accelerating.

Past economic and social policies have contributed to over-employment on state-owned and collective farms, resulting in low labour productivity. As non-agricultural activities have largely collapsed, household plots have now assumed even greater importance for farm workers. In the deteriorating economic situation, agriculture will continue to represent the only possibility of maintaining a decent livelihood for most former farm members, and it will also need to absorb labour from other sectors.

Selection of farming systems for analysis

Of the eleven major farming systems identified in the region, three have been selected for further analysis on the basis of their potential for reducing poverty and increasing agricultural production; as well as their demographic and economic importance:

- Mixed Farming System;
- Large-scale Cereal-Vegetable Farming System; and
- Extensive Cereal-Livestock Farming System.

MIXED FARMING SYSTEM

CHARACTERISTICS OF THE SYSTEM

In terms of ownership, management, farming traditions and production patterns, the Mixed Farming System, covering some 85 million ha, is typical of those Central European countries that seek accession to the EU[17]. Although heterogeneous, Central Europe has generally good agro-ecological conditions. The types and

Box 4.3 Basic Data: Mixed Farming System	
Total population (m)	99
Agricultural population (m)	16
Total area (m ha)	85
Agro-ecological zone	Subhumid
Cultivated area (m ha)	35
Irrigated area (m ha)	4
Cattle population (m)	14

quality of soils vary widely, from poor sandy soils to rich *chernozems*. Annual precipitation ranges from 300 mm in the southeast, to more than 3 000 mm in the mountainous parts. In the warmer parts of the region, severe droughts sporadically affect crop production and yields. Despite this, the irrigated area accounts for little more than 10 percent of the 35 million ha of cultivated land. This land is located in the plains, which are separated by mountain and hilly areas more suitable for livestock production. There are an estimated 14 million head of cattle within the system.

The total population of the farming system is 99 million, of which 36 million live in rural areas with about 16 million economically active in agriculture. Although the incidence of poverty is low by regional standards, there are vulnerable groups exposed to more severe poverty, including minorities, marginal groups, unemployed and unskilled labourers, and people living in marginal areas.

Many private, family farmers cultivate land with obsolete machinery obtained from former co-operatives or at auctions, but those operating larger farms have succeeded in buying new machinery. In order to minimise costs, farmers frequently limit cultivation and apply low doses of fertiliser. The most important crops are winter wheat, sunflower, oilseed rape, fodder crops and a smaller proportion of spring barley and alfalfa. Corn, sugar beet and pumpkins are grown on the better soils. However, the area of high value crops is not great. Livestock production in stables often complements crop production and crops are partly used as feed. Smaller diversified farms (see Box 4.4) rely heavily on income from livestock. The system also contains a number of larger, specialised livestock farms, with animal numbers in the range of 30 to 70 pigs, 10 to 30 dairy cows or 15 to 40 fattening steers, depending on the species specialisation.

[17] Although the Baltic States (Estonia, Latvia and Lithuania) have similar characteristics with respect to accession, due to the differences in agro-ecological conditions and natural resource base the dominant farming system variant in those countries is based on fodder for livestock and forestry production (see Forest Based Livestock Farming System).

Box 4.4 A Typical Family Farm of the Mixed Farming System

A typical mixed crop livestock family farm operates 20 ha of cultivated land, mostly owned by the family, with leased land wherever there is such possibility. It has four to five members, with a labour force equivalent to 1.6 fully employed persons. Most of the work on the farm is done by family labour. Main crops are wheat and barley (20 to 30 percent), maize for grain or silage (30-40 percent) and oil crops (5 to 15 percent). Two-thirds of on-farm income originates from livestock production; with 2 or 3 fattening pigs, 1 to 5 milking cows and 1 to 3 fattening steers, as well as poultry, being typical. Crop production would account for the other third. Production technology is based on mechanised cultivation, certified seed, fertilisers (60 to 80 kg/ha of nutrients) and limited amounts of pesticides.

TRENDS AND ISSUES IN MIXED SYSTEM

The decline in input use and changes in cropping patterns resulting from land privatisation have affected yields. As the amount of land operated by private farmers has expanded, its use has generally become less intensive. In some parts of the system, crop production is also subject to frequent natural disasters (drought and floods), against which there is no effective insurance system. Due to the reduced levels of input use, crop yields have significantly decreased, especially on the small family farms. The relative price of inputs has increased compared to output prices, with consequent declines in the use of inputs. Although fertiliser use has generally started to increase, there are huge differences between countries due to different pricing policies. The cost of inputs is also affected by interest rates which are still high in many CSEE countries.

At present, many family farms are small and fragmented, but structural reforms and adjustment to the EU model of agriculture are expected to promote land consolidation and to increase farm size to a range of 20 to 120 ha. It is also expected that, wherever there are off-farm income opportunities, these will be used to supplement family incomes and that part-time farming will become common.

Farmers still cannot be certain that they will be able to sell their produce and receive timely payment. Access to inputs is also difficult, due to local monopolies created by uncontrolled privatisation of the non-land assets of former state and co-operative farms. The new owners, often former farm managers, lease out farm machinery, supply farmers with inputs, and also act as intermediaries in the sale of farm products. Increased commercialisation and linkage into the food distribution chain is inhibited; not only by the lack of market support institutions and information, but also by the lack of management capacity and knowledge. Efficient markets for farm inputs and products have yet to emerge and this impedes the successful operation of the newly privatised agricultural sector.

In the course of EU accession, the candidate countries are adjusting their institutional and policy frameworks. Although much progress has been made in a number of areas there is still insufficient awareness, particularly at the local and farm level, concerning the extent of necessary changes. It is essential to arrive at a clear definition of property rights, and to draft and implement related legislation that will enable the development of fully functional land markets and efficient rural credit systems. This would facilitate access to new technologies and improved farming practices, with a beneficial impact on yield and productivity, as well as on the environmental performance of farms.

PRIORITIES FOR MIXED SYSTEM

The priorities for improving the farm systems of poor farmers relate to: (i) intensification of existing production patterns; (ii) enterprise diversification; and (iii) increased farm size through better land tenure and land markets. In addition, off-farm income will be a further important source of poverty reduction.

Small and fragmented holdings reduce the efficiency of family farms but, since land markets are still not fully functioning, there is limited possibility of increasing farm size in the medium term. At the same time, in a number of countries, substantial areas of land are left unused, as many newly reinstated landowners have no interest in farming. It is, therefore, necessary to facilitate and improve the terms of land leasing in ways that poorer farm households can benefit. In the longer term, together with the improved functioning of the land market, land consolidation programmes should be developed. In conditions of restricted farm size, intensification – and in some cases specialisation – would be beneficial in order to improve competitiveness and to enhance income generating opportunities.

Marketing channels, designed for the large-scale production that existed in the past, have not been replaced by appropriate market support mechanisms, thus leaving newly established family farmers without efficient facilities to market their produce. Furthermore, there has been insufficient integration of production and post-production phases to assure food quality that could compete with subsidised imports. As a consequence, not only export but also domestic markets are difficult to access for small family farms. In many cases, development and promotion of local markets should be a priority measure. In order to exploit new market potential, farmers need better information and decision support services, as well as management and organisational skills. These services and skills can be promoted by better farmer co-operation and an increased participation by farmer' interest groups and organisations. There are positive examples of farmers organising themselves, even in situations where there is little government support or a suitable institutional framework.

The trend towards further restructuring of large corporate or co-operative farms, and enlargement of small family farms, should be accompanied by measures to increase off-farm employment opportunities in rural areas. In addition, the orientation towards the EU model of agriculture also implies an integrated approach to rural areas – not only to provide space for agricultural activities but also to create possibilities for development of a range of off-farm activities and services (e.g. rural tourism, protection of the landscape and the environment). In all countries that are candidates for accession, past and recent EU-supported programmes in agriculture have been used to support infrastructure and institutional development. Promotion of alternative and supplementary on-farm and off-farm activities is needed in order to facilitate new opportunities created by rural development programmes, to open new possibilities of income generation and diversify livelihood systems.

LARGE-SCALE CEREAL-VEGETABLE FARMING SYSTEM

CHARACTERISTICS OF THE SYSTEM

The Large-scale Cereal-Vegetable Farming System is typical of the less advanced transition countries with good agro-ecological conditions – for example Ukraine and Moldova – but can also be found in neighbouring countries. It covers a total of 100 million ha, of which just under 40 million ha are cultivated. Annual precipitation ranges from 360 mm (for

Box 4.5 Basic Data: Large-scale Cereal-Vegetable Farming System

Total population (m)	68
Agricultural population (m)	15
Total area (m ha)	100
Agro-ecological zone	Subhumid – semiarid
Cultivated area (m ha)	38
Irrigated area (m ha)	4
Cattle population (m)	24

example in the Crimean peninsula where irrigation is necessary to satisfy the summer crop water requirements), to 1 600 mm in the Carpathian mountains of Northwest Ukraine. Droughts are frequent in the southern and eastern areas. However, only 10 percent of the cultivated area is irrigated and is found mainly in areas where the groundwater level has fallen significantly due to excessive drainage.

Total population is nearly 70 million, while the agricultural population is estimated at 15 million. Most farms range in size from 500 to 4 000 ha, but there are still examples of huge farms exceeding 10 000 ha. These latter farms are associated with large rural communities of 500 to 800 persons, many of whom are employed there. Farm employees also work their household plots. The main crops are wheat, barley, maize, sunflower, sugar beets and vegetables. There are nearly 25 million cattle within the system.

TRENDS AND ISSUES IN LARGE-SCALE CEREAL-VEGETABLE SYSTEM

The system is characterised by a remarkably high production potential. This potential was not fully utilised during the Soviet period and productivity has fallen since. The natural resource base that gives the system a high crop yield potential includes the *chernozem* and chestnut soils extending through Ukraine into neighbouring Russia and further into Central Asia. These soils are among the prime wheat soils of the world. Crop yield constraints are low annual rainfall and for wheat, high temperatures during the grain-fill period. Rainfall is not sufficient to allow any appreciable leaching, and very little of the rain percolating into the soil ever reaches the groundwater or the rivers. However, melting snow on frozen land can cause run-off with consequent erosion. During the 1980s, typical average yields achieved by the collective and state-owned farms were 3 t/ha for winter wheat and 25 to 30 t/ha for sugar beet[18], but these have since declined to as low as 2t/ha for cereals and 10 t/ha for sugar beet. However, experience has shown that cereal yields, even on large collective farms, can reach 7 to 8 t/ha and can be maintained at that level without any apparent negative effects on the environment. Sugar beet yields can reach 60 t/ha with relatively simple technologies.

The technique that unlocked the production potential in the West European cereal farming systems in the late 1970s was the synergistic interaction between nitrogen fertiliser and modern fungicides[19]. The technology package is simple; involving moderate nitrogen and phosphate applications, a modern fungicide and a simple growth regulator. Available machinery can be used for cereals, sugar beet and oilseeds, but hydraulic sprayers frequently need an improved filter system and new nozzles. However, farm managers have not yet adopted these

[18] By way of comparison, West European yields were approximately double those levels and continue to rise.

[19] The acceptance and use by farmers of this new technology spread very rapidly and created a demand for much increased extension services. The quantity of fungicide to be applied is limited and raises no environmental risk, particularly given the reduced soil leaching.

technologies, as the cost is high relative to current yields. Nonetheless, deep-rooting crops grown on deep, structurally robust and fertile soils are a highly efficient use of land in this system. In the black-soil belt of Ukraine, the ecological and technological potential is at hand for the recovery of the crop sector – possibly even in the short term. Winter wheat, spring malting barley, sugarbeet and oil crops, particularly sunflower, but also possibly spring oilseed rape, are crops that link in with the industrial processing sector and in which this system already has a competitive advantage or is likely to develop one.

The former organisation of labour, with an abundant labour force and limited individual responsibility, has left a legacy of poor motivation and appalling work practices, affecting workers as well as management. A culture of defensive management has developed, using information to deflect blame rather than to enlighten and improve management and productivity. This is perhaps the most intractable feature of the large farms in the system.

While in the long run business management and some form of empowerment training is critical, agronomy training – including training in Integrated Crop Management (ICM) – is even more crucial if sustainable agricultural practices are to be established and maintained. Established private farmers need access to the same kind of training programmes, concentrating on farm business management, crop production technology, ICM and marketing. A number of farm employees are not directly involved in agricultural operations, but work in activities such as catering, teaching, transport or machinery repair. Access to appropriate training can encourage these groups to provide services as small private enterprises. This can make it possible for large farms to divest themselves of these activities in order to concentrate on core agricultural operations.

Private farms have no access to agricultural extension services. The large corporate farms still have their in-house expertise, but this is unlikely to be adequate in an emerging free market system. An effective extension service is therefore needed to support both the private farmers and the large-scale farms with technical information and advice. This would cover the whole range of agricultural activities from livestock enterprises – most pertinent to small private farms – to crop production and marketing. A situation where the input supply sector alone would cater for information demand must be avoided. Agrochemical suppliers are already providing advice as part of their sales campaign, but can cover only a small segment of the total need and only with a certain amount of bias.

PRIORITIES FOR LARGE-SCALE CEREAL-VEGETABLE SYSTEM

The main strategies for the reduction of poverty in small farm households are: (i) increased farm size (or at least, individually operated area); (ii) intensification of existing production patterns; and (iii) enterprise diversification.

Continuation of farm privatisation remains the highest priority with a view to creating well-managed family farms. This will provide a livelihood for most of the existing rural population and reduce poverty, as well as producing a significant share of the future overall agricultural value added. In the process, attention must be given to the distribution of land and asset shares to individuals in collective farm enterprises; as well as to the possibility of workers retaining these when they leave. However, this would still be insufficient guarantee to give complete confidence to all would-be new entrants. The reasons that farm workers are so hesitant to start their own farm – even though private farms are performing better than large-scale farms – need to be better understood, because this form of privatisation represents an important means of reducing poverty. For example, the possibility of providing some initial assistance, in the form of a small loan for working capital, might be explored.

In parallel, programmes to raise agricultural productivity through introducing efficient cereal growing technology from Western Europe will provide this system with the best chance of rapidly reviving agriculture. Success on this front would make farms profitable and allow them to re-capitalise, particularly in terms of soil fertility and equipment (see Box 4.7). Such programmes should emphasise: collaborative work between farmers and scientists to validate and adjust

Box 4.7 Natural Resource Use and Economic Viability of Farming Systems in Southern Ukraine[20]

The unsound use over a long period of available physical, financial and natural resources on cultivated lands became obvious in the late nineties, when crop yields fell by over 30 percent from earlier levels. Poor farm management, inadequate use of fertilisers and pesticides and unchecked soil erosion caused nutrient depletion and land degradation. An imbalance between cultivated land, natural pastures and forested areas, combined with inefficient tillage technologies, led to negative environmental effects and inappropriate natural resource use.

However, successful examples of adaptation of large-scale farms to a more sustainable pattern of resource use do exist in Southern Ukraine, based on: (i) modified crop rotations that exclude unprofitable, previously heavily subsidised crops; and (ii) land conservation schemes incorporating leguminous crops and pastures with grazing cattle. Oversized and complex farms have been split into smaller, specialised and more manageable units.

The introduction of new production patterns with improved technology has increased output and profit. Before restructuring, the farms were indebted and losing money; with the new programmes sufficient revenues were generated to repay the debts. In addition, there has been a positive impact on water balance and soil quality, and increased landscape biodiversity. The use of soil-conserving crop production technologies has had a positive influence on soil fertility and organic matter content.

[20] Martinenko 2001.

techniques; training and short visits to farms in Western Europe; plus access to technical assistance and specialised equipment parts. Private farmers are expected to respond faster than large farms and should be the primary group to be involved. Communication will also be important to build awareness and acceptance in the farming community, as well as in government circles and the private sector.

Human resource development is vital to turn around and diversify the Large-scale Crop-Vegetable System. Farm managers need training in financial and strategic business management, they also need courses in human resource development and management. Farm workers need technical skills, as well as empowerment training. It is from their ranks that private farmers can emerge.

EXTENSIVE CEREAL-LIVESTOCK FARMING SYSTEM

CHARACTERISTICS OF THE SYSTEM

The system is typical of semiarid regions of the Russian Federation and Northern Kazakhstan, but also covers some areas in Southern Kazakhstan and neighbouring Turkmenistan and Uzbekistan. The average length of the growing season is 125 days. Annual precipitation ranges from 200 to 400 mm per annum. Rainfall is most

Box 4.8 Basic Data: Extensive Cereal-Livestock Farming System	
Total population (m)	98
Agricultural population (m)	14
Total area (m ha)	425
Agro-ecological zone	Semiarid
Cultivated area (m ha)	106
Irrigated area (m ha)	2
Cattle population (m)	14

prevalent during spring and fall. Winters bring little snow (200 to 300 mm), many sunny days and strong winds. Summers are dry with hot, dry winds. This is the *steppe* area with natural grassland and soils that vary from black chestnut soils in the north to brown forest and lighter soils in the southern part of the zone. Historically, this area was the home of herdsmen migrating over long distances to avoid extreme winters and to seek seasonal pastures. There was very little sedentary agriculture. During the Soviet era, pastoralists were collectivised and livestock production intensified based on cultivated and irrigated fodder. By the mid-1980s, this approach had resulted in a large population of sheep, accompanied by serious degradation of pastures and reduced productivity of livestock operations.

The system extends over 425 million ha, of which 106 million ha are cultivated. The total population of the system is almost 100 million, but the agricultural population is estimated at only 14 million. This region was famous for its huge state and collective farms, which were built through the legendary *Virgin Lands Programme* that literally transformed the *steppe* from grassland pastures to highly mechanised farms for wheat production. Wheat cultivation was characterised by a very input-intensive technology to smooth out variability arising from climate-induced changes in cropping conditions. Some farms were as large as 300 000 ha, including croplands and extensive pastures. Farm and community were one and the same. During the restructuring reforms, former state and collective farms have been officially privatised and transformed into production co-operatives, partnerships and joint-stock companies, private farms and family farms. Farms are generally large, the average extent depends on the agro-climatic conditions of the area. Larger farms registered as production co-operatives have an average size of about 14 000 ha, but there still are examples of much larger farms. Corporate partnerships and joint stock companies average about 8 500 ha; and relatively small, so-called peasant, farms about 450 ha.

Box 4.9 A Typical Farm of the Extensive Cereal-Livestock Farming System

A typical production pattern on this type of farm consists of wheat and barley on 60 to 65 percent of the cultivated land, some 15 to 20 percent each of hay and fodder crops, and a small area of industrial and vegetable crops. The major crop is rainfed wheat, primarily spring wheat, with fallows every two years in the drier parts, every 3 to 5 years elsewhere – the fallow being used for grazing. Average wheat yields are 0.8 t/ha. Other crops are fodder (grass) and sunflower. The number of hectares per farm worker varies, depending on size, from 4 to 10 ha. Production technology is based on mechanised cultivation with mostly worn-out machinery. Due to financial difficulties, the use of mineral fertilisers is minimal, on average 5 kg/ha. Pesticides are also applied in inadequate quantities. Quality seeds are used on only 20 percent of the wheat area.

Production co-operatives, partnerships and joint stock companies account for as much as 80 percent of the total agricultural land. Within these large-scale farms, household plot production has assumed increased importance, accounting for about half of value-added in agriculture. Principal outputs are wheat and barley, hay and some industrial crops combined with traditional breeds of sheep, cattle and horses. Livestock production is based on summer pasture grazing and winter stall-feeding. As a result of livestock privatisation, about 85 percent of the animals are privately owned. Agricultural output fluctuates from year to year depending on weather conditions.

TRENDS AND ISSUES IN EXTENSIVE CEREAL-LIVESTOCK SYSTEM

The productivity of labour and other resources within the system has been decreasing in recent years and is now very low. The decline in production is due to a number of factors, including initial confusion surrounding the transition, reduced purchasing power of the population following the drop in food subsidies and deteriorating economic conditions, the collapse of former domestic and export markets, declining input use, and deteriorating irrigation infrastructure and machinery stock, associated with the breakdown of the cash economy. Over decades of Soviet central planning, the system rarely used criteria of economic efficiency, regional specialisation or competitive advantage based on world markets. An additional factor contributing to the sharp decline in wheat productivity is the progressive degradation of the resource base, as a result of years of unsustainable cropping patterns. Some 20 percent of the land that is particularly unsuitable for cultivation has now been taken out of wheat.

The financial situation of large-scale farms has continuously deteriorated, resulting in a downward spiral of increased indebtedness, growing inability to buy inputs and reduced productivity. Wages are not paid regularly, paid in kind, or paid after months or years. Some farm workers have been reduced to half-time employment or sent on leave; receiving basic food rations and fodder as payment. As a consequence, the role of household plots in sustaining livelihoods has greatly increased.

Land reform measures have formally dissolved the Soviet-style collective farms, but farm restructuring has often been flawed. Farm members did not receive sufficient information about their rights to land and assets, nor were they adequately informed about possible choices related to the formation of new legal entities – including peasant or family farms. Many were not ready to engage in private farming, as they had insufficient experience in farm management or technical farm activities, and were concerned about lack of access to inputs and services. Because of these reasons and sometimes under pressure from the former manager[21], many pooled their land and non-land assets to form new large co-operative farms, with little or no change in the former collective style of management. For most of these newly organised farms, restructuring has not brought about much efficiency gain and their financial condition continues to deteriorate. Moreover, land remains under state ownership, which makes access to credit difficult and also decreases incentives to invest in productivity-improving technologies.

However, the situation is improving in some areas. For example, in Kazakhstan, the new bankruptcy policy has led to the creation of thousands of new independent entities, most of which are peasant farms. This approach has two objectives: (i) to write off farm debts and so permit access to bank credit; and (ii) to accelerate changes in farm sizes, ownership and management so that they can become more efficient and viable. New forms of ownership and management have also been introduced, such as contract farming, or farm acquisition by large grain or industrial companies providing for vertical integration. The outcome is not positive everywhere as, after debt write-off, some farms still retain the former style

---

[21] World Bank 2000d.

of management. Restructuring is, however, proceeding fast in the southern areas, which have more favourable agricultural conditions and where the majority of the poor live; as well as in the irrigated zones of the northern part. Farms in less favourable areas seem to prefer to go bankrupt and close down. In the process, many farms are bought by outsiders and stripped of any valuable movable property, leaving the farm workers without equipment. Additionally, the ongoing restructuring involves the transfer of social services to local governments. This entails a risk of the poor losing access to health, educational and social services.

Constrained by a lack of working capital, farmers have reduced input use to low levels which may be unsustainable. The major problems are in the areas of fertilisers, pest control and seeds. Locust infestation has been particularly severe in the past few years. The seed sector may be hardest to revive, in the absence of a proper legal and regulatory environment and the lack of clear policies. The state of disrepair of agricultural machinery is also a cause for serious concern. Moreover, the type of equipment now needed is different from that formerly produced: it should be smaller, lighter, and more precise. Such equipment is not affordable by the majority of farms.

Agro-processing, distribution and marketing appear to be the weakest links in the agricultural system. Proximity to urban areas, and thus potential direct access to markets, is an important factor influencing the profitability of farms. There is sufficient processing capacity in the region but most of the units are antiquated and inefficient. Inadequate and poor-quality equipment for storage, processing, transportation and product handling contributes to heavy post-harvest losses and low prices for producers. Former state-owned enterprises continue to enjoy a monopolistic position in the industry and constrain producers' access to free, competitive markets, as well as restraining entry of new capital, technology and management. Barter still dominates trade, representing over 80 percent of total sales.

PRIORITIES FOR EXTENSIVE CEREAL-LIVESTOCK SYSTEM

The main strategies for poverty reduction are: (i) increased size of smallholder farms and livestock herds; and (ii) intensification of existing patterns of production. Although average farm sizes have been reduced, there are still many very large farms, and only some have been divided into family units. Completing the land reform and restructuring process is a major priority in order to increase farm sizes of poor households.

Because of the agro-climatic conditions in the crop-livestock regions – low and extremely variable precipitation combined with strong winds – improving wheat cultivation requires agronomic and soil conservation practices that enable moisture retention during the winter, utilise summer precipitation efficiently, and address serious wind erosion problems resulting from cultivation. Because weed control and efficient use of moisture have been identified as essential in improving the productivity of grain production, conservation tillage is a potentially useful technology. It has already been developed successfully in similar agro-ecologies in other countries and should be explored further for this system. Alternative rotations and crop diversification, that would provide farmers with greater flexibility and protect the resource base, should also be investigated.

The major constraints to livestock development are the insufficient feed base, poor animal health management resulting in high morbidity, and generally poor technical and financial management. Traditional breeds are well adapted to the local conditions and the more extensive management that is now required. For sheep breeds, the promotion of those selected for wool quality may not be in the interest of small-scale producers until local prices for wool improve. The traditional fat-tailed meat breed requires less fodder during winter, can be maintained on grazing in semiarid areas, and is more profitable. There is a large potential for using natural pastures to cut production costs, by improved grazing management; for rehabilitation of forage seed production; and for distribution of new forage species to livestock producers. Considerable work is required on developing a policy and legal framework for more efficient pasture use with a focus on enhancing and preserving pasture variability, preventing land grabbing by the influential, and ensuring security of tenure and user rights of small-scale producers.

Agricultural research has remained largely in the Soviet pattern and research activities have dwindled due to lack of funding. The system is greatly oversized and needs to start responding to the needs of both large and peasant farms through more practical and demand-driven research programmes. Competitive grant schemes would enable governments to use available budgetary funds more effectively for agricultural research, and to mobilise private-sector resources. There is a large gap in the agricultural advisory services in the region. In the Russian Federation, there was no need for an independent extension service as former state and collective farms used their own technicians, in addition to the technical services provided by the government specialists. However, following farm restructuring, farm technicians have started to operate their own farms and are no longer available to advise other farmers who need their services. There is an urgent need for efficient, market-based advisory services in agriculture; these will require partial public financing, at least initially and particularly for small family farms, as described in Box 4.10.

> ## Box 4.10 Advisory Services in Extensive Cereal-Livestock Farming Systems[22]
>
> Many of the technologies promoted in the Soviet period have become unsustainable in the new economic environment, in particular because of high input costs. Technologies for reducing production costs are not widely available. In the meantime, the breakdown of the previous systems of information dissemination has created a void. Land reform and farm restructuring have also created new kinds of production units requiring advisory services. However, governments have not been able to establish new services and have generally given limited priority to advisory systems because of their perceived high cost and the need to reduce public sector staffing and budgets.
>
> Recent World Bank and Asian Development Bank-assisted projects aiming to support agriculture and farm privatisation in Kazakhstan have included initiatives to facilitate access to credit through commercial banks, establishment of advisory services, and technical assistance to local governments and research institutes[23]. These initiatives focus on farms that may qualify for commercial bank loans, based on readily marketable collateral. A large proportion of farms, including small-scale peasant farms, do not qualify and would be left out of these initiatives, with their owners or workers continuing to remain in the poverty trap, unless alternative approaches are developed for improving employment opportunities and incomes.
>
> Governments within the region tend to favour a 'cookbook' approach which assumes that a simple menu of recommendations can be applied to solve all problems facing farmers. However, the issues affecting the lives of the rural population are complex. A flexible participatory strategy to address such issues is needed. Unless staff understand the underlying purpose and value of eliciting farmers' views and incorporating them into programmes, advisory and extension services are unlikely to become credible, effective and sustainable.

STRATEGIC PRIORITIES FOR EASTERN EUROPE AND CENTRAL ASIA

This section highlights some of the major challenges in the region and suggests possible approaches and investment opportunities. Table 4.2 ranks the potential of each system for agricultural growth and for poverty reduction, and indicates the relative importance of five major household strategies for poverty reduction. The assessments are based on expert judgement, and the score for the region has been calculated as a weighted average based on proportion of agricultural population (see Table 4.1).

There is substantial scope for both agricultural growth and poverty reduction, although the two are not necessarily completely inter-dependent because of,

---

[22] Meng 2001.

[23] The World Bank assisted Agricultural Post-Privatisation Assistance Project, ADB-assisted Agricultural Support Programme, and the proposed ADB-assisted Farm Restructuring Sector Development Programme.

Table 4.4 Potential and Relative Importance of Household Strategies for Poverty Reduction in Eastern Europe and Central Asia

Farming System	Potential for agricultural growth	Potential for poverty reduction	Strategies for poverty reduction				
			Intensi-fication	Diversi-fication	Increased Farm Size	Increased off-farm Income	Exit from Agriculture
Irrigated	High	Moderate	4	3	I	I	I
Mixed	Moderate	High	3	2.5	2	1.5	I
Forest Based Livestock	Moderate	Moderate	3	2	2.5	I	1.5
Horticulture Mixed	Moderate	Moderate	4	2	2	I	I
Large-scale Cereal	High	Moderate	2.5	2	4	I	0.5
Small-scale Cereal-Livestock	Low	Moderate	3	2	2	I	2
Extensive Cereal-Livestock	Low	Moderate	3	I	4	I	I
Pastoral	Low	Moderate	2	I	2	2	3
Sparse (Cold)	Low	Low	I	I	I	3	4
Sparse (Arid)	Low	Low	1.5	I	0.5	2	5
Urban Based	Low	Low	2	2	0	2	4
Average for Region			2.7	1.8	2.3	1.4	1.8

Source: Expert judgement.
Note: Total score for each farming system equals 10. Assessments refer to poor farmers only. Average for region weighted by agricultural populations of systems derived from Table 4.1.

inter alia, the distribution of land. With regard to the strategies of poor households for escaping poverty, production intensification holds the greatest promise on a regional scale, followed by an increase in farm size (among poor farmers). Much of the size gain is expected to derive from further land distribution, although improved land market functioning (both formal and informal) are likely to contribute over the next 30 years. It is also expected that substantial numbers of households will leave agriculture for other occupations. The following public actions are designed to support households in implementing these strategies. These conclusions need to be interpreted in the context of declining and ageing rural populations[24].

[24] Contrary to expectation, some studies suggest that older people fare better than younger couples with children (D'Avis, *pers. comm*).

Since future developments are expected to include further privatisation, structural adjustments and market liberalisation, it is likely that some of the systems characterised by small size and private or family ownership will gain in significance. After almost 10 years of reforms, the differences between the CSEE and Baltic countries on the one hand, and the CIS countries on the other, have been accentuated. Due to the adoption of more comprehensive transition policies the transformation of agriculture is most advanced in Central Europe and the Baltic, agricultural production has started to pick up again, and labour productivity is increasing – thanks in part to the creation of alternative job opportunities outside agriculture. In contrast, the transformation of agriculture in the CIS countries is still in its early stages. The large-scale farm units have still survived in many of those countries, and distortions in production, pricing and marketing of 'strategic' products continue. For these reasons, emphasis is given below to discussion of the CIS countries, where many of the issues are far more acute and solutions are less readily at hand.

POLICIES, INSTITUTIONS AND PUBLIC GOODS

Attempts to reform large-scale farms through a number of international projects in Russia and the Ukraine[25] have not been particularly successful so far. The restructured farms are still too large for efficient management, and are only marginally more efficient in terms of yields and market orientation. In most cases, only a handful of family farms were created in the restructuring process.

If reforming the core farm management structure fails, a different approach is needed; one that would take into account the whole farm community. It is significant that household plot production has increased sharply during the past decade and now represents almost 50 percent of total output value. However, household plot farmers are not yet ready – or not allowed – to become private farmers. Rather, a symbiotic relationship tends to develop between the small production units and the mother farm[26], the former possibly specialising in labour-intensive activities and the latter in providing services (access to inputs, tractors, and sometimes marketing). Farm workers need household plots to feed their family, while farm managers' positions appear to depend more on the relationship they maintain with the workers' community than on their actual performance in managing the corporate farm. Such a form of association might provide a possible framework for transforming large-scale farms, even if it entails the creation of a large number of family farms that are perhaps, initially too small to be economically efficient. This may be preferable to the alternative of large-scale liquidation of the mother farms, if in the process those farms are stripped of all

[25] Lerman and Csaki 2000.
[26] Serova 1998.

valuable assets and workers forced to leave - as is happening in marginal areas of Kazakhstan.

In countries where farm restructuring is not complete it is suggested that other avenues for farm restructuring be tried, giving more emphasis to social dimensions and less to the need to retain large farms for the sake of increasing national output. Even in relatively marginal areas of the Extensive Cereal-Livestock Farming System, a farm with 40 to 50 ha of cultivated land with access to pastures, provides a family with a better livelihood than can be obtained within the large farm; and the family farm contribution to the national economy is greater. The requisite minimum land area can fall to less than five ha in the higher-potential areas of the Cereal-Vegetable Farming System.

The best arrangements, final outcomes and ways to reach them, will differ from place to place. Two other ways could be envisaged; one leading to small private farms serviced by a medium-sized corporate farm[27], leasing its land from ex-members and providing contractual services. The alternative would lead to fully independent small farms; services being provided by individuals among them (e.g. tractor owners for machinery services) or by various co-operation mechanisms. The first solution would have the merit of retaining certain core services requiring specialised skills and capital-intensive equipment (e.g. mechanical workshops), until the private sector can effectively provide them. Specific issues that would need to be addressed to promote such solutions would again differ with location, but generally include the need to write off the debt of the former large farm. Land tenure arrangements would preferably ensure freehold and free transferability of titles, at least for the cultivated land. For pasture land, communal leasing arrangements may be preferable for optimum management and to avoid exclusion of the poorest.

Although structural change in the farming sector is not yet complete in the CSEE countries, most of the land is now controlled and farmed by individuals in all but two of those countries. The share of land under state control remains high in some countries, however, and land markets are generally only weakly developed, although this is now rapidly evolving, particularly in the countries moving towards EU accession. The basic requirement is to develop a land tenure system that facilitates secure and equitable access to land. This will comprise land administration functions that are generally provided by the public sector in developed market economies; including registration, plus valuation and planning – together with support for their associated institutions. It also includes capacity-building related to the appropriate professional skills and professional institutions that are associated with these and other activities related to land markets in the private sector. With the basic land registry now being compiled, attention is focusing on the enhancement and strengthening of land administration structures

---

[27] In Russia, many agricultural officials are exploring ways of maintaining large-scale units, provided they are efficient and can attract, foreign direct investment and improved technologies (D'Avis, pers. comm).

to support market transactions. Mechanisms are required to ensure fair, transparent and secure access to land and natural resources – whether through ownership or leasing – and to protection property rights.

New professional skills need to be acquired, particularly in the market-related fields of valuation and real estate management. The main focus will therefore need to go beyond the current emphasis of establishing formal land tenure institutions of modern cadastres – plus land registration systems – although these will continue to be important priorities. There will be a need to extend this support to include the development of the other institutions broadly considered under land administration, in order to produce relevant professional skills and institutions. Given the globalisation of capital and the rapid development of international accounting and valuation standards, valuation skills are seen as an important issue in this context.

Land reform policies that focus exclusively on creating efficient large farms, hoping that workers will find work either within those farms or elsewhere, may be doing more harm than good. Any agricultural policy – particularly in countries where large-scale farms still prevail – needs to be tested for its potential impact on labour and poverty. Specific rural poverty alleviation policies are needed which, *inter alia*, must improve access of the poor to objective information on land and non-land property rights; as well as involving civil society in protecting the rights of the poor. In designing rural poverty alleviation initiatives, the importance of rural communities and rural livelihoods must be recognised. In particular, attention should be given to non-agricultural aspects of rural life, such as health, education, infrastructure and non-agricultural economic activities. Participatory methods, involving NGOs where possible, can facilitate such an integrated approach to local development and poverty alleviation.

TRADE LIBERALISATION AND MARKET DEVELOPMENT

Marketing of agricultural products is one of the major bottlenecks faced by producers in the region, particularly in light of the importance of diversification for poverty reduction. However, the current situation differs between the two sub-regions.

In the CSEE countries, the macro-economic environment has become more favourable in recent years (except in most of the Balkans), and prices are to a large extent open to world market influences. While support for agriculture and protection of domestic markets has increased in the past 4 to 5 years, it is generally below EU levels. Increased convergence is expected in the years to come. The challenge will be to retain methods of support that serve efficiency and competitiveness, rather than protecting inefficient farm structures.

In most CIS countries, the situation appears much worse than it was before transition. Economic reform has often meant the collapse of the previous system, based on state controlled allocation of raw and processed products and the consequent specialisation of certain regions or republics in the production of agricultural products. However, a predicted process of 'natural' transition to a market economy appears – after 10 years – to have failed to establish an alternative marketing infrastructure or associated support services. This has contributed to increased poverty amongst producers and the development of a barter economy during the 1990s. Entire countries, whose economies are based on agriculture and which have seen their traditional allocated or centrally-determined production and distribution mechanisms disappear, have fallen into poverty. This is the case in Moldova, Armenia, Georgia (specialised in horticultural products such as fruits, vegetables, juices, wines) and to a lesser extent in Macedonia.

The root causes of this situation include: (i) the overall economic crisis throughout the region, leading to a dramatic decrease of purchasing power among the population and hence lower demand for agricultural products; (ii) the inefficiencies and obsolescence of local large scale, often technically bankrupt, processing industries, and their obstruction of alternatives approaches to marketing and market development; (iii) various trade barriers common throughout the region, which reduce competition among intermediaries, hamper exploration and testing of new market opportunities, and in general, limit the opportunities for farmers to specialise in activities where they have a comparative production advantage; (iv) the current inability to penetrate other markets such as the Western European countries for a number of reasons such as protection measures, difficulties in reaching quality standards, lack of trade development strategies, and difficult transportation conditions; (v) on the production side, the weak position of producers - being scattered, producing small quantities, of a limited range of products of uneven and often low quality; and (vi) lack of market information.

It seems very difficult to find successful marketing projects in the region that could serve as examples. At policy level, while price and trade policies will need further attention and improvement, understanding the workings of informal barriers to trade – and how these could be lowered – is equally important. Policies should also consider addressing legal impediments to market development, the need to improve quality by *inter alia* promotion of standards, and favouring the emergence of new types of private smaller scale processing industries. Ultimately, however, policies can do little without effective implementation. Barriers to entry and growth of new enterprises frequently exist in contravention of national legislation and policy declarations, and are linked to established power groups unwilling to see the evolution of systems outside their control. In this respect, the problems faced in developing an efficient and functioning marketing sector in the region is inextricably tied to the progress of open and efficient private enterprise in general – an area with ramifications far beyond agriculture.

Strengthening local institutions will also be of the utmost importance in trying to encourage and support the development of new marketing structures. This could include the development of producers' organisations (e.g. co-operatives, marketing groups) and of professional organisations organised around specific products or ranges of products and which would aim at improving the flow of information between actors (e.g. market requirements) and facilitating their contractual arrangements.

INFORMATION AND HUMAN CAPITAL

In addition to political will and financial resources, the renewal and vitalisation of the agricultural research systems, discussed below, will require a major focus on training and education. Farmers and their service providers will need training in: technical and agronomic aspects of their respective enterprises; planning and management; accounting and administrative skills; and marketing. This massive task can only be achieved if the efforts and the costs are distributed across government, local training and advisory services and the beneficiaries themselves.

The former command economy was operated without an extension system: technical specialists were available on the farm and used prescribed techniques to meet centralised orders. So, while research is dilapidated, extension is still non-existent. Advisory services need to be actively developed, particularly for small family farms. Their role should not be limited to technical aspects, though these are important. Due to the paucity of well-adapted techniques, advisors need to develop skills in simple, farmer-participatory experimentation in order to test such things as different varieties, or new systems of resource management and conservation. Their work should also cover training and advice in farm management; business plans; accounting and book keeping; and credit, applications. Some of these services could be partially paid for by the farmers. Farmers should also become active in a new farm advisory system by developing networks to exchange information, plus arranging meetings and visits to share new knowledge, not only of production systems but also of planning for the market.

Most services will need public funding, at least in the initial stages. However, the pitfalls of large public extension systems should be avoided, as they are too expensive for national budgets to support. This situation can be avoided through quasi-market mechanisms ensuring that advisors work for the benefit of farmers. Various formulae can be used to this end, including coupons – although cumbersome – competitive grants, or payments to providers according to a work programme that has been established with groups of farmers. A gradual and flexible development of the system, allowing close adaptation to local situations and emphasising quality services, should be preferred over quick coverage. Programmes to support development advisory services need to place a very strong emphasis on training, particularly in participatory methods and in farm management.

For large farms, private services must be envisaged from the start, but publicly funded training for providers is justified, as well as some start-up financial assistance. Information services also need to be developed to reach large number of farmers and provide them with information they can use directly. One of the main domains to consider is awareness building concerning farmers' rights, e.g. regarding land, public health and market information.

SCIENCE AND TECHNOLOGY

The potential for overall productivity improvement through better technologies is generally high and thus intensification of family farm production is considered to be the most important pathway, at regional level, to poverty reduction. Some of the best opportunities lie in developing conservation agriculture in semiarid zones, particularly in the Extensive Cereal-Livestock Farming System; and everywhere introducing reduced tillage and more precise land preparation and sowing practices. Another promising avenue of improvement is the intensification of grain production in the Large-scale Cereal-Vegetable Farming System, through introducing and adapting some of technologies developed in Western Europe. However, this should proceed with caution as many farmers in Western Europe, after 40 years of intensification and specialisation, are facing surpluses, environmental damage and the breakdown of rural communities.

Re-instating fodder crops in crop rotations – and developing feed and pasture management systems well adapted to local situations – is one way of combating these effects, while at the same time reducing dependency on grain for livestock feed and benefiting from better systems of crop-livestock integration. A further source of improvement is through better water management in irrigated systems; in order to reduce overall consumption, limit environmental damage, and increase productivity.

Research systems can be revitalised. They need to be reorganised and properly funded, even though this is a slow process requiring a long-term investment. Starting with incentives to change ways of working and address practical farmers' problems is a sound strategy, and is being effected with some success in several countries by means of competitive grants. This change must be accompanied by efforts to improve farmer participation in priority setting and engagement in the evolution of national research strategies. Significant investments are justified in infrastructure, equipment, training and core programmes once there is agreement on objectives, priorities and strategies. There should be a clear realisation that a few well-equipped centres are superior to a large number of dispersed and specialised facilities; especially as a growing proportion of experimentation will be done on farmers' fields. A network of on-farm research activities by farmers' groups, based within distinctive agro-ecological or socio-ecological regions, could be linked to these key centres. In revitalising research it is important to introduce more social scientists into the system and to move away from the highly centralised technocratic approach to research and technology development.

Rehabilitating research systems is a long-term process. Farmers cannot wait for the research centres to produce the requisite technologies so shortcuts are needed. Part of the technology can be borrowed from elsewhere and adapted to local conditions. Horticulture and irrigated agriculture, for example, could benefit from technology transfer. In the CSEE, technologies suited to local situations can generally be borrowed and adapted with relative ease from EU countries, when not already available locally. This is hardly the case for most of the CIS countries. Agroclimatic conditions that are close to those found in the region's Extensive Crop-Livestock System, for example, may be seen in northern America where large farms also dominate. However the socio-cultural and economic context is very different and a simple transfer of technology is generally not feasible. Even where adaptation is relatively easy, as in the case of the Large-scale Crop-Vegetable System, introducing better cereal technology to farm managers has been difficult. Again, there are important lessons to learn from the rapidly changing structure of agriculture in Europe; and from the United States, which might soon see the development of very different technologies to those that have dominated agriculture for the past 30 years.

Rainfed cropping under a variety of moisture, soil or temperature constraints – and limited capital resources – needs careful adaptation to local circumstances. This is a case where Participatory Technology Development (PTD) may be the most effective way to produce, verify, adapt and disseminate new technology. In such an approach, farmers themselves are trained in experimentation, and with the help of scientists decide on objectives and methods. Admittedly, there are still only few examples of successful PTD in CIS countries, and the current evidence (e.g. from Swiss-funded extension projects in Kyrgyzstan) is that PTD takes time and significant technical assistance in order to be successful. But in a number of domains there is no alternative to local technology development. Areas that would benefit most from a PTD approach include conservation agriculture (including zero or reduced tillage), improvement of livestock feeding systems and improvements in farm management.

NATURAL RESOURCES AND CLIMATE

The challenges raised by the excessive expansion of irrigated systems, and the difficulty of rehabilitating and maintaining them, have already been mentioned. Solutions to contain further degradation and develop sustainable systems, particularly on-farm, through the establishment of participatory management systems are being successfully developed in several countries. At the same time, it must be realised that a significant part of these systems was developed in areas that can be successfully cultivated without irrigation, even though this will require drastic improvements in agricultural practices. Conservation agriculture, explored by a number of USSR scientists but not favoured under the previous system, will allow better use rainfall water, increase yields, and reduce drought risks and production costs. This is in addition to its benefits in terms of soil conservation and build-up of soil organic matter. It should not be forgotten that these systems were primarily developed for the production of cash crops, such as cotton and sugar cane. The markets and prices for these products been weak in recent years and the net returns from continuing to grow them are likely to be low and risky. Alternatives include reducing irrigation in order to develop more sustainable systems and rehabilitate the environment, or switching to intensive food crop production in order to improve the health and income of local people, or some combination of both.

Scarce resources and poor pasture management have put severe pressure on the natural resource base in the Pastoral Farming System of Central Asia, resulting in the deterioration of natural vegetation and extensive soil erosion. The challenge is to develop new systems of pasture management that preserve the resource base and regulate access without excluding the poor. Such systems will differ according to local conditions, and need to be developed jointly with concerned communities. They would generally emphasise protection and rehabilitation of areas of intense grazing close to the villages and fuller exploitation of remote pastures. For the farmed areas, individual management through cut and carry 'meadow' systems may be preferable to common grazing. More remote resources would remain under local administration or state responsibility, which generally allows for a range of grazing management interventions – taking into account the user rights of nomadic and transhumant groups. Technical interventions may include enrichment of grazing areas and degraded slopes through sowing well-adapted species, with or without minimum cultivation, in conjunction with livestock control and concurrent re-introduction of fodder crops. To implement such systems successfully would require a parallel development of communal range management systems (see the case study from the Syrian *Steppe* in the Middle East and North Africa region in Chapter 3), in which resource users have an active role in planning, implementing and policing the system. Such systems also require strong social capital and organisation to be effective.

CONCLUSIONS

There is substantial scope for both agricultural growth and poverty reduction in the region. With regard to the strategies of poor households for escaping poverty, production intensification holds the greatest promise on a regional scale, followed by increased farm size. Although it is impossible, based on the foregoing regional analysis to prescribe specific national actions, the overall challenge of reducing hunger and poverty in the region demands three strategic initiatives. These are all concerned with building the capacities of local institutions – both in the public and private sectors – in order to take advantage of farm restructuring and economic liberalisation. In the public sector, this implies acquiring the capacity to switch from a planning role in a command economy system to a supporting and guiding role. In the private sector, it means acquiring the knowledge and skills to operate within an open economy. Moreover, mechanisms are needed for farmers to access and participate effectively in new institutions, including producer groups. Other measures, such as the rehabilitation of viable irrigation schemes and the establishment of rural finance mechanisms, also merit regional priority. However, they will not operate effectively unless local capacities in related areas are first enhanced.

The inter-linked initiatives are as follows:

Improved resource access. Improved land tenure systems are needed to encourage the efficient use of land and the emergence of viable private farm units. Components include: completing land distribution processes; continuing support and broader development of land administration systems; encouraging formal transfer of land (through renting, leasing or sale) and through appropriate valuation; and developing real estate management skills.

Re-oriented and strengthened agricultural services. Viable farming systems require new types of *post-privatisation* services. Components include: the provision of mixed public/private sector advisory services; training; and the dissemination of information in order to improve technical, managerial and marketing skills of privatised farms.

Expanded market development. Functional markets are essential for food and other agricultural products, agricultural inputs and for labour. Components include: supporting efficient organizations of producers, traders, processors; investing in market infrastructure (including market and price information systems); improving the quality of food products in order to comply with international norms; and addressing legal impediments to efficient marketing.

SOUTH ASIA

...

REGIONAL SETTING

CHARACTERISTICS OF THE REGION

South Asia, as defined in this book, comprises eight countries including Afghanistan[1]. Agriculture accounts for a significant part of GDP throughout the region, and has grown at a remarkable overall rate during the past 30 years as a consequence of the Green Revolution. Nevertheless, the region has a greater number of undernourished and poor than any other developing region, and more than two-thirds of these reside in rural areas.

The South Asia region contains a population of 1344 million people[2], more than one quarter of the population of the developing world. Of these, 970 million (72 percent) live in rural areas. Approximately 150 million households, with 751 million people, can be classed as agricultural[3]. The combination of high population and limited land area (514 million ha), means that the rural population density in South Asia – at 1.89 persons per ha – is higher than in any other developing region. Moreover, the large proportion of inhospitable terrain has led to the concentration of most of the population on less than half of this land area, resulting in severe pressure on natural resources in many places.

The long history of human settlement has resulted in the utilisation of a wide diversity of natural resources for agriculture. In agro-ecological terms[4], 20 percent of the region's land consists of steeply sloping hills and mountains containing only five percent of the total population. Nineteen percent is densely populated, humid or moist subhumid lowland containing the bulk (43 percent) of the region's people; while 29 percent is dry subhumid and still heavily populated,

---

[1] See Annex 3 for the countries in the region.
[2] FAOSTAT.
[3] FAOSTAT.
[4] See Annex 5 for an explanation of agro-ecological zones.

as it contains 33 percent of the population. The remaining 32 percent is semiarid and arid lowland supporting only 19 percent of the region's inhabitants. Hill and mountain areas are found in all the countries, but predominate along the southern slopes of the Himalayan range across India, Bhutan, Nepal, Pakistan and Afghanistan. These hill areas have suffered from particularly extensive deforestation and soil erosion.

The humid and moist subhumid agro-ecological zones, which benefit from seasonal monsoon rains and more than 180 growing days per annum, are located in Bangladesh and around the northeastern, eastern and southern fringes of India, and cover the centre, west and south of Sri Lanka. With large areas of alluvial soils and a high proportion of the land under intensive rice cultivation, these areas support a particularly dense population. The dry subhumid areas, characterised by 120 to 179 growing days each year, cover most of the Deccan Plateau in Central India. The northwest of India, most of Pakistan and Afghanistan are semiarid or arid with less than 120 growing days, low population density and large areas of desert. Throughout the region, there are about 74 million ha of forest (14 percent of total land area), 49 million ha of grazing land and about 213 million ha of cultivated land and permanent crops – equivalent to less than 0.16 ha of agricultural land per capita. Freshwater resources are relatively scarce

Of the 1.2 billion people worldwide living in dollar poverty, over 43 percent are found in South Asia. Of these, the vast majority live in rural areas. Despite improvements in national food security over the last three decades, benefits have not yet reached the entire population of the region and FAO estimates that 254 million people are still undernourished. Indicators of other dimensions of poverty, such as female illiteracy (59 percent), child mortality (89 per 1 000 in children under five years), and child malnutrition (51 percent)[5], also point to extensive poverty. The rural poor are particularly vulnerable to droughts, floods and other natural disasters. According to IFAD estimates[6], about 66 percent of the vulnerable population in India are small farmers and 2 percent are artisanal fishing families. Women are particularly disadvantaged; female-headed farm households have far lower average incomes than equivalent male-headed farm households.

Of the eight countries in the region, only the Maldives and Sri Lanka have achieved middle income status. Average per capita income is low: with a GDP of US$440 per capita. Official development assistance in 1998 amounted to only US$4 per capita (cf. US$21 per capita in Sub-Saharan Africa) and represented only 0.9 percent of regional GNP. Historically, the agriculture sector has generated the surpluses that have supported the growth and development of

---

[5] World Bank 2000a.

[6] Jazairy et al 1992.

Major Farming Systems
SOUTH ASIA

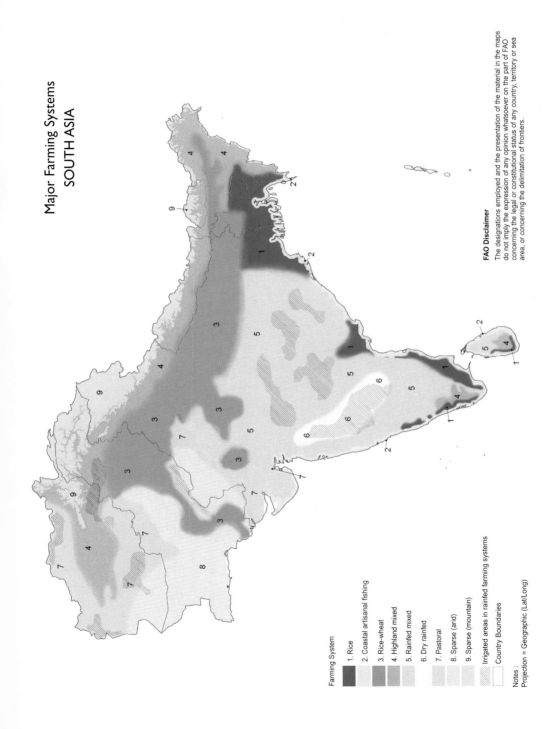

Farming System

1. Rice
2. Coastal artisanal fishing
3. Rice-wheat
4. Highland mixed
5. Rainfed mixed
6. Dry rainfed
7. Pastoral
8. Sparse (arid)
9. Sparse (mountain)

Irrigated areas in rainfed farming systems

Country Boundaries

Notes :
Projection = Geographic (Lat/Long)

other sectors of the economy. This process is most advanced in India and Pakistan, where GADP comprises 27 percent[7] and 24.6 percent[8] respectively of national GDP. The value added from agriculture in 1999 was 28 percent of regional GDP[9]. The sector employs 59 percent[10] of the labour force and generates 16 percent of the value of total exports[11].

MAJOR FARMING SYSTEMS IN SOUTH ASIA

For the purposes of this analysis, eleven broad farming systems have been identified. The geographical distribution of nine of the farming systems is indicated in the accompanying Map. The Urban Based and Tree Crop Farming Systems are not mapped. The main characteristics of the major farming systems, including the land area and agricultural population as a proportion of the regional total, principal livelihoods and prevalence of poverty, are shown in Table 5.1. A brief description of each farming system appears in the following paragraphs, and four are analysed in greater depth in subsequent sections.

Rice Farming System

This farming system is dominated by intensive wetland rice cultivation[12] by farmers and sharecroppers in fragmented fields with or without irrigation. Of the total system area of 36 million ha, an estimated 22 million ha – or more than 60 percent – is under cultivation. Some 10 million ha, or 43 percent of the cultivated area, is irrigated. Of the total system population of 263 million inhabitants, 130 million are classified as agricultural (17 percent of the regional total). The system is concentrated in Bangladesh and West Bengal, but smaller areas are found in Tamil Nadu and Kerala States of India, and Southern Sri Lanka. The system contains 50 million bovines, used for draft Power, milk and manure, and considerable number of small ruminants. Poor farmers operate extremely small areas, and rely on off-farm income for survival. Poverty is extensive and also quite severe.

Coastal Artisanal Fishing Farming System

In a narrow band along the major part of the coast of Bangladesh and India, and around the Maldives, households supplement artisanal (inshore) fishing with food production – often rice and such cash enterprises as coconuts, livestock and

---

[7] Government of India 2000.
[8] Government of Pakistan 1998.
[9] World Bank 2000a.
[10] FAOSTAT.
[11] FAO 1998b.
[12] Intensive is used here to indicate the growing of two or more crops of paddy during the year.

Table 5.1 Major Farming Systems in South Asia

Farming Systems	Land Area (% of region)	Agric. Popn. (% of region)	Principal Livelihoods	Prevalence of Poverty
Rice	7	17	Wetland rice (both seasons), vegetables, legumes, off-farm activities	Extensive
Coastal Artisanal Fishing	1	2	Fishing, coconuts, rice, legumes, livestock	Moderate - extensive
Rice-Wheat	19	33	Irrigated Rice, wheat, vegetables, livestock including dairy, off-farm activities	Moderate - extensive
Highland Mixed	12	7	Cereals, livestock, horticulture, seasonal migration	Moderate - extensive
Rainfed Mixed	29	30	Cereals, legumes, fodder crops, livestock, off-farm activities	Extensive (severity varies seasonally)
Dry Rainfed	4	4	Coarse cereals, irrigated cereals, legumes, off-farm activities	Moderate
Pastoral	11	3	Livestock, irrigated cropping, migration	Moderate - extensive (especially drought induced)
Sparse (Arid)	11	1	Livestock where seasonal moisture permits	Moderate - extensive (especially drought induced)
Sparse (Mountain)	7	0.4	Summer grazing of livestock	Moderate (especially in remote areas)
Tree Crop	Dispersed	1	Export or agro-industrial crops, cereals, wage labour	Moderate (mainly of agricultural workers)
Urban Based	<1	1	Horticulture, dairying, poultry, other activities	Moderate

Source: FAO data and expert knowledge.
Note: Prevalence of poverty refers to number in poverty, not depth of poverty, and is a relative assessment for this region.

vegetables. The main livelihood is threatened by over-exploitation of the common resource, both locally and by larger well-equipped fishing boats. Total land area is estimated at five million ha with nearly half under cultivation. Coastal land resources are also under pressure from the high population density along the coastline, and from the expansion of modern and capital intensive acquaculture enterprises. One third of the cultivated area, or 0.8 million ha, is under irrigation. Of the total system population of 45 million, about 18 million are classified as agricultural. Off-farm income constitutes a significant source of livelihood, especially for poor households. The management of the system is complex from many points of view – the complexity associated with lying on the interface between marine and terrestial ecosystems is aggravated by the complexity of numerous stakeholders with conflicting objectives. Poverty across the system ranges from moderate to extensive.

Rice-Wheat Farming System

Characterised by a summer paddy crop followed by an irrigated winter wheat crop (and sometimes also a short spring vegetable crop), the Rice-Wheat Farming System forms a broad swathe across Northern Pakistan and India, from the Indus irrigation area in Sindh and Punjab, across the Indo-Gangetic plain to the northeast of Bangladesh. Total system area is 97 million ha with an estimated 62 million ha – more than 60 percent of the land of the system – under cultivation. An estimated 48 million ha, or 78 percent of the cultivated area, is irrigated. The system has a significant level of crop-livestock integration, with an estimated 119 million bovines which produce draft power and milk, as well as manure for composting. Around 73 million small ruminants are kept, principally for meat. Of the total system population of 484 million people, 254 million are classified as agricultural. The Rice and Rice-Wheat Farming Systems together contain 40 percent of the cultivated land in the region and produce the bulk of the marketed foodgrains that feed the cities and urban areas of South Asia.

Highland Mixed Farming System

This farming system, generally intermediate between the rice-wheat plains of the lowlands and the sparsely populated high mountain areas above, extends across the entire length of the Himalayan range, from Afghanistan to the extreme northeast of India, as well as in isolated areas of Kerala and Central Sri Lanka. Major products include cereals, legumes, tubers, vegetables, fodder, fodder trees, orchards and livestock. Total system area is 65 million ha with an estimated 19 million ha – about 29 percent – under cultivation. While most cultivated land is rainfed, an estimated 2.6 million ha, or 14 percent, is irrigated. There are about 45 million bovines and 66 million small ruminants. Of the total human population of 82 million, nearly 53 million are classified as agricultural. The prevalence of poverty, which is aggravated by remoteness and the lack of social services, is rated between moderate and extensive.

Rainfed Mixed Farming System

This predominantly rainfed cropping and livestock farming system occupies the largest area within the sub-continent and, with the exception of a small area in Northern Sri Lanka, is confined entirely to India. Total system area is 147 million ha with an estimated 87 million ha (59 percent) under cultivation. Rice and some wheat are grown, as well as pearl millet and sorghum, a wide variety of pulses and oilseeds, sugarcane, and vegetables and fruit. An estimated 14 million ha, or 16 percent of the cultivated area, is irrigated. There are an estimated 126 million bovines and 64 million small ruminants, which are partially integrated with cropping. Of the total system population of 371 million, 226 million are classified as agricultural. In many instances, relatively small areas are irrigated from reservoirs and in recent decades, tubewells have contributed to an elevated level and stability of cereal production. Vulnerability stems from the substantial climatic and economic variability. Poverty is extensive and its severity increases markedly after droughts.

Dry Rainfed Farming System

Located in a 'rain shadow' surrounded by the Rainfed Mixed Farming System in the Western Deccan, this farming system has a higher proportion of irrigation than the moister surrounding areas, allowing it to support a similar range of irrigated and rainfed crops despite the drier climate. Total system area is 18 million ha with an estimated 10 million ha – about 53 percent – under cultivation. An estimated 3.5 million ha, or 36 percent of the cultivated area, is irrigated – and this irrigation is a central determinant of the farming system. Of the total system population of 45 million, nearly 30 million are classified as agricultural. Because of the prevalence of irrigation, vulnerability is somewhat lower than in the neighbouring Rainfed Farming System, and thus the level of poverty is moderate.

Pastoral Farming System

Across the semiarid and arid zones, from Rajasthan in India through Pakistan and Afghanistan, transhumant pastoralists keep mixed herds of livestock. The system includes scattered pockets of irrigation which mitigate the extreme seasonal vulnerability of pastoralists. Total system area covers 55 million ha, and it supports an estimated 12 million cattle and 30 million small ruminants, as well as a significant number of camels. There are scattered areas of cultivation amounting to an estimated 6.8 million ha, of which nearly two thirds (4.6 million ha) is irrigated and sown to rice, wheat and other food and fodder crops. Off-farm income is an important source of livelihood. Of the total system population of 27 million, around 21 million are classified as pastoral or agricultural. In aggregate terms, this farming system is not of great importance, supporting only three percent of the human population and less than 10 percent of the livestock of the region. The level of poverty is moderate to extensive, and is periodically accentuated by droughts.

Sparse (Arid) Farming System

The land area of the system is estimated at 57 million ha, supporting an estimated 16 million bovines and 29 million small ruminants. About 1.7 million ha is cultivated, practically all under irrigation. There are some scattered irrigation settlements in the arid areas; in most cases used by pastoralists to supplement their livelihoods. The rest of these areas are utilised for opportunistic grazing where water is available for livestock. The human population is 23 million, of which 9.6 million are classified as pastoral or agricultural. There is a gradual transition from the Pastoral System to this system, which has moderate to extensive poverty that is often severe after droughts.

Sparse (Mountain) Farming System

This system lies at altitudes above 3 000 metres along the mid level and upper slopes of the Himalayan Range and occupies an estimated area of 34 million ha with a population of 3 million people, of whom 2.8 million are classified as agricultural. A number of small settlements depend on potatoes and buckwheat, plus cattle and yak herds. Cultivated area is 1.9 million ha, or only five percent of total area, and only around 10 percent is irrigated. There are an estimated 10 million cattle and yaks, and nine million sheep and goats. During the summer, herders graze cattle and yak on the higher slopes. Generally, household incomes are supplemented by seasonal migration and in some cases by trade, mountaineering and tourism. Poverty tends to be moderate overall, although more prevalent in remote areas.

Tree Crop Farming System

This scattered farming system comprises plantation companies and smallholders producing substantial areas of tea, rubber, coconuts and other tree crops. It is estimated that the system covers three million ha of land, with some 1.2 million ha of annual and permanent cropland. Concentrations of this system are found in the lowlands of Sri Lanka (especially coconuts), Kerala in India (including spices), and the upland areas of India, Nepal, Bangladesh and Sri Lanka (tea estates). The estimated agricultural population is seven million. Poverty is moderate and largely confined to agricultural workers. Given the dispersed nature of this system, it is not distinguished on the map.

Urban Based Farming System

In most large towns and cities in the region the intensive production of perishable high-value commodities – such as milk and fresh vegetables – has expanded. These are generally commercial systems with high levels of external inputs and with effective links to the surrounding rural areas for stock feed and fodder. The system has an agricultural population of 11 million, and contains around 12 million head of bovines (cattle and buffaloes).

REGION-WIDE TRENDS IN SOUTH ASIA

Population, hunger and poverty

The region's 1999 population of about 1 344 million [13] is expected to increase by approximately 1.4 percent per annum to 1 650 million in 2015. Thereafter, population growth is expected to slow to about 1 percent per annum to reach 1 920 million by 2030. The proportion of the total population living in cities (presently 28 percent [14]) has increased markedly over the last four decades and is expected to continue to expand, reaching 53 percent in 2030.

A key factor affecting the pace and direction of change will be the increase in human mobility – reflected in rapid urbanisation and more off-farm employment, especially for adult males. In some cases this mobility will lead to the adoption of more extensive, low labour systems of production – such as paddy cultivation rather than cotton cultivation – so as to provide the best returns per labour day for periods that can be fitted-in with off-farm employment. It is also likely to be reflected in an improved asset position on farms; more mechanisation, and also an increase in the area of land per operator. As greater numbers of adult males migrate seasonally and semi-permanently in search of alternative livelihoods, it is anticipated that women farmers will assume greater responsibilities for the management and operation of farms.

The absolute number of undernourished people in the region, some 284 million in 1995-1997 [15], has remained stubbornly high, as shown in Figure 1.2 in Chapter 1, but is projected to decline dramatically – to 82 million by 2030. This represents a decline from 23 percent of the population to only four percent. Average food intake was estimated at 2 424 Kcal per person per day in 1995-1997 and is expected to increase to 2 790 Kcal by 2015 and to reach 3 040 Kcal by 2030. The quality of the diet is also expected to improve, with consumption per head of both meat and dairy products forecast to double over the period from 1995-1997 to 2030.

Poverty levels are high throughout the region, although lower in Sri Lanka than elsewhere. In India, some 44 percent of the population live on less than US$1 per day, and 86 percent on less than US$2 [16]. Figures are slightly lower, but comparable, for Nepal, Pakistan and Bangladesh. Although figures for Afghanistan are not available, it is estimated that approximately 530 million people within South Asia live on less than US$1 per day. According to World Bank projections, those in 'dollar' poverty should decline from the current level of 40 percent to between 18-25 percent by 2030, depending on the growth scenario selected.

---

[13] FAOSTAT.
[14] World Bank 2000a.
[15] FAO 2000a. Except where specifically noted, quantitative information in this section is derived from FAO (2000a).
[16] World Bank 2000b.

Natural resources and climate

The area of land under annual cultivation and permanent crops in the region is estimated at 213 million ha (49 percent of total land area) and is expected to show only a marginal increase by 2030. Additional land area would come principally from grazing and forest land, and would therefore involve significant investments, as well as some foregone production. Estimated increases in development of cultivated land would be greater but for losses to buildings and civil works in existing urban centres [17].

Soil erosion in the highland and rainfed watersheds is widespread and is being aggravated by heavy grazing and the loss of nutrients from cropland. Overgrazing has also led to soil degradation in large areas of the Mixed and Pastoral Farming Systems. Severe soil management problems also confront the intensive Rice and Rice-Wheat Farming Systems where yields are increasing more slowly, or even stagnating in some high intensity areas. This is attributed by some analysts to deteriorating soil physical condition, declining organic matter and unbalanced fertilisation – with over-reliance on nitrogen fertilisers, relative neglect of other major and micro-nutrients, and declining use of animal manure [18].

The overall scarcity of water resources in the region, and their geographic distribution, has shaped the development of South Asia's farming systems. The region's irrigated land area is forecast to grow slowly, from 85 million ha to 95 million (44 percent of cultivated land) in 2030. The high cost of developing new, environmentally sustainable, irrigation systems – and the reluctance of donors to finance large irrigation projects – may lead governments to place greater emphasis on modernising existing irrigation schemes and the improvement of water use efficiency [19]. This will involve participatory management or transfer of ownership to users, improved design of operating systems, better drainage and cost recovery. Considerable potential remains for improving water management through better rainfall conservation and use; further development of water storage; and conjunctive use of groundwater. Increased on-farm water conservation can be achieved through conservation agriculture; including mulching, bunding and windbreaks.

Shortages of groundwater in some localities have already started limiting the use of tubewells within the intensive Rice and Rice-Wheat Farming Systems [20]. Such shortages are bound to worsen over the next three decades. It has been estimated that, if present rates of increase of overdraft continue, as much as one-third of irrigation blocks may be over exploited by 2020 [21]. The Rainfed Mixed

---

[17] It is possible that average farm size will increase somewhat by 2030, as a result of continued migration of rural population to urban areas and because of economies of scale, particularly through mechanisation.

[18] Tran and Nguyen 2001.

[19] A recent World Bank supported water resources sector review calls for a shift of emphasis from development to management.

[20] Even though groundwater resources in these farming systems are replenished annually, unlike other regions.

[21] Government of India and World Bank 2001.

and Pastoral Farming Systems will also be constrained by the limited availability of both ground and surface water for crop and livestock production. There will be strongly increasing demand for water from urban and industrial users during the coming decades. As a result, local water markets are likely to develop, with agriculture at a disadvantage except in the case of high value crops. As labour costs rise, it is likely that irrigation water will increasingly be used to replace labour in land preparation and weed control in rice. Increasing pressure on water resources also seems to have given rise to problems of declining quality of drinking water – including widespread arsenic poisoning in Bangladesh.

Due to high population densities, forest resources are under threat in all countries of the region. Although FAO data indicate a slight increase of forest and woodland cover throughout the region, to 85 million ha in 1994, there is evidence of deforestation occurring during the 1990s at the rate of 0.13 million ha (0.2 percent per annum). The pressures causing deforestation are expected to increase still further, particularly in the Highland Mixed Farming System – little forest remains in most other farming systems of the region. In many instances, deforestation results from increasing pressure to obtain agricultural land, but conflicts of interest between individuals and forest departments have also contributed. The growing realisation that forest communities have to be fully involved in forest management, and that forests need to be managed for the benefit of such communities, has done much to overcome the latter factor.

Climate change is projected to have a significant negative impact on agricultural production within the region. The frequency of storms which batter the coastal areas of Bangladesh and Eastern India is expected to increase. Not only will the variability of climate cause fluctuations in yield, but average yields of rainfed crops could drop by a substantial amount[22].

Science and technology

Agricultural research in South Asia has been strengthened dramatically over the past 40 years through reorganisation of the National Agricultural Research Systems (NARS); with the establishment of central co-ordinating bodies[23], decentralisation into regional research centres, greatly enhanced manpower and increased investment. The NARS in the region have benefited greatly from the strong linkages and networks they have established with International Agricultural Research Centers (IARCs), such as IRRI, CIMMYT and ICRISAT, building on their participation in the development of green revolution technology. More recently, the many NARS have shifted their emphasis to meeting the post-green-revolution challenges of stagnant yields and resource management, by developing technologies for resource-poor farmers and farmers in sub-optimal crop environments.

---

[22] Fischer et al 2001.

[23] The pro-active leadership of these Councils is demonstrated by their long-term strategic planning.

Increasing demand, changing consumer preferences and degrading resources within the region will continue to pose new challenges to these agricultural research systems, and increasingly complex and diversified technologies will be required to meet these challenges. The high returns to agricultural research in marginal lands[24], the growing role of women in farm household decision making and the emergence of new areas of integrative research (agroforestry, biotechnology, etc.), will require the development of new skills and inter-disciplinary research efforts. Although private-sector research will make increasing contributions to the development of new technologies for improving the profitability of commercial ventures, the focus of public-funded agricultural research is likely to remain the resource-poor small farmer.

Returns from past agricultural research in the region (e.g. the HYV-fertiliser-irrigation technology) seem to have been concentrated in certain systems[25], such as the Rice and Rice-Wheat Farming Systems. Emerging problems require a better mixture of upstream (basic or strategic) and downstream (adaptive and participatory, farm-level) research. A major issue is that much of the present agricultural research effort fails to address many topics of most interest to farmers, e.g. improved low-input crop husbandry practices and minimised production risks.

Use of inorganic fertilisers in the South Asia region has expanded rapidly in recent decades; from three kg of plant nutrients per ha in 1970 to 79 kg/ha in the mid-1990s. The rate of consumption is expected to continue to increase, albeit more slowly. Application rates are high in irrigated, intensive farming systems compared to dry and risky production environments. In some of the more remote areas, such as the Sparse (Mountain) Farming System, high transport costs can easily exceed the material cost.

In some cases there is considerable wastage of nutrients – particularly nitrogen in irrigated and wetland cultivation – due to low efficiency in the use of fertiliser. Severe losses by volatilisation occur in Pakistan, which is a large consumer of nitrogen fertiliser. The future rate of increase in total fertiliser use is expected to decline, although the rate of decline will depend to some extent on progress in raising the efficiency of fertiliser use. Nitrogen losses from volatilisation, leaching and runoff could, therefore, remain constant or even diminish.

At present, use of fertilisers for paddy is constrained by low rice prices. The use of fertilisers in the coming decades will be influenced by fertiliser prices (likely to increase in real terms), commodity prices (likely to decrease), use of organic fertilisers (likely to increase) and fertiliser use efficiency (also likely to increase). The possibility of significant contributions from the use of Biological Nitrogen Fixation (BNF) cannot be discounted[26]. In parallel with the increase in fertiliser use, the demand for agricultural chemicals has grown, although moderated somewhat by the spread of IPM.

[24] Fan *et al* 2000.
[25] Anderson 1994.
[26] FAO 2001.

Paddy rice has traditionally been the most important single crop in South Asia and it has increased in importance over the last 30 years – principally as a result of the green revolution – with yields increasing by an average of almost two percent per annum over the period 1970 to 2000. Rice area has also increased but more slowly (see Table 5.2), resulting in production of 2.5 percent over the last 30 years, to 184 million tons. Production is forecast to further increase in the period to 2030. Wheat production has shown by far the strongest growth among the cereals in recent decades with increases in both yields (nearly three percent per annum) and land area (1.4 percent per annum) to achieve an overall increase in production of more than 250 percent to almost 100 million tons in 2000. This growth is expected to continue in the period to 2030. By contrast, coarse grains such as millet and sorghum, have seen declines in harvested areas in the last three decades, and only small increases in yields have avoided absolute declines in outputs of these crops.

Fruits and vegetables have equalled wheat production trends in recent years, showing that diversification of traditional cultivation patterns is already well underway. Harvested areas have increased faster than for any other crops. The modest increases projected in irrigated area, and improvements to established irrigation schemes, are likely to encourage even greater diversity of cropping in the future. When combined with the growing demand from urban and international consumers, as well as improved marketing and processing channels, additional strong growth in fruits, vegetables and other non-traditional products is anticipated.

Table 5.2 Trends in Crop Area, Yield and Output in South Asia, 1970-2000

Crop	Harvested Area 2000 (m ha)	Yield 2000 (t/ha)	Production 2000 (m tons)	Average Annual Change 1970-2000 (%)		
				Area	Yield	Production
Rice	60	3.1	184	0.5	2.0	2.5
Wheat	39	2.5	98	1.4	2.8	4.3
Millet	13	0.8	10	-1.7	0.7	-1.0
Sorghum	11	0.9	10	-1.6	0.7	0.5
Maize	8	1.7	14	0.4	1.0	1.6
Pulses	27	0.6	15	0.3	0.2	0.5
Oilcrops	42	0.2	10	1.3	1.4	2.6
Vegetables	8	10.7	71	1.7	1.2	3.0
Fruits	3	1.3	40	3.0	1.2	4.3

Source: FAOSTAT.

Cultural factors strongly affect livestock production and consumption throughout the region. Cattle numbers have shown only moderate growth from some 230 million head in 1970 to 277 million head in 2000 (see Table 5.3); an annual growth rate of about 0.6 percent over the entire period. Buffalo numbers have increased faster, by 1.9 percent per annum over the same period, although the rate of growth has declined during the past decade. Similar rates of growth have been seen for small ruminants, which totalled 321 million in 2000. The largest increases in livestock numbers and production have occurred in poultry. Intensive, large-scale production to meet urban demand has already developed in most countries of the region. In the period 1970-2000, the rate of increase in number of poultry was 3.8 percent per annum.

Table 5.3 Trends in Livestock Populations and Output in South Asia, 1970-2000

Species	Million Head 2000	Ave Annual Change 1970-2000 (%)
Buffalo	122	1.9
Cattle	277	0.6
Small Ruminants	321	2.1
Poultry	742	3.8
Product	Output 2000 (million tons)	Ave Annual Change (%)
Total Meat	8	3.2
Total Milk	105	4.2
Total Wool	1	0.9
Total Eggs	2	6.2

Source: FAOSTAT.

For meat, milk and eggs, output has grown more rapidly than livestock populations, suggesting that production efficiency has improved in recent decades. Buffalo and cattle numbers have increased by an average of less than one percent per annum, and small ruminants by just over two percent, while dairy output has risen by over four percent. With increased incomes, meat consumption (particularly poultry meat and eggs, sheep and goat meat), and demand for dairy products, are expected to continue their significant expansion. However, the large ruminant population is expected to stabilise or even decline as tractors replace both draught buffalo and oxen. The management of the remaining animals will increasingly intensify and focus on productivity – probably more than compensating for this decline.

Trade liberalisation and market development

The recent trend towards increased market liberalisation is expected to continue over the next decades. Commercial farmers may be exposed to declining terms of trade, especially for cereals in international markets. Significant diversification is expected in almost all farming systems; partially in response to intensified external competition for previously protected domestic markets in the case of basic staples such as rice, and partially as a result of increasing export opportunities. South Asia could build upon its dominant world position in a few niche markets – such as that for mango and cashew products – and develop a wide range of competitive fruits, spices, colorants and other tropical products. Given the large number of expatriate South Asians living in the industrialised countries, and the popularity of regional cuisine, it is also to be expected that considerable growth will occur in processed foods. This tendency is likely to accelerate as advances in packaging and transport technology allow fresh breads, curries and other perishable products to be delivered to western markets at economical prices.

Although rural populations in South Asia may provide only limited markets for imported foodstuffs in the medium term, the large and expanding urban markets will become increasingly important consumers of both regional and extra-regional produce in the coming decades. Urban-based agriculture will expand and intensify in response to this demand. Dairying is expected to grow still further, as will processed dairy products; while poultry, lamb and goat consumption will expand rapidly. Vegetable and vegetable oil production will also continue to grow strongly. As international labour markets develop, remittances from overseas work will increase and a significant proportion will flow into agriculture and rural investment in general. These cash incomes are an important source of livelihoods in many marginal rural areas – for example in the Highland Mixed Farming System – and often finance farm improvements.

Policies, institutions and public goods

A large proportion of the increase in foodgrain production during the Indian Green Revolution occurred in the 10 percent of districts with adequate local infrastructure – especially for water management, transport, and electricity for tubewells. On the other hand, agricultural development in many areas of the region has been constrained by a lack of infrastructure. In particular, the shortage of roads in remote and sparsely populated areas pushes up transport costs for both inputs and marketed produce, while the lack of health and educational services reduces labour productivity[27].

Most countries in the region have policies that favour urban areas and the manufacturing sector rather than the rural and agricultural sectors. Intervening in the market to maintain food prices artificially within reach of the increasing,

[27] While attention to the HIV/AIDS-agriculture linkages has focused on Africa, it is conceivable that AIDS will also cause major suffering and affect agricultural productivity during the coming 30 years elsewhere, including rural South Asia.

politically articulate urban population may also aggravate already low internal cereal prices, thus exacerbating the bias against rural communities. Because the majority of the poor are located in rural areas, poverty reduction efforts should be targeted towards increased agricultural income.

Decentralisation and local institutional performance will be key issues in the development of most farming systems. Line departments have already given up some of their functions to the private sector. They have also begun to hand over others to empowered rural communities and this trend will become more pronounced in the future. However, this transfer may not take place very rapidly and the quality of its implementation will require monitoring, given the close relationship between rural community constituencies and politicians. Another far-reaching change that is occurring in association with decentralisation, is the growing role of women in *panchayat* (local council) and district-level decision making. There is also an increase in public-private partnerships for agricultural development, which will have far reaching effects on deciding agricultural research priorities.

Local institutions in some parts of the region (e.g. India) are being mandated to play a larger role in land administration, but often lack the capacity to discharge such functions properly. In general, land reforms in the region have met with limited success in improving access to agricultural resources. Land ceilings have had some limited impact, but larger farmers have often found ways to maintain their holdings. The implementation of these programmes is rendered difficult by the inadequate state of land records in some areas.

Information and human capital

By 2030, the majority of farm households will be literate and numerate, and nearly all younger people – including women – are expected to have a basic school education. However, continuing investment in rural education is required not only to support this transformation, but also to address two other key human resource needs: (i) equipping workers with the skills necessary to transfer from agriculture to the off-farm economy; and (ii) ensuring that those remaining in agriculture possess the skills needed to manage the emerging knowledge-intensive farming systems. Although total labour requirements in agriculture are not likely to increase, improved skills are required to raise efficiency and productivity. Such local increases of human capital would underpin the development of small-scale local rural industry, perhaps along the lines of some of the more successful examples of rural industry found in China.

The shift to commercial, knowledge-intensive, farming systems requires a greatly improved flow of information to farmers, as well as support services concerned with new technologies and market information. This is emerging as a key issue and is a promising area for public-private partnerships. In some areas cellular telephone communications are revolutionising the availability of market information, for example, in Bangladesh. A number of computer-based systems for farm extension have shown promise, such as the touch-screen systems tested by the Swaminathan

Research Foundation. The improvement in the information flow across the government-NGO interface is well documented[28].

It is widely recognised that an information revolution will occur in rural South Asia, although its full effects cannot be predicted. However, without doubt, the wide availability of market information will substantially improve the efficiency of the system and increase access by smallholders. It may also be that widespread dissemination of technical information through multiple channels will lead to a redefinition of the role of agricultural extension.

Selection of farming systems for analysis

Four of the farming systems outlined in the previous section have been selected for analysis, using criteria based upon agricultural population, the incidence of poverty, and apparent potential for agricultural growth and poverty reduction in the coming 30 years:

- Rice Farming System;

- Rice-Wheat Farming System;

- Rainfed Mixed Farming System; and

- Highland Mixed Farming System.

Most of the poor inhabitants in the region live within these four farming systems, which also contribute more than three-quarters of the regional GADP. They are described in more detail in the following sections.

RICE FARMING SYSTEM

CHARACTERISTICS OF THE SYSTEM

The Rice Farming System covers about seven percent of the land in the region (see Box 5.1) and encompasses much of the old and well-developed wetland rice areas, particularly Southern Bangladesh and South Punjab, but also including coastal zones of Tamil Nadu and Kerala and the wet zone and irrigated parts of the dry zone of Sri Lanka. Land is generally farmed by owner operators

Box 5.1 Basic Data: Rice Farming System	
Total population (m)	263
Agricultural population (m)	130
Total area (m ha)	36
Agro-ecological zone	Humid
Cultivated area (m ha)	22
Irrigated area (m ha)	10
Bovine population (m)	51

---

[28] Farrington and Thiele 1993.

Box 5.2 A Typical Household of the Rice Farming System

A typical poor sharecropping household with five family members within the Rice Farming System cultivates 0.4 ha of irrigated land in West Bengal, India. A second irrigated rice crop and a short vegetable crop follow the kharif (monsoon) rice crop. Modern rice varieties are transplanted in both seasons, producing typical yields of 1.9 and 2.4 t/ha, of which the sharecropper retains one third since the landowner provided the land, as well as a draught buffalo and crop inputs (including fertiliser, about 150 kg/ha of nutrients and chemicals for about four sprays per season). The household owns two goats and some ducks and chickens and plans to join with a relative to purchase a milking buffalo. Both adults work for about 120 days a year on nearby large farms and in a local factory. The household has a very low annual income, and is vulnerable to low crop yields or lack of labour earnings due to sickness or lack of work opportunities.

---

or sharecroppers. Farm size tends to be bi-modal, with a large number of tenants and sharecroppers with small areas of the order of 0.3 to 1 ha (see Box 5.2), and a few medium to large owner-operated farms that could be from 4 to 10 ha or more. Rice is invariably grown in the wet season. In the dry season a second rice crop, or another less water-demanding crop (e.g. coarse grains, oil seeds, legumes, vegetables), will be grown.

In most cases, the system is supported by supplementary irrigation in the monsoon season and full irrigation in the dry season. Because of the limited resource base of the farming system and the fact that these areas are generally close to urban areas, off-farm employment is common. The strategic importance of rice as a food staple and the generally easy access have resulted in well developed extension services. With virtually continuous paddy cropping there are limited fodder resources except for paddy straw to support ruminants, which generally include milk and draught animals – buffalo, or oxen in the drier areas, where these have not already been replaced by tractors. Nevertheless, this farming system contains a significant proportion of the region's cattle and dairy animals, the latter principally because of proximity to large urban centres.

Most farmers know the value of using fertiliser and improved seed. Nevertheless, uptake of improved varieties has not always been enthusiastic. This is largely due to lack of high quality certified seeds, the poorer taste of some new varieties, their lower tolerance to early or late transplanting – and the sometimes marginal increase in yield compared to local varieties. Typically, farm households must supplement their food production with off-farm income in order to ensure food security.

Considerable diversity exists within the system, with a transition to the Rice Wheat System in the northern areas of Bangladesh and in Bihar State, while in more southern parts of this zone, aquaculture is widely practised and households tend to keep more cattle – including dairy cattle – and more poultry. The southeastern areas of the system in Tamil Nadu and the southwestern parts in Kerala have less risk of cyclones and floods and tree crops are more common.

Despite increasing diversification in recent years, households still tend to depend on a limited crop income that is vulnerable to fluctuating yields, or even complete failure in flood and cyclone prone areas. The major source of vulnerability, however, is failure to find work in the vicinity, or inability to work because of sickness – a frequent occurrence. There are few traditional mechanisms to which the poor can turn in time of need; access to government safety nets, such as employment guarantee schemes, is often inadequate. In this respect, poor small farmers are just as vulnerable as landless rural workers.

TRENDS AND ISSUES IN RICE SYSTEM

During the coming 30 years, land availability per capita is expected to decline because of population increase and the loss of land to urban expansion. This loss may be aggravated by land degradation, including soil erosion and salinisation. Moreover, increasing water scarcity in agriculture is expected, as demand for water grows in domestic and industrial sectors. However, some market-driven land consolidation can also be expected, together with gradual reduction in sharecropping. Education levels for both men and women are expected to increase substantially. Widespread adoption of hybrid rice – both existing and future new varieties – is expected, except in deepwater and other unfavourable rice ecologies.

The declining terms of trade for rice, and increasing costs of production, will induce diversification of production to include *inter alia*, dairying and aquaculture. Intensive pressure on land will limit the availability of fodder and lead to a decline in the population of buffaloes. Draught buffalo power will be replaced by two-wheel tractors, which will also be widely used for local transportation. Increased labour costs will favour mechanisation of other operations, such as sowing, weeding and threshing. Given the declining profitability of rice, only a modest increase in external input use is expected – with no significant increase in the riskier flood-prone areas. The gradual decline in rice profitability, and increasing population pressure, will force many male household members to seek an increasing part of their income from off-farm sources. In these cases, women will shoulder an increasing burden of farm work. Overall, there may be a gradual improvement in household food security and a modest reduction in poverty.

Some improvement is expected in public infrastructure and other aspects of the socio-institutional environment affecting agricultural production. In particular, transport, educational and health facilities will improve. These will be associated with significant decentralisation of decision-making to the district and the local *panchayat* levels. At the local level, farmers' organisations are also likely to grow stronger. The prevailing feminisation of poverty in large areas of South Asia will most probably begin to be reduced. With the enforcement of the one-third quota for women in local office, local governance will increasingly reflect the needs of women, who are currently disproportionately represented among the very poor.

As public sector research and extension budgets decline during this period, greater emphasis will be placed on the private sector, farmers' organisations, and upon individual farmer experimentation and technology sharing. The enhanced role of farmers and the private sector in advisory services will tend to improve the relevance of extension messages. The success of the Grameen Bank in Bangladesh has generated a plethora of micro-finance activities throughout the region. There is likely to be an increase in seasonal and permanent out-migration, and a slow growth of the off-farm rural economy.

The main issues driving the evolution of the system are the currently low and declining paddy prices combined with increasing labour costs. These make it increasingly unattractive to use high rates of fertiliser application and consequently inhibit the growth of rice productivity. Low domestic paddy prices are largely a reflection of declining world prices. In some instances, however, this trend is exacerbated by government attempts to keep rice prices low in order to satisfy urban populations – using price controls and monopoly purchases with countervailing subsidies on fertilisers, irrigation and other inputs[30].

PRIORITIES FOR RICE SYSTEM

In order to make substantial progress in reducing poverty in this system, the following household strategies to escape poverty need to be supported in the following order of importance: diversification; increased off-farm income; intensification of existing production patterns; and exit from agriculture. While intensification and diversification in this farming system require some attention to natural resources – soil management and flooding in particular – the major problem is the low and progressively declining producer price for rice resulting from unfavourable terms of trade. This can only be countered in the long run by using more efficient production practices, thereby increasing the comparative and competitive advantage of local rice production. An effective programme of research and extension to improve labour and factor productivity is needed to improve farmers' production practices. In order to maintain adequate incentives to farmers it will also be necessary to avoid urban bias in trade and economic policies.

The productivity of the Rice Farming System can be increased through intensification, although with a different emphasis to that of the earlier variety-

---

[30] It is estimated that subsidies and transfers account for nearly 40 percent of Government of India expenditure (World Bank 2000a).

chemical based intensification. Despite major investments in irrigation infrastructure in the past, many schemes still perform poorly. Upgrading these systems to improve irrigation security, plus the introduction of tubewells for conjunctive use of groundwater, generally results in significant increases in production and farm incomes. Water user associations are an effective means of improving water use efficiency[31]. Box 5.3 shows that small adjustments in policies and technology can unleash major investments in the rural sector which, in turn, increase productivity and reduce poverty.

Box 5.3 Critical Policy Changes for the Spread of Shallow Tubewells, Bangladesh

Major changes in the farming system arose in Bangladesh during the 1990s, resulting from a dramatic expansion of Shallow Tubewells (STW) that could be traced to specific policy changes. These included liberalisation of the import of engines, pumps and tubewell supplies (allowing full private sector participation) and abolition of STW siting restrictions (arising from recognition that the tapped groundwater was replenished annually). In 1989, some 70 000 small pump engines (at around US$200 each) were imported and were widely used for low-lift irrigation by private sector operators. Irrigation water was supplied to farmers against a 25 percent share in the crop. Since the demand for pumps far exceeded the supply, pump operators made fertiliser application a condition for access to irrigated water supply. As a result of the ensuing boom in fertiliser use, grain production in Bangladesh rose sharply and the production target of 20 million tons was achieved by 1990, at no cost to Treasury.

Other areas in which interventions can increase the productivity of this farming system are research and extension; farmer training (particularly in farm management, IPM[32] and other crop production practices); mechanisation of operations such as weeding and threshing; land consolidation and leasing mechanisms to increase operated field sizes and, over time, operated farm sizes; and, improved post-harvest handling and milling. Box 5.4 shows the potential for joint intensification and diversification of irrigated rice systems in Bangladesh.

Where systems are already quite intensive, further opportunities for improving productivity through diversification appear to involve the incorporation of income-generating enterprises such as dairying, aquaculture, horticulture and local value-added processing[33]. Where the risk of flooding is low, aquaculture can

[31] In Gal Oya and Mahaweli schemes in Sri Lanka, some 500 000 farmers have organised into 33 000 water user associations, with improved cropping intensity and reduced irrigation problems.

[32] In excess of 80 000 farmers have been trained in IPM and related improvements in rice, cotton, sugarcane and oilseeds.

[33] These opportunities related to specialised market opportunities or unused farm resources, such as fish production in paddies after pesticide use is discontinued, can be termed 'niche' or 'patch' improvement of systems (Pretty 2000).

Box 5.4 Intensification and Diversification in Irrigated
Rice Farming Systems[34]

Intensification and diversification both offer opportunities to boost food security and incomes among poor smallholders within the intensive irrigated Rice Farming System. These possibilities have been demonstrated in both the Young Bramaputhra floodplain and the Chittagong coastal plain areas of Bangladesh.

Major interventions for intensification of rice production include: land selection based on crop suitability; the use of improved seeds sown at the recommended rate; balanced and timely fertiliser use; optimum dates of sowing and harvesting; and plant protection measures. The introduction of irrigated boro cropping has increased the food security status of the community in the lowland areas and created extra employment opportunities for the landless. An assured high-yielding boro crop in the lowland has, in turn, encouraged farmers to diversify their cropping patterns in other, slightly higher-lying types of land, thus increasing the overall productivity of their farming system.

However, in other parts of the system, higher financial benefits have been derived from the development and intensification of associated livestock, fisheries and homestead production systems than from intensification of rice production. Some farmers practise rice-fish culture during the transplanted *aman* rice season, but the majority avoid this option due to the risk of flooding.

provide additional income in inter-harvest periods. Duck or chicken raising provides other possibilities; although in order to be adopted all of these potential enterprises need to show better returns to labour than the operator could get from off-farm income-generating activities. Their widespread adoption would also need some strengthening of the relevant support services.

Whether farmers chose crop intensification strategies or crop diversification strategies in a specific area depends not only on the individual circumstances of the farm household, but also on the availability of appropriate technologies; this in turn is linked closely to the effectiveness of agricultural research related to the zone.

The system can also be improved by diversification into vegetable or other cash crops where there is nearby urban demand – as demonstrated by the expansion of horticultural production around Bogra in Bangladesh[35]. A combination of these practices can, in favourable circumstances, lead to highly productive and profitable integrated, intensive farming systems. Similarly, dairying has been a traditional engine of growth for smallholder farming systems in South Asia. One well-known dairy scheme is the Milk Vita programme in Bangladesh (see Box 5.5).

[34] Hoque 2001.
[35] As witnessed during the implementation of Government of Bangladesh/FAO/ADB Horticultural Development Project.

> ### Box 5.5 Smallholder Milk Marketing[36]
>
> From a modest start that involved providing 4 300 very poor, often landless, households in remote rural areas of Bangladesh with a complete package of improved milk production technologies, village level organisational skills and a milk collection-processing-marketing system, a two-tier co-operative has grown into a successful commercial dairy enterprise. Today, milk is collected from 40 000 farmer-members, organised into 390 primary village co-operatives, then processed and distributed to all the major cities in the country. Since start-up, regular earnings from milk have increased ten-fold in real terms. The resultant increase in cattle numbers and savings also serves as a cushion against the devastating effects of severe flooding that regularly afflicts the country.
>
> Democratically elected milk producer and distributor co-operative members are now in the majority on the **Milk Vita** Board of Directors. This prepared the ground for the government to withdraw from day-to-day management of the co-operative, thus enabling the board to hire professional managers. In turn, this improved performance and created a platform for expansion to bring more poor people into the milk collection network. The **Grameen Bank** is currently adapting the model to reach out to some of its poorest female clients involved in inland fish farming.

RICE-WHEAT FARMING SYSTEM

CHARACTERISTICS OF THE SYSTEM

The Rice-Wheat Farming System covers 19 percent of the land in the region (see Box 5.6), and occupies a broad swathe of land from Northern Pakistan, through the Indo-Gangetic plain including the Terai of Nepal, and the Gangetic plain in Uttar Pradesh, Bihar and West Bengal, to finish in Northwest Bangladesh. The farming system is characterised by a

> ### Box 5.6 Basic Data: Rice-Wheat Farming System
>
> | | |
> |---|---|
> | Total population (m) | 484 |
> | Agricultural population (m) | 254 |
> | Total area (m ha) | 97 |
> | Agro-ecological zone | Dry subhumid |
> | Cultivated area (m ha) | 62 |
> | Irrigated area (m ha) | 48 |
> | Bovine population (m) | 119 |

'summer' (monsoon-season) wetland rice crop and a 'winter' (cool, dry season) wheat crop – sometimes followed by a short 'spring' vegetable crop) – see Box 5.7.

Poverty and household food insecurity are widespread, principally among landless agricultural workers and sharecroppers. In some areas cotton is part of

---

[36] Dugdill and Bennett 2001.

> **Box 5.7 A Typical Household of the Rice-Wheat Farming System**
>
> A typical poor Rice-Wheat sharecropping household with two adults and three children cultivates 0.8 ha of irrigated land in Uttar Pradesh, India. The *kharif* (monsoon) rice crop is followed by a wheat crop, and sometimes a short vegetable crop. The modern rice variety produces a typical yield of 1.9 t/ha, of which the sharecropper retains two-thirds. Wheat yields average about 2.5 t/ha. The household owns a share in a milking cow and the milk is delivered daily to the village milk collection centre. The cow is fed straw, weeds and other herbage that can be cut from the field and path perimeters. Both adults work as labourers, for about 160 days a year, on nearby large farms and in a local factory. The household has a combined average income just beneath the international poverty line, and is vulnerable to low crop yields, loss of the milk cow and to lack of labour income.

the system, but its cultivation is constrained by its high labour requirements and the long duration of the crop. Commonly, some form of irrigation supports the system. It contains large populations of cattle, sheep and goats. Livestock are more common than in the Rice Farming System, although often they may not be strictly a part of the farm system but consist of large cattle herds owned by landlords or businessmen. These cattle graze the stubble after harvest and return to wastelands or uplands during the crop season. Substantial heterogeneity exists within the farming system chiefly in terms of access to land and water resources.

With the development of improved varieties of both rice and wheat, and the use of irrigation and fertiliser, the Rice-Wheat Farming System has shown remarkable increases in production. However, in recent years the declining or stagnant yields and factor productivity of the system have given cause for concern and are the subject of an on-going research programme by the Rice-Wheat Consortium for the Indo-Gangetic Plains.

The western parts of the system in Pakistan tend to have fewer animals and are more mechanised. In these irrigated areas, away from major flood-prone districts, vulnerability is associated with price variation, crop pests and inability to earn sufficient off-farm income. It is not an easy system to manage. In particular, wheat sowing must follow immediately after the rice harvest if subsequent wheat yields are to be satisfactory. Over time, the system has expanded into areas where groundwater is not so easily accessible and because irrigation supply is unreliable, farmers have to transplant at the onset of the monsoon. In order to maintain flexibility they continue using traditional varieties, but these are slow maturing. Consequently, all too often, wheat is sown late, thereby depressing yield as high temperatures affect the plants while they are setting seed.

TRENDS AND ISSUES IN RICE-WHEAT SYSTEM

Average farm size will continue to grow gradually due to permanent and seasonal out-migration of youth, although the bimodal farm size pattern is expected to be accentuated in the coming decade. Later, it is expected that the number of sharecroppers and small farms will diminish. Land close to urban centres will continue to increase rapidly in value, while some observers expect an increase in absentee ownership. The practice of sharecropping can be shown to have some advantages, but has the big disadvantage of perpetuating a traditional and largely immutable operating system within which innovation is difficult or impossible to promote.

The decline in soil productivity, due *inter alia* to excessive reliance on unbalanced application of mineral fertiliser, is likely to continue depressing wheat and rice yields for some time to come. No definite answers have yet emerged from research in this area[37]. Similarly, the build-up of soil salinity and sodicity in the dry, western areas of this farming system – caused by poor water management – will also continue until appropriate steps are taken to improve water control at farm level. Reversing these trends will depend on the success of future research and extension, as well as on policy decisions favouring balanced fertiliser use and efficient utilisation of water.

There has been a rapid expansion of tubewells in some areas such as Western and Central Uttar Pradesh, resulting in declining water tables. Efforts to regulate groundwater abstraction have had limited effect and with millions of private tubewell owners, the task of conventional regulation through licensing and monitoring has proved insurmountable. It is clear from recent evidence gathered in Gujarat and Rajasthan[38] that as the exploitable aquifers are depleted and degraded, it is likely that some groundwater-dependant irrigation farmers will have to convert, wholly or partially, to rainfed cropping. There will be increasing levels of mechanisation, especially for primary tillage, which is already noticeable in the Pakistan Punjab where most draught oxen have disappeared. The typical enterprise pattern is expected to shift towards more dairy, horticulture and feed grains. Because of the availability of feed grains and crop by-products, plus the proximity of major urban markets, this farming system is a likely location for the expansion of specialised large-scale, industrial poultry production.

Overall, most farmers are expected to achieve both household food security and increased farm household incomes by the year 2030. There may also be a gradual decline in poverty among the landless as wage rates rise – even if opportunities for agricultural employment diminish. Some improvement in infrastructure is probable; particularly better roads. Decentralisation will bring decision making

---

[37] However, some promising minimum and zero till resource conservation technologies have been tested in the field, and are currently spreading rapidly - it is estimated that 100 000 acres will be under these improved methods this year in Haryana (Hobbs, *pers. comm*).

[38] Moench 2001.

closer to the farm, and in the process women will have a greater role in local governance. It is expected that farmers' organisations will be strengthened. Funding of public-sector research and extension will decline, and the private sector and farmers' organisations may play a bigger role in experimentation and advisory services; which may improve the efficiency of the dissemination of technical information. Modest growth of the off-farm rural economy is expected.

PRIORITIES FOR RICE-WHEAT SYSTEM

In order to make substantial progress in reducing poverty in this system, the following household strategies to escape poverty need to be supported (in order of importance): diversification; increased off-farm income; intensification of existing production patterns; increased farm size; and exit from agriculture. There are a number of worthwhile options for supporting these poverty pathways that will also have direct impacts on agricultural growth, although the opportunity cost of labour will be a critical determinant of the viability of interventions.

One high priority is to tackle the resource conservation issues; such as declining soil fertility, development of salinity and sodicity problems on irrigated land in western areas, and groundwater depletion in zones irrigated by tubewells. Research is being conducted to develop technologies that can improve the level of soil fertility, which has fallen as a result of the continuous, intensive cereal production practised since the Green Revolution started. However, governments sometimes pursue policies that work at cross-purposes with such research efforts. For example, the continuance of heavy subsidies on urea fertiliser in India, while at the same time deregulating the prices of P and K fertiliser, is causing an imbalance in fertiliser use among farmers – particularly resource-poor farmers practising the rice-wheat rotation. As a result, there is continuous mining of P and K nutrients in the soil causing long-term damage to soil productivity.

As mentioned above, an important factor contributing to the development of salinity and sodicity in irrigated areas of this farming system is the inefficient use of water, particularly at farm level. The highly undervalued price of water from canal systems and the heavy subsidies – up to 100 percent on shallow tubewells, 25 to 50 percent on pumps, plus varying rates on electricity for pumping – are all incentives for excessive use of water by farmers, with consequent waterlogging. Depletion of water tables by indiscriminate sinking of tubewells has also been encouraged by these same subsidies, as well as by the absence of appropriate monitoring and regulatory mechanisms. While waiting for governments to deal directly with these policy issues, another option would be to improve moisture conservation by employing a range of techniques such as zero tillage, use of plastic and other mulches, and planting of windbreaks. Improvement of irrigation security would also materially improve the system, by allowing the adoption of short-duration rice varieties, more timely wheat sowing and production of spring vegetables.

Many of these resource management technologies are scale-neutral and thus poor smallholders – although perhaps not sharecroppers – will gain from their adoption. The need for close co-ordination between water management, fertiliser use, pest control and other husbandry practices, has resulted in the development of Integrated Crop Management (ICM) systems[39]. The dissemination of ICM practices to farmers could be a good option for increasing rice yields and reducing the cost of rice production in South Asia. In some countries the active participation of women in these practices will also be a challenge. Another approach that would be appropriate, especially in rainfed areas susceptible to erosion or where labour costs are high, is Conservation Agriculture (CA), in which minimum tillage is practised to obtain better moisture and soil conservation. The objective should be to let farmers choose those approaches and practices that best suit their conditions and circumstances.

Good opportunities also exist for better integration of ruminant livestock into smallholder farming systems; with profitable conversion of crop by-products, increased use of manure, and possibilities of regular cash income from dairying. The treatment of straw, using urea or other chemicals to increase its value to livestock, is likely to be adopted more widely. Such labour-intensive expansion of livestock production on smallholder farming systems will increase output and reduce poverty. Large-scale industrial production of animals, especially dairy and poultry, will also expand. The expansion of livestock enterprises will stimulate feed production and the development of a feed industry. It will be desirable to site industrial livestock production units so as to minimise feed transport costs and to contain environmental problems involved in processing. Since industrial livestock production will boost output but not reduce poverty to any significant degree, the challenge will be to promote linkages – between industrial livestock production and smallholder livestock production – which benefit poor farmers. Investments in industrial livestock production in this zone are likely to be short term, since in the medium and longer term the locus of feed production and industrial livestock production may shift to the Rainfed Mixed Farming System, where land values and population densities are lower.

The system can easily incorporate many other forms of diversification, including the introduction of fruit trees or other cash crops in situations where land is owner occupied – but this would normally not be possible under sharecropping arrangements. Diversification will generally require investments in marketing, transport infrastructure, research, extension and other support services. Although governments may continue to provide certain categories of seed and planting material, it is expected that farmer co-operatives and the private sector would progressively take over this activity. Similarly, the demand for technical and market information could be addressed through public-private partnerships.

---

[39] ICM has been effectively applied to increase rice yield and productivity in Australia, Egypt, the Republic of Korea and the FAO project BGD/89/045, Thana Cereal Technology Transfer and Identification in Bangladesh.

HIGHLAND MIXED FARMING SYSTEM

CHARACTERISTICS OF THE SYSTEM

The Highland Mixed Farming System incorporates the cultivation of a range of cereals, legumes, tubers, fodder, fodder trees and livestock (see Box 5.8). It stretches in a narrow band across upland areas of Pakistan, India, Nepal, and Bangladesh, occupying the area between the plains below and the generally uninhabited mountain areas above. There is also a small area in

Box 5.8 Basic Data: Highland Mixed Farming System	
Total population (m)	82
Agricultural population (m)	53
Total area (m ha)	65
Agro-ecological zone	Moist subhumid
Cultivated area (m ha)	19
Irrigated area (m ha)	3
Bovine population (m)	45

Central Sri Lanka. In total, the system covers about 13 percent of the land area of the region. In the more remote areas, where mineral fertilisers are very costly or unavailable and distance to markets is prohibitive, the flow of nutrients to cultivated land is generally only from grazing or cutting of fodder trees from woodland areas at higher altitude. However, in more accessible areas, such as the central highlands of Sri Lanka, the opportunity for successful vegetable production, particularly potatoes, can result in a highly intensive system of commercial production. Similarly, in the hills of Himachal Pradesh there has been a large expansion in horticulture, particularly apple orchards. Generally, ruminant livestock are an important part of the system as they provide draught power, milk, manure and cash income. A typical farm household is described in Box 5.9.

In most cases the existing communities have lived in these areas for thousands of years, often as tribal societies that originally practised shifting cultivation. In fact, two thirds of the global indigenous population live in Asia, many of whom reside within the Highland Mixed Farming System. Most, however, have now adopted

---

Box 5.9 A Typical Household of the Highland Mixed Farming System

A typical poor Highland Mixed farm household in Central Nepal has five family members and owns 0.5 ha of land, of which 0.2 ha is cultivated with irrigated wetland rice followed by a poorly-irrigated wheat crop (both for home consumption), and the remaining 0.3 ha of upland is cultivated with maize for food and millet for the preparation of alcohol. The farm has some fruit trees and produces some vegetables. One ox, one cow and several goats are raised, all of which depend upon herding on overgrazed communal grassland and forest. Some oranges and the offspring of livestock are sold. Vulnerability is high. The only possibility to build up capital is through seasonal migration to the Terai or India for wage labour.

more settled agriculture. In some areas, these original communities have been joined by people from lower down the slope, pushed up by population pressure and this has led to ethnic tensions in certain cases. In some instances there are also cases of land speculation where forest areas are cleared by 'farmers' with the support of a local landowner or businessman. In most instances farmers in these areas do not have land titles and some communities may well be living inside the boundary of the forest as recognised by the forest department. The most important issue overall is the ever-increasing population pressure, caused both by reduced mortality rates and by immigration by 'lowlanders', which can make the already fragile system unsustainable.

TRENDS AND ISSUES IN HIGHLAND MIXED SYSTEM

For many of these upland areas, particularly where there has been little development assistance, the trend has been one of a general deterioration in incomes, living standards and the overall environment. A reduction of forest cover on the upper slopes, unimproved agriculture and continuous cultivation on steep slopes – often with thin or poor soils – have led to impoverishment of communities that now barely eke out an existence. They have virtually no cash income and women have to walk progressively further to secure their water and fuelwood needs. Soil and water conservation under these conditions is generally poor, and erosion and the decline of soil fertility can pose grave threats to household survival.

Generally, there are few local opportunities for young people, who often leave to find work elsewhere leaving behind an ageing resident population. The difficulties experienced by shifting cultivators in adapting to sedentary cultivation has also been a factor. As in some other systems, the situation has not been helped by the general insecurity of land tenure – most families having settled either on common land or within forest boundaries. In some areas, social cohesion is absent or very poorly developed – each family becoming increasingly a law unto itself, with none of the normal hierarchy of village councils or headmen. This lack of social capital makes it difficult to resolve individual land ownership disputes or to obtain agreement on the use and management of common lands. Both of these are pre-requisites for development, being essential for the introduction of improved technology, land use guidelines, and the application of soil and water conservation methods. Several other factors aggravate the lack of social capital, including a low level of education and the paucity of communications facilities.

There are, however, a few promising developments, which are worthy of note. Pockets of cash crop or livestock production have sprung up and have provided the basis for the improvement of the whole farm systems. Examples include apples in Himanchal Pradesh, citrus in Eastern Nepal, virus-free potato planting material in Pakistan and vegetable seed in Nepal. In these examples, production was linked to well-organised collection and marketing, often with private sector involvement. Sound technical and marketing information underpinned all cases. Road access has been a determining factor in permitting the expansion of milk production, but is of less importance for non-perishable products such as vegetable seed.

PRIORITIES FOR HIGHLAND MIXED SYSTEM

In order to make substantial progress in reducing poverty in this system, the following household strategies to escape poverty need to be supported (in order of importance): exit from agriculture; diversification; increased off-farm income; and intensification of existing production patterns. Emigration can be facilitated by measures to improve rural and urban labour market function and the provision of basic education and vocational skills, focused on the poorer parts of the system.

With regard to diversification and intensification, lessons drawn from the few pockets of successful development provide the directions for strategic interventions (see Box 5.10). In scattered areas with reasonable market access or strengthened social capital, for example along the milk collection routes outside major Hill cities such as Kathmandu, intensification of production is evident. To the northeast of Kathmandu, the production of fresh vegetables has expanded and the resulting cash income has led to increased input use on other crops. In some areas, the extensive planting of farm trees for fodder and timber – substituting for the loss of access to forest resources – is increasing the natural capital of the farms and reinforcing the basis for nutrient recycling through crop-livestock integration[40]. Other examples have shown how community empowerment improves resource management and incomes; even those of the poorest within a village. This is achieved through communal management of common resources, and group action to increase production through the acquisition of improved germplasm and inputs, plus better marketing[41].

The critical component in the strategy for development in the hill areas must be to arrest land degradation through soil and water conservation, as part of an overall programme to improve living standards – a strategy that could be termed conservation by stealth. Since traditional engineering techniques for soil conservation are expensive and often not sustainable, a variety of biological integrative activities is required. This could involve a range of measures including: integrated crop and livestock husbandry; agro-forestry; introduction of perennial cash crops such as coffee or fruit trees (where this is feasible and markets are available); planting of fodder crops; stall feeding of livestock; community managed

---

[40] Several technology packages have been successfully tested, including those from Pakribas and Lumle in Nepal, and also permaculture in Jajarkot, Nepal. The development of apple industry in Himanchal Pradesh was often cited as a major development success, but the industry has recently come under pressure from apples imported from East Asia.

[41] As demonstrated in the FAO/UNDP Farm level Applied Resource Management Programme.

Box 5.10 Crop-Livestock-Forestry Interactions for the
Highland Mixed Farming System[42]

In Nepal a number of innovative interventions have been successfully tried out on a pilot
scale. These could form some of the elements in a strategy to deal with the severe challenges
of the Highland Mixed Farming System viz.: sloping land, poor soils, seasonal moisture stress,
limited growing periods, population pressure and fragmentation of holdings (over 60 percent
of farms are less than 0.5 ha. in the Nepalese part of the system), as well as isolation from
markets. One of the more promising innovations studied was the transition from extensive
grazing to zero grazing with cut-and-carry stall feeding of large ruminants. Stall feeding had a
wide-ranging beneficial impact on a range of factors, including labour availability, school
attendance of children, adoption of new fodder species, nutrient recycling, the management
of crop residues, breed improvement and reduced livestock numbers. An additional effect has
been to permit the production of fruit tree seedlings over larger areas as open access grazing
declines. Because of the need to establish livestock development committees to manage the
breeding programme, social fencing to protect fodder areas, and veterinary care within the
community; increased community co-operation and the empowerment of local institutions
has been fostered. Other promising interventions within the system included: (i) use of
farmers' varietal assessment, permitting simultaneous selection for a wide range of required
characteristics and quicker release of varieties; (ii) participatory integrated watershed
management for improvement in living standards and encouraging alternative livelihood
opportunities; (iii) leasehold forestry, involving the hand-over of degraded forest land to
households below the poverty line, raising their incomes and improving the ecological
conditions in the hills; and (iv) community forestry management in which National Forest
areas in Nepal are transferred to local community management.

animal health services and, provision of drinking water. The outcomes of these
measures can be further enhanced by under-sowing wetland rice with leguminous
fodder species such as Egyptian clover (*Trifolium alexandrianum*) before the basin
dries out. This would improve livestock feed supply and also provide green manure
for the following crop.

Since remoteness and high transport costs usually make the use of mineral
fertilisers difficult or impractical, development of livestock enterprises such as
dairying or goat production – with emphasis on improving nutrition, stall feeding
and collection of dung – appears to be a good entry point in attacking poverty in
upland areas. Where this can be accompanied by introduction of a cash enterprise,
such as orchard fruit or vegetables, the chances of a significant reduction in poverty
are much improved. Finding suitable cash crops for the more remote areas may,
however, be difficult. Nonetheless, even in remoter areas there may be

[42] Kiff and Pound 2001.

opportunities for production of high-value, low-bulk commodities such as vegetable seeds, spices or medicinal plants.

All components of the programme need to be implemented in a participatory manner with the full involvement of the local community and joint support of government and NGO partners. A supportive policy environment must exist or be created, as this will facilitate local decision-making and allow local development and management of resources – especially in view of the difficulty of communicating with central or even district authorities. Devolution of decision-making authority will also help to build social capital, which is sometimes lacking in hill-dwelling peoples. Participatory research and extension services will be needed to support households and communities during the adoption and adaptation period. Projects aimed at development of upland watersheds now stress the importance of full community participation in all aspects of design and implementation. Such projects also include helping local communities to develop the ability to take charge of their own affairs and to manage the land and water resources in their area as one of their objectives, while still being able to request technical advice from the respective government agencies.

In some instances, rural development interventions must be broader still, in order to include education and health clinics. Establishment of high-quality, vocational training schools will foster the remittance economy that often constitutes an important source of rural household income and helps to reduce land fragmentation and maintain viable farm sizes.

RAINFED MIXED FARMING SYSTEM

CHARACTERISTICS OF THE SYSTEM

The Rainfed Mixed Farming System covers nearly 30 percent of the land in the region (see Box 5.11), almost entirely within Central and Southern India, although there is a small area in Northern Sri Lanka. The system is not supported by any large irrigation system, but in many instances relatively small areas irrigated from tanks reduce vulnerability to drought

Box 5.11 Basic Data: Rainfed Mixed Farming System	
Total population (m)	371
Agricultural population (m)	226
Total area (m ha)	147
Agro-ecological zone	Dry subhumid
Cultivated area (m ha)	87
Irrigated area (m ha)	14
Bovine population (m)	126

and permit dry season cropping. This traditional tank-based supplemental system has been further enlarged in recent decades by the use of tubewells.

Overall, however, being mostly dependent on rainfall, the system faces relatively high levels of risk, and introducing new technology is therefore difficult. Crops grown within the system include wheat, barley, vegetables and fodder crops in the cooler northern areas, while maize, sorghum, finger millet, vegetables, chickpea, pigeon pea, green gram, black gram and groundnuts are more common in the warmer climates of Southern India. Smaller areas of soybean, rapeseed, chilli, onions and sesame are grown mainly as cash crops. Double cropping is possible only where irrigation is available. In Southern India and the Dry Zone of Sri Lanka, where land holdings are smaller, farmers prefer to grow wetland rice on any irrigated land available, as well as in the poorly drained valley bottoms during the wet season. The above-mentioned coarse grains, pulses and oilseeds are grown on the upper parts of the landscape. Some fruit trees such as mango are grown in home gardens. Box 5.12 describes a typical household in this system.

Box 5.12 A Typical Household of the Rainfed Mixed Farming System

A typical rainfed mixed poor farm household with six family members cultivates 3 ha of land in Madhya Pradesh, India. The crops include one ha sorghum (post-rainy season) with a yield of 1.3 t/ha, about 0.5 ha of chickpea yielding 0.85 t/ha, 0.2 ha of pigeon pea yielding 0.5 t/ha, 0.3 ha of groundnuts yielding 0.6 t/ha, 0.2 ha of rapeseed yielding 0.7 t/ha. The household owns two head of cattle, several goats and some poultry. It has a combined average income just beneath the international poverty line, and it is also vulnerable to crop failures.

Livestock are an important part of the farming system – which supports the largest share of cattle, sheep and goats in the region – and they usually provide the major part of the farm family's cash income, particularly through sales of adult animals or young stock, since most areas are too remote for commercial milk production. As infrastructure improves, however, dairy production is becoming more important in some areas.

While the total area covered by the system is larger than the preceding Rice-Wheat Farming System, the heavy reliance on rainfed agriculture imposes a much lower population density – about half that of the latter system. A large proportion of the rural population in the Rainfed-Mixed Farming System lives in chronic poverty, aggravated by periodic drought-induced severe transient poverty (see Box 5.13). Agriculture is oriented towards subsistence; while most areas are poorly served by infrastructure and services, and are remote from markets. Agricultural extension services in these areas are typically weak, farmers mostly use traditional technology with a strong bias towards risk avoidance. Land tenure is often an issue and farmers may not have sufficiently clear titles to their land to be able to use it as collateral for obtaining institutional credit.

Box 5.13 Seasonal Vulnerability

Seasonal vulnerability is a critical dimension of livelihoods in the Deccan Plateau and is sometimes considered as one measure of poverty. Crop failure is more likely than in any other major cropping area in South Asia, but traditional coping mechanisms have weakened. New forms of risk reduction for smallholders, such as rainfall insurance, may offer promise.

TRENDS AND ISSUES IN RAINFED MIXED SYSTEM

Enterprise patterns have been changing fairly rapidly, despite only moderate market access. Vegetable and dairy production have expanded where tank irrigation is available, driven by market forces. There has also been a boom in oilseeds, fuelled by significant production subsidies[43] and this growth is likely to continue. It is expected that there will be increasing scarcity of fresh water resources as agricultural and urban demands expand. Land degradation, including soil fertility decline, is expected to intensify. Food crop production will increase and the use of hybrid sorghums and millets will become more widespread. Soybean and mung beans may, to a significant degree, replace traditional pulses. The system is expected to become more commercial, with a modest increase in the use of external inputs and further mechanisation. Livestock productivity is expected to increase through the spread of stall-feeding and in response to better market access. Although household food security will improve, there will still be food deficits in drought years.

With regard to the external environment, some improvement of transport infrastructure and social services is expected. Government agencies will decentralise to a significant degree and the role of women in local decision making may be strengthened in some countries. Whilst the scope of public sector research and extension will contract, there will be a greater role for farmer organisations in the provision of agricultural services. Limited expansion of the off-farm rural economy is expected.

PRIORITIES FOR RAINFED MIXED SYSTEM

In order to make substantial progress in reducing poverty in this system, the following household strategies to escape poverty need to be supported (in order of importance): diversification; then intensification, increased off-farm income and exit from agriculture (all of equal importance) and finally increased farm size.

Little can be done to significantly reduce poverty within the Rainfed Mixed Farming System without increasing the overall water security of the farm

---

[43] Gulati and Kelley 1999.

household, which not only underpins intensification and diversification, but also greatly improves the quality of life of the household. In the past, this has generally entailed improving the availability of water for drinking and irrigation by repairing existing tanks, improving diversion works from streams and increasing the scale of water harvesting, as well as acquiring more low-lift pumps and tubewells. These improvements will require social mobilisation and participatory planning if they are to be sustainable.

However, in future the emphasis must shift to the maximisation of moisture and soil conservation for increased production. Conservation agriculture will also reduce the impact of climatic risk. The approach includes measures such as timely cultivation, minimum tillage, rapid seeding with early-maturing varieties, mulching and – where the low opportunity cost of labour in the dry season and the nature of the soil make it an option – bunding and tied ridging. In this area new technology is being adopted slowly at best. More sophisticated methods, such as the use of plastic film for water conservation, are absent altogether. Where adequate and secure drinking water is available, one good entry point is the improvement in livestock production through planting of fodder grasses and stall feeding. This in turn can lead to a build-up of fertility, better rainfed crops and more arable by-products for animal feed. Box 5.14 outlines the potential of water harvesting which is discussed further in the accompanying case study.

Box 5.14 Water Harvesting [44]

In semiarid and subhumid areas water harvesting offers millions of poor people a pathway to water, food and economic security. Successful cases show how improved water management provides increased domestic water and crop income. This in turn permits increased livestock numbers and ultimately expanded tree crop production. In the process, the status of natural resources and the watershed are improved, and village income can double. Experience shows that community organisation is an essential pre-requisite for successful water harvesting.

Since the farming system depends for its survival on rainfall and possibly groundwater, appropriate measures are required in the upper catchments to make sure that tree cover is adequate to reduce run-off and to encourage infiltration and percolation that can recharge local aquifers. Improvements to the system will require inputs from a spectrum of disciplines, including irrigation engineering, forestry, fodder production, livestock husbandry and horticulture, in addition to traditional arable crop agronomy. The introduction of horticulture and fruit crops has historically been constrained by remoteness from markets. This can be overcome in areas where there is some comparative advantage for fruit and vegetable production, if private sector interest in establishing processing plants can be generated.

[44] Abstracted from Case Study 4, Annex I.

Some research stations claim to have developed packages of practices suitable for this rainfed farming system. In general, adoption of these recommendations is disappointingly low, but this can be explained by farmer's aversion to risk, or by shortage of labour or other resources to implement improvements. Successful projects or programmes of assistance need to have a wider focus, rather than merely being concentrated on agriculture-related measures. Provision of reliable drinking water is generally the first priority need in these areas. Other social services including health clinics and primary schools, are also normally lacking.

The development of markets is less important than in the Rice-Wheat Farming System. However, access by poor households to land, water and forest resources will be a critical issue. Similarly, access to sources of information is important for the intensification and diversification of these systems. Conversely, the expansion of information dissemination systems will be important and is expected to accelerate the diversification of part of the system towards high value enterprises – after food needs are met.

STRATEGIC PRIORITIES FOR SOUTH ASIA

South Asia's total agricultural population is second only to East Asia and the Pacific, yet it is experiencing a much higher population growth rate. Compared with several other regions, South Asia has relatively little high potential land with fertile soils plus good irrigation or rainfall. The region has a long history of intensive agriculture, which has led to substantial resource degradation in some locations. During the past 30 years – against all odds – the research and agricultural support services of the system have generated growth in food production in excess of population growth, and reduced the proportion of people living in poverty. The opening of the region's economies has had a profound effect on farming system dynamics in the past decade. Farming systems in the region are likely to evolve rapidly during the coming 30 years, as technologies, institutions and markets change, and the pace of change is expected to accelerate.

Available projections suggest some improvement in indicators related to hunger and poverty in coming years, albeit at a slower rate than those implied by the international development goals for halving of hunger and poverty[45]. In order to meet these goals, increased effort by public and private organisations and farm communities is required. Table 5.4 indicates the potential for growth and poverty reduction within each of the farming systems in the region. Although the Tree Crop System, with its focus on relatively high value products with considerable scope for productivity gains, has perhaps the highest potential for growth, major gains in

---

[45] FAO 2000a.

Table 5.4 Potential and Relative Importance of Household Strategies for Poverty Reduction in South Asia

Farming System	Potential for agricultural growth	Potential for poverty reduction	Strategies for poverty reduction				
			Intensi-fication	Diversi-fication	Increased Farm Size	Increased off-farm Income	Exit from Agriculture
Rice	Moderate	Moderate	2	3	0.5	2.5	2
Coastal Artisanal Fishing	Low	Moderate	0	3	0	3	4
Rice-Wheat	Moderate - high	High	2	3.5	1	2.5	1
Highland Mixed	Moderate	Moderate	1	3	0	2	4
Rainfed Mixed	Moderate	Moderate	2	3	1	2	2
Dry Rainfed	Moderate - high	Moderate	2	4	1	2	1
Pastoral	Low	Low	1	1	1	2.5	4.5
Sparse (Arid)	Low	Low	0	1	0	2	7
Sparse (Mountain)	Low	Low	0.5	1.5	0	3	5
Tree Crop	High	Moderate	2	3	1.5	2.5	1
Urban	Low	Low	1	3	2	4	0
Average for Region			1.8	3.1	0.8	2.3	1.9

Source: Expert judgement.
Note: Total score for each farming system equals 10. Assessments refer to poor farmers only. Average for region weighted by agricultural populations of systems derived from Table 5.1.

poverty reduction are more likely to come from the Rice-Wheat System where poverty is widespread and severe.

Table 5.4 also indicates the relative importance of five household strategies for escape from poverty. Clearly, given their importance across many different systems, strong support will be needed both for small farm diversification and for growth in employment opportunities in the off-farm economy. Measures that assist farm households to leave agriculture will be an important third priority, and would need to include improved rural education and vocational skills training. There is also substantial potential for poverty reduction by means of intensification of existing production patterns, largely through improved water management and adoption of improved technologies. Given the pressure on land, there is only limited opportunity for poverty reduction through the expansion of the farm or herd size of poor households. The following sections summarise the strategic priorities for actions, under the areas of policies, markets, information, technologies and natural resources.

POLICIES, INSTITUTIONS AND PUBLIC GOODS

Most countries in the region have policies that effectively favour urban areas and the manufacturing sector rather than rural areas and the agricultural sector, i.e. there are national trade and price distortions with a negative impact on the commercialisation of farming. For example, the need to maintain food prices within the reach of the increasing, politically articulate, urban population causes some governments to keep inter-harvest food prices artificially low by releasing stocks of grain as prices rise; thus adversely affecting farmgate prices. Because the majority of the poor are located in rural areas, poverty reduction efforts should be targeted towards increased farm household income. Moreover, successful rural poverty reduction has a positive impact on urban poverty reduction, but the converse is not true. There is a substantial advocacy challenge in this area, for which coalitions of civil society organisations are well placed to assist government.

Decentralisation and the strengthened performance of local institutions will be key strategic priorities for the development of most farming systems. Line departments in most countries have already given up some of their functions to the private sector, and plan to hand-over other functions to empowered communities. This trend is likely to become more pronounced in the future, but may require careful monitoring to ensure effective functioning, given the close relationship between rural community constituencies and politicians. Rural development will ultimately depend heavily on the effectiveness of local institutions, including community institutions. For this reason performance-based incentive schemes will be desirable. Public resources should be invested in the capacity building of local organisations, at both community and district levels. Another far-reaching change which is occurring in association with decentralisation and which needs to be encouraged, is the growing role of women in local level decision making, for example, *panchayats* in India. The growth of public-private partnerships for agricultural development should also be promoted, as they will have far-reaching effects on determining agricultural research priorities.

A high proportion of the increase in foodgrain production during the Indian Green Revolution occurred in districts with good irrigation facilities and adequate local transport. Agricultural development in many other areas of the region, however, has been constrained by a lack of infrastructure. In particular, the shortage of roads in remote and sparsely populated areas pushes up input and product transport costs[46] and the lack of health and educational services reduce

---

[46] Fan *et al* (2001) report higher rates of return for investment in roads and research in rainfed areas than in irrigated areas in India. Notably, their poverty reduction potential was also higher.

labour productivity[47]. Investments in roads and educational services should, therefore, be an essential ingredient of a strategy for increasing agricultural production and rural development.

Traditionally, irrigation water was available without cost in many areas – and was often seen as a way of supporting farmers and keeping down food prices. However, significant improvement in water management will only be possible if realistic water charges are introduced. In the case of surface water systems, better arrangements are required to provide an equitable balance between the benefits accruing to downstream users of irrigation water and electricity, and the well-being of the communities living in the upper catchment above and around the dam.

A double benefit, to growth and to poverty reduction, could result from an overhaul of obsolete land tenure policies and regulation. Increased operated size of fields and, over time, of farms will facilitate improved resource management and also intensification and diversification. In addition, open access resource regimes need to be converted to managed common poverty situations, within an effective legal framework.

The linkages between proper broad-based agricultural productivity growth and off-farm rural economic growth are well established[48]. However, less attention has been given to the integration of farm and off-farm economies, and in particular the types of developments which are simultaneously mutually reinforcing and which foster poverty reduction.

TRADE LIBERALISATION AND MARKET DEVELOPMENT

The three significant global issues that affect this region are: (i) gaining access to developed country markets in OECD countries; (ii) declining terms of trade for agricultural commodities; and, (iii) the continuation of subsidies for agriculture in developed countries. The terms of trade for rice, wheat and other foodgrains have been declining and the ongoing opening of economies exposes farmers to these forces, especially in the intensive Rice and Rice-Wheat Farming Systems. While some producers in these intensive systems may have the potential to remain internationally competitive, additional market development will inevitably be needed even in these favourable areas. Generally, market-related priorities within intensive systems need to address two issues: (i) reducing risk associated with monoculture activities by promoting enterprise diversification and value adding local processing; and (ii) the development of alternative income sources for landless and sub-marginal producers. There are many minor products that also generate income for poor households through the market; of which dried manure cakes and fodder are two important examples.

---

[47] While attention to the HIV/AIDS-agriculture linkages has focused on Sub-Saharan Africa, it is conceivable that AIDS will also cause major suffering and affect agricultural productivity during the coming 30 years in rural South Asia.
[48] See Chapter 1.

Producers in other systems with less potential in traditional products will need to develop market strategies that exploit alternative advantages. In relatively high poverty areas, such as the Highland Mixed Farming System, labour intensive activities such as horticulture and dairy have provided successful diversification pathways, but only if market access is sufficiently developed. These systems may thus require a particular focus on market-related infrastructure development, such as access roads and market facilities. However, less successful and more isolated households will leave the system, leading to a need for training and other exit support services.

Notwithstanding the attention being given to global issues, functioning local commodity markets and price information systems are of more direct interest to most smallholders. The experience of the recent past has demonstrated that market-led growth does not necessarily lead to benefits for the poor unless strong institutions are in place. Considerable investment is needed in these areas, and especially in the more remote farming systems such as the Highland Mixed and Pastoral Farming Systems. Similarly, further development of rural financial services, including micro-finance and linkages to mainstream banking, are needed for the full potential of farming systems to be realised.

INFORMATION AND HUMAN CAPITAL

Investment in rural education is required for two principal reasons: (i) to equip workers with the skills to transfer from agriculture to the off-farm economy (whether locally or through permanent emigration); and (ii) to equip those remaining in agriculture to manage the emerging, knowledge-intensive, farming systems. Although total labour requirements in agriculture are not likely to increase, improved skills are required to increase efficiency and productivity. These local increases of human capital are needed in order to underpin diversification towards high value skill intensive enterprises as well as the development of small-scale local rural industry.

In addition, further investment in the training of professionals for research and agricultural support services is required. There emphasis should be placed on two aspects. First, mature and older professionals need to be updated in modern approaches and skills for agricultural development. Second, some advanced tertiary training institutions should incorporate soft systems approaches to agricultural education.

The shift to commercial knowledge in intensive farming systems requires a greatly improved flow of information concerning technologies and markets, to both farmers and support services. This emerges as a key issue and is a promising area for public-private partnerships. Publicly funded and managed information systems – particularly those providing market data – have generally proven to be of only limited value in strengthening the position of small farmers, while incurring substantial long-term operating costs. Technologies have been demonstrated which enable effective village level access to computer, or Internet based, information. A high priority for investment in the coming 30 years would be empowering small farmers to access Internet based information on markets, services and technologies.

SCIENCE AND TECHNOLOGY

Notwithstanding the existence of a range of technologies that are ready for adaptation and adoption by farmers, there is a continuing need for research efforts that respond to farmers' needs and to a number of strategic priority production problems; including soil degradation in the intensively cultivated systems, continuing germplasm improvement in food crops and, perhaps of greatest importance in the long run, effective biological nitrogen fixation (BNF) to boost cereal productivity through rotations with legume crops. There is already substantial capacity and a number of proven successes in the larger National Agricultural Research Systems (NARS) to exploit modern research techniques including: the potential of biotechnology, e.g. in the development of new genotypes possessing high yield potential and resistance to biotic stresses. Other potentials lie in the field of animal reproduction; recycling technologies such as biogas[49]; and value added through new agro-processing technologies.

The germplasm banks held by the NARS and the Consultative Group on International Agricultural Research (CGIAR), the latter under FAO custodianship, will be an important resource for public sector research and are also being utilised in private sector plant breeding efforts. Investments in support of agricultural research and extension – including livestock, forestry and fishery – will pay off handsomely if carried out using a problem oriented, farmer-centred multi-disciplinary approach. Two priority foci would be: (i) maintaining and expanding public research capacity, while at the same time ensuring its responsiveness to farmer needs; and (ii) concurrently building partnerships between the public sector, the private sector and farmer organisations. Demand-driven research structures will therefore be essential in the future.

In many countries in the region, the utilisation of inorganic fertiliser shows considerable scope for efficiency improvement. In the short run, priority should be given to better on-farm integrated nutrient management, combining inorganic and organic nutrient sources, and economic incentives for balanced fertiliser use – with reduced greenhouse gas emissions as an added advantage. These improvements should be combined with technological improvements,

[49] The benefits of biogas could be extended to high altitudes if cold tolerant digesters could be developed, which could have significant positive impacts on reduced deforestation, reduced women's work and improved recycling of nutrients to crop production.

such as more cost-effective slow-release formulations, in order to reduce losses of plant nutrients. In the long run, breakthroughs in BNF, if they occur, could have a major impact on agriculture.

It is conventional wisdom that vigorous agricultural growth has to be established in order to prime the off-farm rural economy, and that both these sub-sectors are interdependent through consumption, production and labour market linkages. However, agricultural policy and development planning will need to take account of the increasing degree to which the roles are reversed. In many cases, off-farm employment is priming the rural farm economy and the growth of agriculture depends on investments derived from off-farm sources, including remittances. The typically lower return per labour day in agriculture compared to off-farm employment, as well as the seasonality of such off-farm employment, have important implications for labour availability on the farm – particularly at times of peak labour demand. Socio-economic research is needed concerning the impact of this phenomenon on the farm enterprise, as well as to identify the means by which farmer can adjust to the demands of off-farm employment. The policy implications for government also need to be better understood, e.g. the need to facilitate the provision of mechanised land preparation and harvesting services by farmer companies or the private sector.

NATURAL RESOURCES AND CLIMATE

Natural resources will come under increased pressure, as a result of the growing demand for additional food and other agricultural produce to meet the needs of the expanding population. Population pressure is likely to be more intense in those farming systems already under severe strain, *viz* the Rice, Rice-Wheat and Highland Mixed Farming Systems. Thus, sustainable natural resource management depends on measures that limit increases in population pressure on the natural resource base, especially in marginal areas.

The little forest left in the region will come under ever-greater pressure during the coming 30 years. In most countries of the region forest departments have been slow to change their approach to forest management. This lack of progress has occurred despite ample evidence that sustainable productivity increases can be achieved by a joint system of forest management, which allows benefits to be enjoyed by forest dwelling communities. It seems evident that high priority should be given to re-orienting forestry development policy, and to changing departmental regulations to facilitate the establishment of joint forest management systems. These changes would increasingly empower local communities, while at the same time resulting in more efficient production of forest products. A further change needed in support of such development will be the re-definition of forest boundaries, leading to the development of optimal management systems for joint forest management areas and conventional forest departmental management areas. Such measures should be complemented by incentives for agroforestry, including fodder and commercial species, and community woodlots, for fuelwood and construction timber.

The management of water resources has transnational, national and local dimensions. Equitable agreements on sharing of water among states facilitate optimal water use. At national and local levels, conservation of water resources in cultivated areas will require the establishment of incentives for efficient use and mechanisms for the monitoring and regulation of water use – notably of groundwater levels and water quality. Water resources can be further developed through traditional means, such as construction or rehabilitation of tanks and tubewells, and improved water management.

Significant improvements are also likely to result from the introduction of realistic water service charges. This will be a question of 'when' rather than 'if' since the fiscal burden of running irrigation schemes can no longer be borne by governments in the region. Such improvements will include a wide range of improved management techniques, including laser levelling of irrigation basins, and both sprinkler and trickle irrigation. The greatest contribution in the future is expected from soil moisture conservation by means of mulching, bunding, relay cropping, windbreaks, plus general purpose tree planting, and, most importantly of all, water harvesting. This will include effective techniques for moisture conservation at farm level, through adjustments in cropping patterns, mulching, minimum tillage and relay cropping. Water harvesting has the potential to double the productivity of semiarid and subhumid areas[50].

Soil degradation is a critical issue in most of the farming systems of the region. Priority needs to be given to on-going and new participatory research and extension programmes that address these problems, such as those of the Rice-Wheat Consortium for the Indo-Gangetic Plains which has already led to spectacular expansion of zero-till wheat in the Rice-Wheat Farming System. A number of successful participatory, community-based pilot watershed management projects in the Rainfed Mixed and Highland Mixed Farming Systems have provided the methodology and experience to improve the management of the large number of critical watersheds in the region[51].

Governments are likely to continue, quite correctly, to give greatest attention to the relatively high potential, well-watered cereal producing areas of the Rice and the Rice-Wheat Farming Systems in order to ensure an adequate level of self sufficiency in key staples at acceptable prices. The main technical strategy will be to improve the efficiency of production. The potential is already evident in areas, where relatively cheap tubewells have provided a timely supply of water at

---

[50] Agarwal, pers. comm.

[51] The approach of improved watershed management combined with income generation (which was effectively applied in Tunisia, as described in Box 3.6 of Chapter 3) was pioneered through a global network which included one successful pilot project in the Highland Mixed Farming System in Nepal. Some aspects of this approach could enrich the existing participatory approaches to watershed management in the region.

transplanting – which the state-managed surface irrigation schemes often cannot guarantee – which boost the yields of rice and the following crop. Very significant changes can be anticipated as realistic water chargers are introduced. These will involve a wide range of water management techniques including laser levelling of irrigation basins, sprinkler and trickle irrigation; and the introduction of greater moisture conservation, including zero tillage, mulching, windbreaks and relay cropping.

The high potential areas will also need considerable attention to better soil management. In the Rice-Wheat Farming System, where intensive cultivation and unbalanced fertiliser applications have led to a deterioration in soil structure and fertility, solutions are now being developed to tackle the immediate problem. However, it will be important to develop a range of technologies for sound soil management under highly-intensive, continuous, irrigated cultivation. The need for precision management of fertiliser nutrients is a closely related issue, not only from the point of view of efficiency in use for grain formation, but also to minimise groundwater pollution. Improved pest management will also be necessary, and it is expected that this will be biologically oriented for most crops and, increasingly, for livestock. While these areas will remain quite highly specialised in cereal production, there will be a degree of diversification into high value enterprises – including orchard crops and livestock. Household livelihoods will also diversify, and an increasing share of off-farm income is expected for smallholder households.

The low potential areas, such as the Rainfed Mixed, Highland Mixed and Pastoral Farming Systems, are intrinsically less able than the lowland areas to provide production responses in food crops. Sustainable resource management with water harvesting is required to underpin diversification into high-value produce as market access spreads. The severe poverty prevalent in these areas will probably lead to continuing seasonal and permanent migration, thereby limiting the increase of population pressure on the resource base.

However, there are some significant possibilities for development. A community-based micro-watershed approach, such as that which is succeeding in parts of India, would form a sound basis for the development of the Rainfed Mixed Farming System. Conservation agriculture should be introduced; including the greater integration of livestock and trees into the farming systems – with fodder trees, catch crops and green manure crops. Such programmes would include the introduction of cash enterprises, such as dairying or orchard crops, wherever market access is feasible. Greater attention to soil and water conservation should also form a vital element in such programmes; including zero tillage, mulching, relay cropping, windbreaks and on-farm tree planting. Development of sound and sustainable agroforestry and forestry operations, with participatory management for much of the forest area, will be important in maintaining a good forest cover in the upper catchments, as well as on the large areas of wasteland that currently exist in the region.

CONCLUSIONS

Agricultural development will remain an important component of poverty reduction programmes for the foreseeable future in South Asia. There are some major resource degradation challenges, as well as linkages to the off-farm rural economy, to be taken into account. The main source of reduction of hunger and poverty would be diversification to high value enterprises, including local processing. Increased off-farm income and intensification of existing production patterns are next in importance, followed by exit from agriculture. Increased farm size is expected to be of lesser importance. Four broad strategic initiatives are proposed:

Improved water resource management. Improved water management is essential to support the intensification and diversification of production and to reduce resource depletion, for both surface and underground water schemes. Components include: efficient technologies; conjunctive use; water charges and other regulatory measures; water users' associations; and watershed protection.

Strengthened resource user groups. Strengthening resource user groups is one way to redress the extensive land and water degradation in plains and hills, and protect watershed resources. Components include: resource management groups for watershed management in hill and mountain areas; range management groups in pastoral areas; and policies to encourage effective common property resource management.

Re-oriented agricultural services. The re-orientation of agricultural research, education, information and extension systems to involve farmers fully will underpin the drives for intensification and enterprise diversification and promote sustainable resource management. Components include: models for joint public-private service provision; pluralisitic advisory services; Internet based delivery of market and technical information to small farmers; and the incorporation in higher education systems of interdisciplinary learning and approaches.

Improved rural infrastructure. Returns to transport and health investments are high and beneficial to the poor, especially in low potential and highland areas in the region. Components include: roads; drinking water; schools; health facilities; and effective models for private sector participation.

6

EAST ASIA

AND PACIFIC

• • •

REGIONAL SETTING

CHARACTERISTICS OF THE REGION

The East Asia and Pacific region[1] contains 1 836 million[2] people (just over one-third of all the inhabitants of developing countries), of which 62 percent (1 124 million) are directly involved in agriculture. Considerable variation exists among countries in terms of size and density of population, and the overall proportion living in rural areas. Most people are concentrated in just two countries: China (with 1 278 million inhabitants or 68 percent of the region) and Indonesia (with 205 million inhabitants); respectively the first and fourth most populous countries in the world. Very high population densities occur in some rural areas, for example in Eastern China and the islands of Java and Bali in Indonesia.

The total land area of the region is 1 639 million ha. Forest cover is estimated at 380 million ha (23 percent of land area), of which 170 million ha are considered as dense forest. Cultivated land is estimated at 232 million ha (15 percent of land area) and the remainder consists of grasslands, wastelands, mountains, urban areas and waterbodies.

Some 278 million people[3] (15 percent of the total regional population) are living in extreme poverty, with daily incomes of less than US$1. A quarter of these impoverished people live in China, but significant numbers are found in almost all countries in the region. About 240 million people[4] (13 percent of the total population) are undernourished. Poverty in rural areas is approximately twice as

[1] See Annex 3 for a list of East Asian and Pacific Island countries included in the region. Note that Hong Kong, Australia, Japan, New Zealand, Singapore and Taiwan are excluded.

[2] FAOSTAT.

[3] World Bank 2000a.

[4] FAO 2000a.

high as in urban areas[5]. The incidence of rural poverty ranges from 4.6 percent in China to 57.2 percent in Vietnam. With the exception of China and the Republic of Korea, the economies of the region are strongly agrarian. Although the average contribution of the agricultural sector to total GDP is 13 percent, this figure is heavily influenced by China (17 percent)[6]. In the Republic of Korea, the agricultural sector's added value is only 5 percent, while in Laos, Myanmar and Cambodia it is over 50 percent.

MAJOR FARMING SYSTEMS IN EAST ASIA AND PACIFIC

Eleven broad farming systems have been identified[7], based on criteria discussed in Chapter 1. They are listed in Table 6.1 and their geographical location is indicated in the accompanying Map.

Lowland Rice Farming System

This farming system is found in both humid and moist subhumid agro-ecological zones in well-watered mainly flat landscapes[8]. It covers an estimated 197 million ha and, with an agricultural population of 474 million, it is the most populous system in the region. Cultivated area is 71 million ha, of which about 45 percent are irrigated. Large areas of this system are found in Thailand, Vietnam, Myanmar, South and Central East China, Philippines and Indonesia. Smaller areas are located in Cambodia, Korea DPR, Republic of Korea, Laos DPR and Malaysia. The farming system is dominantly rice-based, with cropping intensity dependent on rainfall distribution, length of growing season and the availability of supplementary irrigation. Important subsidiary crops include oilseeds, maize, root crops, soybeans, sugarcane, cotton, vegetables and fruits in all areas, while wheat is significant in Central East China. Both livestock and off-farm income contribute to household livelihoods. Regional food security depends upon the production from this system. The prevalence of poverty is moderate overall, although it is extensive in Mynamar and Cambodia.

Tree Crop Mixed Farming System

This farming system is found mainly in the humid agro-ecological zone, but also extends into moist subhumid areas, principally on flat to undulating landscapes with poor soils where paddy rice cannot be intensively produced. Total system area is 85 million ha, with an agricultural population of 30 million. Cultivated area is

---

[5] See World Bank (2000a), DPR of Korea, Republic of Korea, Myanmar and Papua New Guinea are excluded due to a lack of the poverty data in the report.
[6] World Bank 2000f.
[7] See Chapter 1 for an explanation of the approach followed for delineation of the farming systems.
[8] See Annex 5 for an explanation of agro-ecological zones and length of growing period.

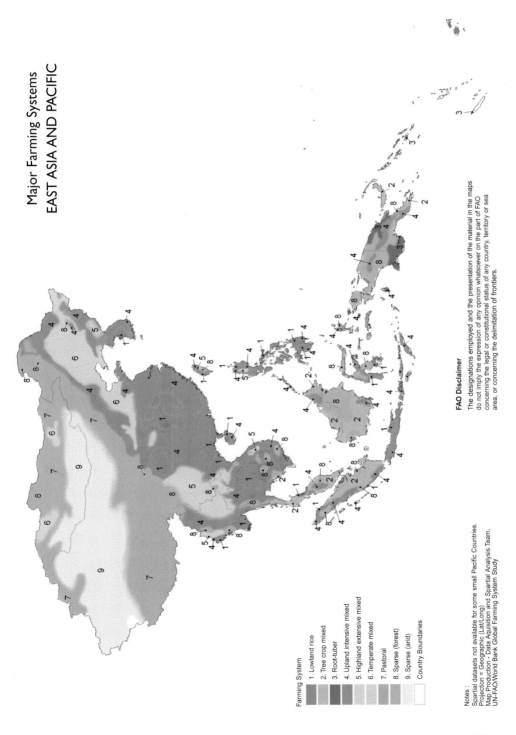

Major Farming Systems
EAST ASIA AND PACIFIC

Farming System
1. Lowland rice
2. Tree crop mixed
3. Root-tuber
4. Upland intensive mixed
5. Highland extensive mixed
6. Temperate mixed
7. Pastoral
8. Sparse (forest)
9. Sparse (arid)
Country Boundaries

Notes :
Spartial datasets not available for some small Pacific Countries.
Projection = Geographic (Lat/Long)
Map Production - Data Aquisition and Spartial Analysis Team,
UN-FAO/World Bank Global Farming System Study

FAO Disclaimer

The designations employed and the presentation of the material in the maps
do not imply the expression of any opinion whatsoever on the part of FAO
concerning the legal or constitutional status of any country, territory or sea
area, or concerning the delimitation of frontiers.

Table 6.1 Major Farming Systems in East Asia and Pacific

Farming Systems	Land Area (% of region)	Agric. Popn. (% of region)	Principal Livelihoods	Prevalence of Poverty
Lowland Rice	12	42	Rice, maize, pulses, sugarcane, oil seeds, vegetables, livestock, aquaculture, off-farm work	Moderate
Tree Crop Mixed	5	3	Rubber, oil palm, coconuts, coffee, tea, cocoa, spices, rice, livestock, off-farm work	Moderate
Root–Tuber	2	<1	Root crops (yam, taro, sweet potato), vegetables, fruits, livestock (pigs and cattle), off-farm work	Limited
Upland Intensive Mixed	19	27	Rice, pulses, maize, sugarcane, oil seeds, fruits, vegetables, livestock, off-farm work	Extensive
Highland Extensive Mixed	5	4	Upland rice, pulses, maize, oil seeds, fruits, forest products, livestock, off-farm work	Moderate
Temperate Mixed	6	14	Wheat, maize, pulses, oil crops, livestock, off-farm work	Moderate
Pastoral	20	4	Livestock with irrigated crops in local suitable areas	Extensive, especially drought induced
Sparse (Forest)	10	1	Hunting, gathering, off-farm work	Moderate
Sparse (Arid)	20	2	Local grazing where water available, off-farm work	Extensive
Coastal Artisanal Fishing	1	2	Fishing, coconut, mixed cropping, off-farm work	Moderate
Urban Based	<1	1	Horticulture, dairy, poultry, other work	Limited

Source: FAO data and expert knowledge.
Note: Prevalence of poverty refers to number in poverty, not depth of poverty, and is a relative assessment for this region.

estimated at 18 million ha, of which little more than 12 percent are irrigated. Significant areas of this system are found in Malaysia, Indonesia, Thailand, Cambodia, Philippines, Vietnam, Southern China and Papua New Guinea. Major industrial crops include rubber, oil palm, coconut, coffee, tea and cocoa, with some other associated crops such as pepper and other spices. Tree crops are grown under both large private estate and smallholder management systems. Smallholders also grow food and cash crops, raise a considerable number of large livestock, and supplement their livelihoods with off-farm income. Coconut plantations are widespread throughout most Asia and Pacific countries. The system has been a traditional source of export earnings in Indonesia and Malaysia, and also a target for substantial private and public investment. The prevalence of poverty is moderate.

Root-Tuber Farming System

This farming system is found in humid and moist subhumid agro-ecological zones in both plain and hill landscapes, typically in areas with low population density. Total system area is 25 million ha, with an agricultural population of approximately 1.5 million. Cultivated area is about 1.2 million ha, less than one percent of total area – no irrigated area is recorded. The system is found in Papua New Guinea and the Pacific Islands generally, and often merges into the Coastal Artisanal Fishing System towards the coastline. Although of minor significance on a regional level, it is the dominant farming system in many Pacific countries. It is based on the use of root food crops (yams, taro, sweet potato), vegetables and fruits (particularly banana), coconut and livestock, supplemented by hunting and gathering in the forest. There is relatively limited poverty in this system.

Upland Intensive Mixed Farming System

This farming system is found in upland and hill landscapes of moderate altitude and slope, in humid and subhumid agro-ecological zones. Total system area is 314 million ha, with an agricultural population of 310 million – the second most populous system, after Lowland Rice, in the region. Cultivated area is 75 million ha of which just under one quarter are irrigated. This is the most widespread and most heterogeneous farming system in the region (even including some remnant shifting cultivation), with major areas located in all countries of East and Southeast Asia. The system is characterised by the cultivation of a wide range of mostly permanent crops, but the specific crops preferred depend on geographic area, agro-climatic conditions, slope, terracing and water regime. A significant crop area – mainly rice – is irrigated from local streams and rivers. Livestock production is an important component of most farm livelihoods (there are 52 million large ruminants and 49 million small ruminants in this system) and contributes draught power, meat, cash income and savings. Off-farm work is an important source of income for many poor households. Poverty is extensive, varying in severity from moderate to very severe.

Highland Extensive Mixed Farming System

This farming system is found in hill and mountain landscapes of high altitude and steep slopes, in both humid and moist subhumid agro-ecological zones. It often lies above the Upland Intensive Mixed Farming System, but with poorer resources and lower population density. Total system area is 89 million ha with an agricultural population of only 47 million. Cultivated area is 8 million ha, of which about one fifth is irrigated. Extensive forested areas occur within the system, some of which have little human habitation and are similar to the Sparse (Forest) System delineated below, but provide grazing to some of the 16 million large ruminants. Major areas are located in Laos, Central and North Vietnam, Northern Thailand, Northern and Eastern Myanmar, Southwestern China, the Philippines and parts of Indonesia. The farming system can be subdivided into permanent and shifting cultivation sub-types. Both sub-types produce crops (including perennial crops such as fruit trees), livestock and forest products. This system provides the principal base for a number of tribal (indigenous) groups. Poverty is moderate to severe.

Temperate Mixed Farming System

This farming system is found in moist and dry subhumid agro-ecological zones in Central-Northern China and restricted areas of Mongolia. Total system area is 99 million ha, with an agricultural population of 162 million. Cultivated area is 31 million ha, of which about one-third is irrigated. The transitional boundary between this system and the Lowland Rice Farming System in Central-Eastern China is not easily defined, and the system also blends into the Extensive Cereal-Livestock Farming System of Southern Siberia and parts of Central Asia (in the Eastern Europe and Central Asia region - see Chapter 4). Major crops are wheat and maize, with smaller areas of rice, cotton, soybeans, sweet potato and rape – depending on local temperature and water conditions – as well as citrus and some temperate fruits. Livestock are important, particularly cattle, pigs and poultry. The prevalence of poverty is moderate.

Pastoral Farming System

This farming system is found in semiarid and arid temperate agro-ecological zones (with less than 120 growing days per annum) in both plain and hill landscapes. The system is extensive in Western China and much of Central and Northern Mongolia. Total area is 321 million ha, but with no more than 42 million people classed as agricultural, cultivated area is just over 12 million ha of which some 20 percent is irrigated in dispersed zones. The farming system is dominated by transhumant pastoralism and characterised by mixed herds of camels, cattle, sheep and goats extensively grazing native pasture. Irrigated crops include cotton, barley, wheat, pulses, peas, broad beans, potatoes and grapes, while sericulture is sometimes practised. Severe poverty, often triggered by drought or severe winters – with consequent loss of livestock – is common in both pastoral and irrigated areas.

Sparse (Forest) Farming System

Although vast in area, the sparse agriculture systems (both forest and arid) are of limited economic importance. The Sparse (Forest) System occurs at moderate to high altitudes to the north and west of the main areas of the Highland Extensive Farming System in Western China and Northern Myanmar, in Northern Mongolia – where it comprises part of the extensive Siberian Sparse (Forest) System – and in the major islands of Indonesia, excluding Java, and Papua New Guinea. The system covers an area of 172 million ha with a population of 23 million people, of whom 15 million are classified as agricultural. On the mainland of Asia small, scattered settlements depend on potatoes and buckwheat, plus cattle and yak herds. In the dense tropical forests of Malaysia, Indonesia and Papua New Guinea, small, scattered settlements (mainly tribal) depend on upland rice, root crops and small and large ruminants, supplemented by gathering wild plants and hunting animals. There are nearly 10 million ha of scattered cultivation, while 14 million bovines and 20 million sheep and goats are also supported. The prevalence of poverty is moderate.

Sparse (Arid) Farming System

The total area of the Sparse (Arid) Farming System, located in Western China and Southern Mongolia, is estimated at 322 million ha, supporting an estimated 9 million cattle and 59 million small ruminants. Only a little over one percent (less than 4 million ha) is cultivated, of which about two-thirds are under irrigation. Two types of irrigation are practised – some large-scale irrigation areas concentrated in the west; and scattered small areas of irrigation used by pastoralists to supplement their livelihoods. There is a population of 24 million people, 17 million of whom are classified as pastoral or agricultural. Apart from these arable areas, the dominant arid areas are utilised for opportunistic grazing. Poverty is extensive and, especially after droughts, severe in this system.

Coastal Artisanal Fishing Farming System

Along the narrow coastal strips in many countries of the region and in many islands (an estimated area of 38 million ha), around 28 million people supplement artisanal, inshore fishing with food production – rice from Java to China and root crops in the Pacific countries – and cash-oriented enterprises such as coconuts and livestock. Cultivated area is estimated at three million ha. The location of the system is not separately mapped. There is a moderate incidence of poverty.

Urban Based Farming System

In most large towns and cities throughout the region, the intensive production of perishable, high value commodities, such as milk and fresh vegetables, has expanded and now employs an estimated seven million people. This farming system – which is also not mapped – is generally characterised as a high external input, commercial system with well-functioning links to the surrounding rural areas for livestock, feed and fodder supplies. Because of the availability of other employment, poverty is generally limited.

REGION-WIDE TRENDS IN EAST ASIA AND PACIFIC

This section describes the most important region-wide trends in terms of: population, hunger and poverty; natural resources and climate; science and technology; trade liberalisation and market development; policies institutions and public goods; and, information and human capital. At the end of the section, four of the regional farming systems described in the previous section of the Chapter are selected for further description and analysis.

Population, hunger and poverty

The region has been settled for many thousands of years but has experienced rapid population growth in the last century, resulting in high population densities in many areas. In response to overpopulation, many governments have introduced birth control programmes that are contributing to falling population growth rates. This trend will continue, although there will be significant variations in the rate of decline among countries. Overall, the population in the region is projected to grow at 0.9 percent per annum to 2.13 billion by 2015[9], and thereafter at 0.5 percent per annum to reach 2.31 billion by 2030. The degree of urbanisation is expected to increase from the current 37 percent to 53 percent by 2030[10]. However, in many of the developing countries in the region, a large proportion of the total population, and the majority of rural people, will continue to be employed in the agricultural sector. Nonetheless, the rural population will age gradually as younger people migrate to cities for jobs. This has adverse implications for socio-economic conditions as well as labour quality and availability in rural areas.

The rapid economic growth experienced over much of the region during the last two decades has resulted in major and widespread socio-economic gains in many countries, but these gains have generally been strongly biased in favour of the urban population. Yet, with the exception of China and Republic of Korea, the regional economies remain strongly agrarian. GADP has been steadily decreasing as a proportion of national GDP, but still remains significant. This trend can be expected to continue in all countries, but a majority of the population will still remain dependent on the agricultural sector by 2030. Socio-economic indicators (household income, poverty, health, literacy, infant mortality, morbidity, longevity, etc.) of the rural population, while gradually improving in most countries, are usually significantly lower than for the urban population. Rural incomes have only

[9] Except where indicated, these data are drawn from FAO (2000a).
[10] For the whole of Asia. Separate data for East Asia are not available.

increased slowly – and perhaps not at all in real terms – and in almost all countries there is a growing disparity between rural and urban incomes.

Average per capita GDP is about US$1000 (US$3500 at parity purchasing power)[11], which is low compared to other developing regions. There are 278 million people (15 percent of the total population) who are considered to be living in extreme (or dollar) poverty, with daily incomes of less than US$1 per day – approximately twice as many in rural areas as in urban areas. A quarter of these people live in China, but significant numbers are found in almost all countries in the region. Furthermore, the rural population remains relatively poorly educated, with significant illiteracy and low school attainment levels in a number of countries. This has an adverse effect on the knowledge and learning skills of farmers. Figure 1.3 in Chapter 1 shows the dramatic reduction in poverty in the region during the period 1978-1987. While some improvements in these factors may occur, it is anticipated that rural/urban disparities will increase in many countries by 2030 unless governments undertake active policy initiatives and make specific plans to redress this imbalance.

The current average food intake is estimated at about 2780 kcal per person per day; 6 percent higher than the average for all developing countries. However, cereals (rice and wheat) contribute a very high proportion of total calorie intake. In the last two decades, the diet in the region has improved significantly, with a 30 percent increase in average total calorie intake, resulting in significant reductions in undernourishment in most countries. By 2015 and 2030, the food intake is forecast to increase to 3020 kcal and 3170 kcal, respectively. In China, the proportion of the undernourished population decreased from 30 percent in 1979-1981 to 13 percent in 1995-1997, and in Indonesia from 26 percent to six percent[12]. Undernourishment increased in only two countries – Mongolia (from 27 percent in 1979-1981 to 48 percent in 1995-1997) and Korea DPR (19 percent to 48 percent) – in the same period. However, a number of other countries still have higher proportions of under-nourished people than the developing world average (18 percent), including Cambodia (33 percent), Lao PDR (33 percent), Thailand (24 percent), and Papua New Guinea (24 percent). Overall, the number of undernourished people in the region has halved in the quarter century leading up to 1995-1997; from 504 million to 240 million (see Figure 1.2 in Chapter 1).

Natural Resources and Climate

Total cultivated land is estimated at 231 million ha, of which 134 million ha are found in China. This is less than 15 percent of the total regional land area. However, only a marginal net increase in cultivated land is expected by 2030, due to the large areas occupied by desert, mountains and other areas unsuitable for cultivation – as well as the loss of productive land to urbanisation. In particular, net

[11] World Bank 2000f.
[12] FAO 1999a.

cultivated land in China has actually decreased over the last two decades and is forecast to continue to decrease gradually over the period to 2030, as urbanisation reduces cropping area faster than new land can be brought into cultivation. Unfortunately, urbanisation removes some of the most productive land, while the newly cultivated tends to be more fragile, less fertile, steeper, more drought-prone and with less soil depth. In the other countries in the region, however, a gradual net increase in cultivated land area is projected up to 2030.

Agriculture is currently smallholder-based with widespread subsistence production. Average farm size has been declining for many decades in most countries. In only few countries has the absolute number of the rural-based population decreased – so allowing larger average farm sizes – as happened decades ago in industrialised countries. By 2030, therefore, it is anticipated that most farms in the region will remain as traditional smallholdings, although the proportion of semi-commercial and commercial farms will increase. The region's renewable water resources account for 32 percent of the total in the developing world. The current irrigation efficiency is low at 38 percent and is expected to increase only slowly to 42 percent by 2030 – still lower than the projected developing world average of 50 percent in that year. Cultivated land under irrigation is projected to expand from the current 71 million ha (30 percent of the total cultivated land) to 85 million ha (35 percent) in 2030. China alone irrigated 51 million ha in 1995-1997 and is expected to bring another nine million ha under irrigation by 2030.

Forest cover[13] is estimated at 380 million ha (23 percent of land area), of which 170 million ha (10 percent of land area) remain dense forest. This area decreased by 0.8 percent per annum (three million ha) between 1990 to 1995, due to unsustainable logging practices, and is expected to diminish further, with little reforestation of natural forests and limited establishment of forest plantations.

With so many low-lying coastal areas on the mainland and the numerous islands, the Asia and Pacific region is particularly vulnerable to floods and maritime storms. The frequency and severity of storms is expected to intensify as a consequence of global warming. In addition, rising sea levels may threaten some islands during the course of the coming century.

Science and technology

Mainly as a result of the adoption of better technologies generated by the CGIAR and national research systems, overall crop production in the region has been increasing at three percent per annum during 1980s – but the rate of increase has been diminishing. Crop yields increased by 3.6 percent per annum during the period 1967-1997, and are projected to grow only at about one-third of this historic rate during the period until 2030. Since little increase is expected in cultivated land area, future growth in crop production will be achieved through

[13] World Bank 1998.

Table 6.2 Trends in Crop Area, Yield and Output in East Asia
and Pacific, 1970-2000

Crop	Harvested Area 2000 (m ha)	Yield 2000 (t/ha)	Production 2000 (m tons)	Average Annual Change 1970-2000 (%)		
				Area	Yield	Production
Rice	74	4.6	344	0.4	1.8	2.2
Wheat	27	3.7	100	0.1	4.0	4.1
Maize	31	4.1	127	1.0	2.7	3.8
Other Cereals	7	2.1	15	-3.5	1.4	-2.2
Oilcrops	47	0.9	41	2.2	3.7	5.8
Roots & Tubers	15	16.3	239	0.1	1.2	1.3
Vegetables	18	17.2	313	4.4	1.5	6.0
Fruits	13	8.4	105	4.7	1.2	5.9

Source: FAOSTAT.

higher cropping intensity and higher crop yield per unit area. However, considerable variation can be noted in growth projections for various crops. While production of paddy rice, the main crop in the region, increased at about 2.2 percent per annum from 1970 to 2000 (see Table 6.2) to reach 345 million tons (200 million tons in China), this rate of growth was lower than that for South Asia. Paddy rice production is projected to increase slowly over the period to 2030.

Wheat has been the fastest growing of the cereal crops, with production expanding by over four percent per annum over the last 30 years, almost all of it due to yield increases. Output is expected to continue to increase during the period 2000 to 2015. The region now produces 100 million tons of wheat per annum compared to only 30 million tons in 1970; almost all of it in China. Substantial increases in the production of maize and barley are also expected, but little increase is anticipated for millet, sorghum, cassava, and pulses. The output of oil crops, such as rape, soybean, maize, sesame, sunflower and oil palm, and fruits and vegetables – already one of the fastest growing crop categories in the region, averaging almost six percent production increases per annum since 1970 – is projected to increase substantially by 2030. The production of cotton is expected to grow moderately, while the output of other fibre crops is forecast to stagnate. The production of beverages, tea and coffee, is also expected to increase significantly. Natural rubber output has grown at an annual rate of 2.7 percent in the past, doubling from 1961 to 5.6 million tons by 1999 and is projected to double again during the next 30 years. Vegetables and fruits have shown very strong growth over the last 30 years, and this is expected to continue.

Over the period 1961-1997, the use of fertiliser increased rapidly at an annual rate of 8.9 percent. As a result, fertiliser application is high, at 147 kg per ha, compared to the developing world average of 90 kg per ha. However, the relatively high level of regional fertiliser consumption is due principally to massive use in China, as the average for the rest of the region is only 93 kg per ha. China consumes 73 percent of all the fertiliser in the region and has twice the application rate of the average in other regional countries. The pace of increase is expected to decline from 2000 to 2030, when average consumption is projected to be 180 kg per ha. Excluding China, the projected annual rate of increase in other countries will be slow, leading to an average consumption will be 106 kg per ha by the year 2030.

Both total and per capita meat and milk consumption have increased rapidly in the last twenty years. Between 1983 and 1993, per capita per annum meat consumption increased from 16 to 33 kg in China and from 11 to 15 kg in Southeast Asia countries, while per capita milk consumption increased from 3 to 7 kg in China and from 10 to 11 kg in Southeast Asia countries.

Most of the strong historical growth in livestock production has been driven by the rapid expansion of the livestock sector in China. Numbers of pigs and poultry in the region increased at high annual rates over the last three decades to reach over 500 and 6 000 million head respectively (see Table 6.3). At present, more than 50 percent of the pigs and 36 percent of chickens and fowls of the world are found in the region. During the period 2000 to 2030, the pace of increase in China will slow down. However, this will still create huge increases in demand for animal feed supplies in China. These extra supplies are expected to come from the conversion of substantial areas of rice and wheat to maize production (as well as an acceleration of maize imports). The scope for increased livestock numbers and meat production in other countries in the region is mostly limited to pigs and poultry, as there is little potential for strong growth in the supply of ruminant meats (see below). The increased production of poultry and pigs will entail greater competition between livestock and humans for cereal grains.

Ruminant livestock are an important source of draught power, meat, savings and income in farming systems throughout the region. Total populations of cattle and buffalo, specialised dairy animals, and sheep and goats, are estimated at 190, 3, and 338 million respectively. While the growth in buffalo numbers in recent decades has been slow – largely due to the expansion of mechanisation – cattle and small ruminant populations have shown strong growth, with annual rates of increases of 1.9 and 2.8 percent respectively for the last three decades. The projected future growth, for the period 2000 to 2030, is moderate for both types of livestock. However, the limited potential for increasing the supply of ruminant feedstuffs is anticipated to be a significant constraint in most countries. Little opportunity exists for improving and expanding native pastures, forages, and sown pastures. Ruminant feed supplies are expected to be mostly dependent on cultivated forages and native pastures rather than grains and concentrates.

Table 6.3 Trends in Livestock Populations and Output in East Asia and Pacific, 1970-2000

Species	Million Head 2000	Ave Annual Change 1970-2000 (%)
Cattle	38	1.9
Buffalo	152	0.3
Small Ruminants	338	2.8
Pigs	501	3.0
Poultry	6 073	5.6
Product	Output 2000 (million tons)	Annual Change 1970-2000 (%)
Total Meat	74	6.9
Total Milk	16	6.1
Total Wool	0.3	2.8
Total Eggs	26	7.7

Source: FAOSTAT.

Trade liberalisation and market development

The region currently accounts for a major proportion of world trade in a number of agricultural commodities, including, oil palm (Malaysia, Indonesia, China, Papua New Guinea and Solomon Islands), rubber (Thailand, Malaysia and Indonesia) and rice (Thailand, Vietnam and Philippines). Countries with a strong positive balance of trade in agricultural products include Thailand, Malaysia and Vietnam, while China, Republic of Korea, Korea DPR and the Philippines have a strong negative balance of trade. Market liberalisation is expected to encourage farm diversification – production and trade of higher-value products – in all farming systems. Growing urban markets and higher per capita incomes will lead to increased internal trade in most countries, with urban and peri-urban agriculture expected to expand and intensify to meet the increasing demand for vegetables and fruits and meat and dairy products.

Policies, institutions and public goods

Many countries in the region are governed under communist-derived regimes (China, Cambodia, Laos, North Korea and Vietnam) or military leaders (Myanmar). In these countries, the political regime has had a marked effect on government policies, laws and regulations, thereby affecting the environment in which businesses and farming have had to operate. Restrictions on trade and prices, rent-seeking practices and the persistence of inefficient government enterprises, all adversely effect the provision of goods and services to farming and private enterprise businesses. In other countries, restrictive and inefficient government bureaucratic practices, and widespread corruption have also had a negative effect on the growth, productivity and profitability of the agricultural sector. Despite these collective shortcomings, policy reforms have been implemented in recent years to improve market liberalisation, government efficiency and good governance, as well as to diminish corruption in the public service. However, it is proving to be a considerable challenge to implement these policy reforms.

Most countries, usually through donor assisted projects, have introduced changes to strengthen their agricultural extension and research systems. While the knowledge, skills and capacity of these services have been upgraded, there is still a need for further strengthening. Whilst the degree of importance given by governments to the protection and management of natural resources (land, water, flora and fauna) and the environment has increased, there is still a need for further upgrading of government institutions concerned with natural resource policy, planning and management. There also needs to be a closer linkage between government agencies concerned with agricultural production and natural resources management.

Information and human capital

Recent advances in information technology have almost exclusively benefited urban, educated populations. Traditionally, agricultural information dissemination to farmers has been delivered by public extension services. This has been through the usual mechanisms of formal and informal farmer training, radio and television presentations, provision of leaflets, field days, etc. In recent years, some countries have introduced computer-based management information systems (MIS), and geographic information systems (GIS), within agencies focused on rural issues. They have also started to develop some basic information programmes on research and extension themes, and even introduced farm decision programmes. Internet based information delivery has the potential to revolutionise service provision to agriculture. However, these developments are only in their infancy and have not reached the general farming public to any extent.

Selection of farming systems for analysis

Four of the farming systems outlined in the previous section have been selected for analysis, using criteria based upon agricultural population, the incidence of poverty, and apparent potential for agricultural growth and poverty reduction in the coming 30 years:

- Lowland Rice Farming System;
- Tree Crop Mixed Farming System;
- Temperate Mixed Farming System; and
- Upland Intensive Mixed Farming System.

These four farming systems contain most of the agricultural poor in the region and also produce more than three-quarters of the GADP. They are described in more detail in the following sections of the Chapter.

LOWLAND RICE FARMING SYSTEM

CHARACTERISTICS OF THE SYSTEM

The Lowland Rice Farming System is the single most important farming system in East Asia in economic and demographic terms, covering some 197 million ha (12 percent of the land area of the region) and containing 825 million people or over one quarter of the region's agricultural population (474 million) – see Box 6.1. It covers both humid (270 to 365 growing days)

<table>
<tr><td colspan="2">Box 6.1 Basic Data: Lowland Rice Farming System</td></tr>
<tr><td>Total population (m)</td><td>825</td></tr>
<tr><td>Agricultural population (m)</td><td>474</td></tr>
<tr><td>Total area (m ha)</td><td>197</td></tr>
<tr><td>Agro-ecological zone</td><td>Moist subhumid</td></tr>
<tr><td>Cultivated area (m ha)</td><td>71</td></tr>
<tr><td>Irrigated area (m ha)</td><td>33</td></tr>
<tr><td>Bovine population (m)</td><td>52</td></tr>
</table>

and moist subhumid (180 to 269 growing days) tropical environment in mainly flat landscapes. Large areas of this system are found in Thailand, Vietnam, Myanmar, South and Central-Eastern China, Philippines and Indonesia. Smaller areas are located in Cambodia, Korea DPR, Republic of Korea, Laos DPR and Malaysia.

Average household incomes are low and poverty is extensive and severe in many areas. Land ownership is secured under traditional or – less frequently – freehold tenure. Traditional rights are not recognised as legal ownership in many countries, but usually ensure long-term use of land. The system is generally well serviced by roads, communications, community, goods and support services.

About 71 million ha, or almost one third of the total area of the system, are estimated to be cultivated. There is considerable variation in intensity of farm

---

Box 6.2 A Typical Household of the Lowland Rice Farming System

A typical rice farm household in Thai Binh Province, Red River Delta, Vietnam illustrates very intensive rice farming (in contrast to the larger farm sizes in Southeast Asian countries). The family of four cultivates a total area of 0.24 ha with a cropping intensity of 190 percent. Two transplanted rice crops (89 percent of the total cropped area of the farm) are followed by small areas of sweet potatoes, maize and soybeans. Modern rice varieties are transplanted in both seasons, producing 2.5 tons per annum of paddy rice (equivalent to 6.5 t/ha for spring paddy and 5.8 t/ha for winter paddy). The yields of the three other crops are 14.6 t/ha for sweet potatoes, 4 t/ha for maize and 1.7 t/ha for soybeans. Total annual household production of these four main crops would total approximately 2.8 t (0.7 t per capita). Power tillers are used for primary tillage, and additional income is earned through provision of transportation services. The household maintains a small piggery. The household income, which has risen rapidly during the past 20 years, is only now reaching the international poverty line.

production. More intensive production systems are found in areas with higher population density and smaller farm size, for example in China. While cultivated area per farm household can reach as much as several hectares in central Thailand, in the Red River Delta it is only 0.24 ha (see Box 6.2). Other locations tend to have sizes between 0.5 and 1 ha (e.g. the Mekong River Delta averages 0.79 ha cultivated area, while in Southeast China it is estimated at 0.67 ha). Average farm household size varies from six persons in the Mekong River Delta to four persons in Jiangsu Province, China.

As its name implies, the farming system is predominantly rice-based, with from one to three harvests per annum depending on rainfall distribution, length of growing season and the availability of supplementary irrigation. Total irrigated area is around 33 million ha, or 45 percent of the arable area in the farming system. This constitutes almost half of the entire irrigated area of the region. The total annual area of rice is estimated at 96 million ha. The second most important crop is wheat (21 million ha), which is sown as a winter crop, mainly in the northern part of this farming system in Central-Eastern China. Other crops, in descending order of importance by area, are vegetables, oilseeds, maize, root crops, soybeans, sugarcane, cotton and fruits. Large and small ruminants, pigs and poultry are a minor but important source of income generation.

Rice is mostly grown on puddled lowland soils under both rainfed and irrigated conditions. Soils are heavy and inherently more fertile than other cropped soils, but natural fertility is declining under conditions of continuous cropping with inadequate or unbalanced nutrient inputs. The average yield of paddy is 3.1 t/ha across the region, but it is heavily skewed by the higher yields obtained in China (up to 8.1 t/ha in Jiangsu Province). High-yielding varieties are used in all countries, but some still have significant areas of lower yielding, traditional varieties because of their perceived higher grain quality and acceptability. Fertiliser use is moderate to high, including the use of both inorganic and organic types. High inputs of organic and inorganic fertiliser combined with the universal use of high-yielding varieties are the main determinant of high yields in China. Rice is mostly transplanted, but germinated seed or seedlings are broadcast in some countries (Thailand and some areas of China) where serious labour shortages occur. Triple cropping only occurs where transplanting is used and there is a continuous supply of water during the year.

Livestock are important for draught power, meat, income and savings purposes. About 29 percent (52 million head) of the total large ruminants (cattle and buffalo) of the region are found in this farming system. Buffalo are very important for draught power in the lower, wetter landscapes with cattle used more commonly in slightly higher parts. Sheep are unimportant, but there are an estimated 36 million goats (12 percent of the regional total). Ruminant livestock graze under extensive conditions and animal health services are generally poorly developed. Pigs and poultry are important for household consumption and sale. In the more extensive areas within the system, animals mostly scavenge during the day with some supplementary feeding. Buffalo will probably decline in importance and numbers in the future, as mechanisation increases. More intensive production systems for pigs and poultry are found in China where a more intensive farming system is generally practised. Animals are usually housed, and productivity levels are higher as a result of better feeding, husbandry and animal health practices.

On-farm fish production is an important source of food and income in this farming system. Fish are cultivated in association with wetland rice fields and in ponds. Rice cultivation has been further diversified in coastal areas in China where rice culture has been combined with other fisheries products, such as crabs, shrimps and pearls. This type of farm diversification has numerous benefits; including improved pest control, nutrient cycling and a higher cash income that can be used to purchase crop production inputs.

The majority of farm households in this system are food secure and sell surplus rice, cash crops, livestock and fish. However, at a national level, most countries are barely able to meet domestic demand; only Thailand and Vietnam are significant exporters of rice. Until the present time, livestock and fish have only been marketed domestically, however small quantities of some other crops are traded internationally.

TRENDS AND ISSUES IN LOWLAND RICE SYSTEM

The rate of production growth of the Lowland Rice Farming System is expected to decline in the coming years due to the limited capacity for expansion of cultivated area, as well as an expected reduction of the historical rate of crop yield increases. Although production intensification will be important, poverty reduction is expected to derive primarily from increased diversification of cropping, as well as non-crop activities such as intensive livestock production and small-scale on-farm aquaculture (fishponds, rice-fish culture, shrimps, crabs, etc.). Rice production may actually decline in some areas as other activities offering higher returns to land use become popular. An increasing proportion of the agricultural population will also obtain a greater percentage of their income from off-farm activities – whether this involves agro-processing, service provision or seasonal migration to urban areas (e.g. construction work). In addition to increased production and incomes, technology changes will emphasise improved sustainability of the natural resource base. Efficiency of irrigation use is also expected to increase, with some expansion of irrigation area.

Specific issues that will have to be addressed if the Lowland Rice Farming System is to achieve significant progress in reducing poverty include: land fragmentation; unbalanced fertiliser use; inefficient use of water resources; inferior seed quality; poor post-harvest management; limited farm diversification; and, the absence of adequate local capacity for agricultural product processing.

Increasing fragmentation of farmland has resulted from a growing agricultural population and the absence of primogeniture to maintain the integrity of holdings. In many instances farm sizes are now uneconomic, and even with the adoption of best practices would still only be marginal in terms of livelihood. If this trend is not reversed, an increasing proportion of farmers will be unable to rely on agriculture to ensure adequate food security and income levels. As a consequence, on-farm employment, and even complete exit from the system (e.g. permanent migration to urban areas), is likely to occur on a much larger scale.

The adoption of intensive methods of crop production, based on high levels of inorganic fertilisers and pesticides, has in many cases lowered the quality of soil and water resources. Continuous rice cultivation, using unbalanced mineral fertilisers and only low inputs of organic manure, is in some situations seriously deteriorating the physical and chemical properties of the soil with adverse consequences on crop yields. On-farm deterioration in the quality of rice for sale, due to poor post-harvest management practices and inadequate storage conditions, is very significant in many areas and leads to reduced revenues from crop sales. There is limited scope for further expansion of irrigation systems. Only a few countries are in the fortunate position of under-exploiting their water resources. In some areas, serious shortages of irrigation water occur in the dry season. However, water use efficiencies are often low.

In most countries, seed is generally of poor quality and not necessarily of the most recently recommended variety, because most farmers retain their own seed for replanting for many seed generations. While research services and private companies have developed new crop varieties – including hybrids – with higher yield potential and better local adaptability, they are often unavailable to the majority of farmers or are unsuited to their production practices. Production of seed of improved rice varieties is undertaken in many countries by government services, but quantities are generally much less than required by farmers. This situation has a serious adverse effect on crop yield and overall crop production.

Historical trends in farm production patterns have been towards the development of rice monoculture systems in lowland areas. The more recent reversal of this trend, towards a more diversified form of production – introducing field crops, vegetables, small livestock and fish into the farming system – has generated both increased incomes and improved family diets. However, opportunities for farm diversification are often location-specific; depending upon markets, infrastructure and other factors, and hence need to be identified on a zone-by-zone basis. In many areas, the productivity of livestock within the Lowland Rice Farming System is low because of extensive management practices. Opportunities to intensify small animal production enterprises need to be identified in relation to the resource situation and market circumstances.

Off-farm income is already a significant part of total household income in many areas. Further opportunities for increasing the value of products need to be identified. In some countries, government agencies still maintain monopolies on the supply of production inputs and also control the price and sale of crop products. Policies and actions need to be adopted to privatise the supply of production inputs and liberalise the marketing of products.

PRIORITIES FOR LOWLAND RICE SYSTEM

The central strategic priorities for improving the farming system relate to: (i) enterprise diversification; (ii) strengthened linkages to the non-farm economy to boost off-farm income; (iii) improved resource management to maintain and even increase current high levels of productivity; (iv) land consolidation to increase field sizes; and (v) an improved level of farm management concentrated on better control of soil nutrients, weeds and pests.

Demonstration, active learning and formal training programmes can catalyse the diversification of farm production (field crops, annual fruits, vegetables, small livestock and fisheries) in order to increase incomes, minimise and spread risks, enhance natural resources and the environment, and improve the diet of farm families (see Box 6.3). Programmes would aim to promote the cultivation of new, higher value, crops with good market prospects. Intensification of village-based, small livestock-production (chickens, ducks, pigs, etc.) should be promoted through effective animal health services, better feeding, better animal husbandry practices and breed improvement. Local feed processing should be promoted by using crop by-products and the cultivation of specific feed crops. Small pond culture, rice-fish culture, and rice-shrimp and crab systems should also be promoted where local conditions are suitable. Diversification is likely to be accompanied by gradual increases in the productivity of existing crops and livestock.

A further high priority area is the introduction of improved post-harvest management practices, processing and storage conditions to reduce losses of crop products – in terms of both quality and quantity. These measures should be accompanied by government divestment to the private sector of responsibility for the production, distribution and sale of improved seeds and planting materials, so as to replace the generally inefficient and inadequate government seed and seedling production services. Reforms need to be accompanied by improvements in marketing systems, through provision of market information, assistance and market facilities in order to prevent product losses and to increase farmers' share of the consumer price.

Development of financial mechanisms to facilitate the use of local resources and gradually expand financial services, is extremely important. In marginal areas, support to local Self-Help Groups (SHGs), to enable them to mobilise savings and to give small short-term loans, may constitute a good starting point. Linking SHGs with formal financial institutions and the use of micro-lending technologies broadens the outreach as well as the sustainability of financial services.

> ## Box 6.3 Intensive Development of the Rice-Based Farming System[14]
>
> The Lowland Rice Farming System in East Asia underpins the food security of several countries in the region. There are considerable productivity gaps between farms, between provinces and between countries. Very high sustained yields have been achieved in some high-performance systems such as in Zhejiang Province, China. However, a high level of management is required, with special attention to soil resources, complemented by continuous refinement of technology through strong production support services. Although rice is still the main crop in lowland areas, diversification is increasing towards high value crops such as oil seeds and vegetables, and other profitable enterprises such as fish production. Current trends suggest that total farm productivity will continue to grow in the coming decade.

Improved management of natural resources can be achieved through implementation of programmes of integrated soil nutrient management to promote increased use of organic manures, crop rotations that include leguminous crops; plus balanced fertilisation to improve sustainability of soil fertility and thereby crop yields. These actions should be accompanied by the implementation of training programmes and demonstrations that emphasise improved efficiency of water use, avoidance of pollution of water resources, communal operation and management, and cost recovery of irrigation systems and efficient drainage systems.

Improved resource management will be facilitated by land aggregation and consolidation, leading to a gradual increase in field sizes and, over time, average farm size. These policy initiatives need to include: (i) issuing of land titles; (ii) development of land markets; (iii) land leasing; (iv) establishment of land banks; and (v) the use of land as collateral to finance purchase of additional land and investment in farm production activities. In addition, governments need to undertake initiatives to provide alternative employment to agricultural workers in rural areas through promotion and development of locally-based industries in order to enhance exit opportunities of farmers and farm workers. This would promote land consolidation, as well as providing off-farm income for households that remain in farming.

A more holistic, integrated form of participatory research and extension should be developed and promoted, with less emphasis on single-crop research. This type of work would place greater emphasis on benefiting from synergies between productive activities, and would consider the whole-farm production system – including the sustainability of natural resources and the protection of the environment. Specific support should be given to the development of research resources, both equipment and human resources, to take advantage of new techniques in biotechnology and genetic engineering. At the same time, there is a need to develop the skills of farmers and extension staff in participatory of farming systems and identification of

---

[14] Wang 2001.

development opportunities, combined with a farmer field school approach to promoting new technologies. These measures should be associated with improvements in the linkages between research and extension to ensure more effective information availability, dissemination and technology development.

TREE CROP MIXED FARMING SYSTEM

CHARACTERISTICS OF THE SYSTEM

This system covers 85 million ha, mainly in Thailand, Malaysia and Indonesia, with smaller areas in Cambodia, Philippines, Vietnam, Southern China and Papua New Guinea, and contains a total population of 49 million with an agricultural population of 30 million (see Box 6.4). The tropical environment of this zone is mostly humid (270 to 365 growing days), with

Box 6.4 Basic Data: Tree Crop Mixed Farming System	
Total population (m)	48
Agricultural population (m)	30
Total area (m ha)	85
Agro-ecological zone	Humid – subhumid
Cultivated area (m ha)	18
Irrigated area (m ha)	2
Bovine population (m)	19

some extension into moist subhumid (180 to 269 growing days) areas. Tree crops have been established under plantation or estate crop systems for the provision of industrial products, beverages and condiments. They are cultivated principally on flat to undulating landscapes on acid soils of low inherent fertility.

The total cultivated area is estimated at 18 million ha and there are only about 2 million ha of irrigation. During the 19th century, extensive areas of tree crops were developed as large private sector estates, particularly rubber and later oil palm in Malaysia and Indonesia. Today, however, there are also significant areas under smallholder ownership and management. Smallholder plantation crop areas are usually a maximum of 2 or 3 ha in size, depending on crop type. Coconut plantations are more widespread throughout most Southeast Asia and Pacific countries and are now mostly smallholder operations.

Coffee and tea plantations are confined to specific agro-ecological areas with higher elevation. Cocoa is usually grown as an intercrop at low elevations under humid tropical conditions. Condiments, cloves, pepper, etc., are usually smallholder crops. While tree crops are the dominant production system, small farms without tree crops are scattered throughout the system, producing food (rice and maize), cash crops (soybeans) and livestock (see Box 6.5). Although large livestock are not very important in this farming system, considerable numbers of small ruminants co-exist with the tree crop plantations in many areas. Incomes of smallholders are moderate and little poverty exists. Where it does exist, poverty is higher among small farmers and landless farm labourers.

Box 6.5 A Typical Household of the Tree Crop Mixed Farming System

A typical smallholder rubber producer has 0.75 ha of land under rubber, assigned by the nucleus estate. The management of the rubber is closely supervised by estate personnel. The rubber is the principal source of household income. In addition, the household grows food crops, including upland rice and maize on a further 0.9 ha. No fertiliser is used on the food crops, so yields are low and the family purchases additional rice. The family of seven also has a perkarangan (multi-storied) homestead garden with a variety of fruit trees, herbs, spices and vegetables, which supplements household food supplies and improves the nutritional quality of the diet, as well as providing a surplus of fruit for cash sale. The household keeps two cattle plus followers, six goats and a dozen free range poultry – the sale of animals also generates small amounts of additional cash income. Vulnerability is relatively low from the point of view of climate, but the system is under pressure because of declining world commodity prices.

Governments in a number of countries have established specialised commodity research stations or institutes for improvement of tree crops, while government operated research extension services have supported smallholder farmers. Crop yields have been rising through the introduction of improved varieties developed by government research or in some cases by large multi-national companies involved in the plantation industry. New higher-yielding dwarf varieties of oil palm and coconut have been developed in recent years that are significantly increasing yields for these crops. Regular applications of fertilisers combined with effective weed control measures are used in productive, well-managed plantations. All these crops require intensive labour inputs for harvesting and processing and therefore profitability is determined by local labour costs. In some countries, such as Malaysia, rising labour costs are now seriously affecting the profitability of rubber plantations and there has been a strategic shift to oil palm cultivation.

Private companies and governments have established large factories, with high investment requirements, to process crops such as rubber, oil palm, tea and coffee. Smallholders supply raw materials or partly processed products to these factories. Smallholder co-operatives are not usually well developed and individual farmers often have no alternative but to accept whatever prices are offered by middlemen or factories for their raw products. Some intercropping is undertaken to increase and diversify incomes, both in the early years of establishment of new plantations and in mature plantations. In some tree crop systems (rubber and coconut plantations) industrial crop production has been combined with livestock production. In more recent times there has been a move to develop alternative products in order to diversify and add to incomes from some plantation crops, for example wooden products from rubber and coconut trees available when old stands are cut and replanted.

TRENDS AND ISSUES IN TREE CROP MIXED SYSTEM

The major factors influencing the future of the tree crop sector will be concerned with: international demand and prices for industrial crop products; replacement of labour-intensive and costly harvesting and processing practices through mechanisation for some crops such as rubber, oil palm and tea; development and adoption of improved production technologies; planting of much higher yielding clones; and, the extent to which there is any significant change in proportion of private companies and smallholder producers. Although world population growth is expected to decline in the future, there will continue to be a strong demand for industrial crop products (plant oils, rubber, beverages, natural fibres, condiments, etc.). However, the price of those products that compete with oil-based synthetic products will be greatly determined by future petroleum prices.

Given the large reported area of immature trees within the system, the tree crop sector is expected to continue its moderate expansion. Prospective annual production increases to 2030 are estimated at 3.4 percent for oil palm, 2.8 percent for rubber, 3.4 percent for coconut, 1.8 percent for coffee and 3.8 percent for tea. It is anticipated that these production increases will come from both area expansion and increasing yields. The extent to which the major private estates will increase their size will depend on overall profitability, but it is anticipated that the smallholder sector will remain important, at least in the medium term. Some plantation (industrial) crops will continue to be grown mainly by smallholders.

The subsequent discussion of issues facing the Tree Crop Mixed Farming System is confined to the smallholder sector. The key issues that have to be addressed in advancing the productivity and income generation of smallholder plantations include: low yield; lack of alternative enterprises; inadequate farmer skills; enhancement in technologies and crop husbandry; primary product processing; and, marketing mechanisms.

Yield improvement has been dependent on government and private research and extension services developing higher-yielding clones with increased disease and pest resistance. However, this research and extension support has been mainly directed to rubber and oil palm and in general, insufficient support has been given to production improvement of other tree crops. Government policies are aimed at assisting smallholder plantation crop production, but government support for expansion of tree crop area must be based on an in-depth analysis of future product demand in order to avoid oversupply and low prices.

Prices for industrial crop products are subject to the considerable variation that occurs in the international marketplace. Many countries have established commodity boards to stabilise prices; generally with very poor results. At the local level, smallholder farmers generally have to accept prices below those ruling in the market because of their immediate need for cash. Returns to smallholders can be increased through improved on-farm processing and collective marketing of products by smallholders' associations. Governments have tried to establish farmer co-operatives for smallholders engaged in many plantation industries. These generally have been weak or have failed altogether as a result of farmers not receiving any material advantage from their operation. Nonetheless, large financial advantages can be obtained from collective purchase of inputs and joint collection, delivery and marketing of products. Alternative modalities still need to be defined for the operation of co-operatives, or farmers' associations or small business companies.

Development of the skills of farmers involved in industrial crop production is usually weak. In many instances, there is inadequate participatory identification of problems, constraints and opportunities for product development and only limited support from government extension and specialised research services. Linkages between government research and extension in information dissemination and technology development are also generally inadequate. There is usually also very little technology transfer to smallholders from private (multinational) companies, even though they often have their own research and extension services directed towards plantation tree crops.

PRIORITIES FOR TREE CROP MIXED SYSTEM

The strategic options for the smallholder sector include increased productivity, diversification of enterprise activities and group organization for business development. Related interventions that would enable significant advancement of the smallholder Tree Crop Farming System include measures to increase production in smallholder plantation systems (rubber, oil palm, coconut, etc.) where considerable scope exists through the introduction of modern clonal materials. As stated above, new clonal materials with very high yield potential have already been developed in some crops, such as oil palm and coconut, and new rubber clones are also being continually developed in commodity institutes. There should be a progressively accelerated replacement of old clonal materials with new, more high-yielding clones.

Regeneration of old plantations must take advantage of intercropping in the early establishment years so as to give an immediate income. Emphasis should be given to local value-adding processing of both product and wood materials. Opportunities also exist for expansion of intercropping in mature plantations to stabilise incomes and reduce risks from price fluctuations; and for households to grow small areas of food crops and keep small stock such as goats, utilising surplus feed and fodder produced around the plantations. Research programmes should be broadened to include more research on the minor tree crops. Research capacity needs to be increased to take advantage of advances in biotechnology and genetic engineering to improve yields and disease and pest resistance.

The establishment of business co-operatives, associations or companies should follow a gradual approach to avoid overloading fragile institutions with multiple functions. Thus it is preferable to start with one main business, e.g. input or output marketing. Once marketing channels and a reliable client base are developed, diversification into other business areas, such as interlocking input supply and credit with output marketing, can be considered. Assistance is required to broaden the outreach of financial services provided by both formal and informal financial institutions to farmers. Business co-operatives, farmers' associations or small companies could gradually expand their activities towards financial intermediation and play an important role in savings mobilisation as a source of funds for credit supply.

In many countries, the government has given insufficient emphasis to extension and research support for industrial crop producers. Consideration needs to be given to the development of private extension support services for smallholder farmers; these could be financed by the smallholder business co-operatives. Skills enhancement of smallholders should not only include training in all aspects of crop production, but also methodologies and practises in post-harvest management and processing of products to maximise quality and price. A farmer field school approach to promoting new technologies should be used, as well as the provision of technical training programmes for farmers.

UPLAND INTENSIVE MIXED FARMING SYSTEM

CHARACTERISTICS OF THE SYSTEM

This system covers some 310 million ha and is the most widespread and diverse farming system in the region with major areas located in all countries of East and Southeast Asia (see Box 6.5). The system contains a total population of 530 million with an agricultural population of 314 million. It is characterised by similar topography, but considerable ecological variation

Box 6.6 Basic Data: Upland Intensive Mixed Farming System	
Total population (m)	530
Agricultural population (m)	314
Total area (m ha)	310
Agro-ecological zone	Various
Cultivated area (m ha)	75
Irrigated area (m ha)	18
Bovine population (m)	52

exists. The system is found in humid and subhumid tropical, subtropical, and temperate environments in upland and hill landscapes of moderate altitude and moderate to steep slope. Soils are generally of low fertility, shallow and susceptible to erosion. Some 75 million ha are cultivated within the system, encompassing a wide range of crops, depending on geographic area, landscape slope, terracing and water regime – see Box 6.6 for a description of a typical farm household system.

Some forested areas are scattered throughout the system, but these have generally been depleted as a result of unsustainable logging practices. Deterioration of natural resources, biodiversity and the overall environment has occurred in many areas. This is a result of high population densities, leading to the extensive cultivation of fragile slopes without the adoption of appropriate soil and water management practices. As a consequence, households are vulnerable to natural disasters and crop failures. Local infrastructure is generally poorly developed. Because most of the population lives in remote areas, links to markets and other systems are scarce. Moderate to severe poverty is found in this system, but with potential to further increase production and incomes there is some opportunity to reduce poverty in the future.

Box 6.7 A Typical Household of the Upland Intensive Mixed Farming System

A typical farm household of five members in Yunnan Province, China, cultivates an area of 0.94 ha (21 percent being irrigated), with a cropping intensity of 84 percent. The main crops grown and their yields are: maize (21 percent of the total cropped area, with a yield of 4 t/ha), rice (16.5 percent of the area, yielding 6.1 t/ha) and wheat (13.2 percent of the area, 2.2 t/ha). Annual farm household production for these three main crops totals is 1.7 t/year; equivalent to 337 kg per capita. Few external production inputs are used. The household has a pig, some poultry and one goat for fattening. The household is food insecure, and has an annual per capita income of only US$166 per annum; considerably below the international poverty line.

Most agricultural production occurs under rainfed conditions, but about a quarter of cultivated area (18 million ha), much of it terraced, is irrigated from local streams and rivers. In some areas, for example in the Philippines and Indonesia, substantial terraces have been constructed for rice cultivation, but in most cases only simple terracing has been developed (e.g. bunding for rice cultivation) and soil and water conservation structures are completely absent. Crops include paddy and some upland rice, wheat, maize, sugarcane, cotton, leguminous pulses, oilseeds, fruits and vegetables. Rice is the staple crop in tropical and sub-tropical areas, being replaced by wheat in more northern latitudes. Both tropical and temperate fruits and vegetables are grown, depending on climatic location. While there are some more extensive areas of commercial fruit and vegetable production, home gardens are widely used for vegetable and fruit production for household consumption and sale of products.

Livestock production is an important component of the system. Livestock are used for draught power, meat production, cash income and as movable assets. Some 52 million cattle and buffalo (28 percent of the regional total), and 49 million goats and sheep (14 percent of the regional total) are found in this system. Pig and poultry production is also very important for meat and cash income. Livestock growth rates and production are generally low, however, because in many countries animals are raised under extensive conditions using poor animal husbandry and animal health practices. More intensive production systems are found in China, particularly for pig and poultry. Where water resources are available, aquaculture is practised, usually combined with rice production. On-farm forestry is limited.

Considerable variation exists in the intensity of crop and farm production within this system, with highest production intensities found in Southern China. In areas of more extensive crop production, many farms operate semi-subsistence production systems with only limited sales of products to meet livelihood needs. Thus, average incomes are low, creating significant poverty and food insecurity. Rural credit is rarely available. Households are vulnerable to the consequences of natural disasters, crop failures and ill health. Rural infrastructure is often poorly developed, particularly in more remote areas, and access to goods and services is poor.

Shifting cultivation is practised in some hill and mountain areas, especially in Southeast Asia, but is mainly confined to the Highland Extensive Mixed Farming System, a subsistence agriculture system characterised by widespread poverty and food insecurity.

TRENDS AND ISSUES IN UPLAND INTENSIVE MIXED SYSTEM

The major factors influencing future changes in the Upland Intensive Mixed Farming System are expected to be concerned with: (i) preservation of the natural resource base; (ii) improvement of technologies for both crop production and watershed management; (iii) diversification into higher-value products; (iv) expansion and intensification of livestock production; (v) development of the rural financial system; (vi) increasing opportunities for improved marketing and off-farm income; and (vii) more responsive agricultural support services.

Major changes in agricultural production are expected to come from intensification and diversification of crop production with little expansion of overall cropped area, and from improved productivity of livestock and tree crops. The trend will be towards agricultural products with higher value, as this system is generally not competitive for the production of cereals for market. Increasing diversification would include an expansion of perennial crops and annual cash crops – as opposed to food crops – and intensification of livestock production. The particular higher-value crops selected for cultivation will depend on local agro-climatic conditions and access to markets; crops which are bulky and perishable will be grown close to larger markets while those with less bulk and longer shelf-life would be cultivated at more remote locations.

Livestock numbers are increasing under very extensive and low input production systems, but productivity and off-take remain low. If present patterns continue, only small increases in livestock numbers can be anticipated because of shortages of feed supplies. However, some intensification of livestock production is expected as a result of an improvement in general incomes and consequent increased demand for livestock products. These changes would increase household incomes and reduce poverty.

A key issue facing the future development of the Upland Intensive Mixed Farming system is the increasing population in hill and mountain areas that is exerting growing pressure on natural resources (soil, water, flora and fauna). Widespread, severe natural resource degradation in many areas has given rise to substantial local costs in the form of lowered yields, mudslides and scarcity of water in the dry season. There are also large downstream costs from siltation of rivers and flooding. The highest priority of farmers is to produce annual food crops to sustain their families. Increasing population pressure has also caused annual crop cultivation to increase on more fragile landscapes and has resulted in a decreased length of the fallow period in shifting cultivation systems. Furthermore, because farmers are poor they are extremely reluctant to invest in field structures to control soil erosion. Collectively, these factors have an adverse effect on farm production and on natural resources. If the majority of families remain in semi-subsistence farming there will be an increasing pressure on natural resources stability in the future, unless considerable new opportunities can be opened up for off-farm employment or exit from the system.

A further critical development issue in highland areas in many countries is lack of security of land tenure. Many governments, because of their political system, are reluctant to give farmers legal ownership of these lands, yet farmers are generally unwilling to invest resources in development without secure land tenure or ownership. Land tenure, land leasing and land markets are policy issues that have to be reviewed in order to promote development in upland and mountain areas.

Government agencies and large timber companies have been responsible for widespread and unsustainable logging of natural forests throughout the system. The area of natural forest has decreased enormously in all East Asia countries in the last two to three decades. Little has been done to replant logged areas or to develop systems of sustainable natural forest management, and the establishment of tree plantations has been limited. The management of village forest resources by communities and the promotion of on-farm agro-forestry systems are important development issues. However, governments have generally been very reluctant to accord responsibility to local communities for managing local forest resources.

Technology development in the past has tended to be focused on specific commodities, rather than on integrated development of a system that is productive, economically attractive, not too complex to manage and that provides a range of land use options in varying agro-ecological circumstances. Because of this single commodity focus, very few technologies have been developed that are economically viable and attractive to farmers while at the same time contributing to environmental and resource regeneration.

Livestock products are a very important source of household cash income in the system and there is considerable potential for expansion of livestock production. However, as in the case of crops, little emphasis has been given to the development of improved integrated livestock production systems – where improvements in feeds, genetic material and husbandry practices are related to other farm activities – and the provision of effective animal health services.

The generally poor development of rural infrastructure in upland areas has seriously affected marketing of products because of very bad communication and transport networks. With a few exceptions, the Upland Intensive Mixed Farming System has received a low priority in government policymaking, and this has aggravated the natural constraints to development that are inherent in these upland areas.

PRIORITIES FOR UPLAND INTENSIVE MIXED SYSTEM

Whilst increasing off-farm income represents the most important household strategy for the reduction of poverty, closely followed by exit from the farming system, there are also prospects for intensification and diversification. Other improvements to the system centre on sustainable natural resource management and more effective agricultural services. Future programmes of assistance should emphasise improved watershed management, conservation farming, water harvesting and introduction of appropriate technologies (see Box 6.7). A holistic approach is essential in micro-watershed management. Experience shows that such programmes must be strongly community-based, with full participation and involvement in management and use of the natural resources. Soil and water management practices and techniques should be promoted as an important means of stabilising yields, ensuring maintenance of soil productivity and increasing crop production. Water-harvesting technology should be promoted where natural circumstances permit interception of surface water flows. Technologies that are introduced and promoted must be holistic, and must provide short-term, medium-term and long-term economic benefits.

The forested areas that are scattered throughout this system mainly occur at higher elevations. Where relevant, future development programmes should strongly promote community management of forests as this has positive effects on environmental management, as well as providing important sources of building materials, income and food for local communities. Furthermore, on steeper lands, agro-forestry systems should be promoted, with contour planting of suitable tree species – for production of fruits, timber, fuelwood and non-timber forest products – to act as conservation barriers and provide additional income generation.

Future programmes of assistance must address the policy issues of land tenure, land leasing and land markets, which are fundamental in promoting development of upland areas. Key priorities would include the establishment of functioning land markets through the establishment or acceleration of cadastral and land titling procedures, and establishment or strengthening financial markets to support purchase and sale of land.

Box 6.8 Transforming Shifting Cultivation in Laos[15]

Shifting cultivation is practised mainly in the highland farming systems through a wide swathe of East Asia, including Vietnam, China, Laos, Thailand and Myanmar, and involves burning small areas of forest to clear land for planting, control weed species and release minerals into the soil. Traditionally, several years of cultivation are followed by long periods in which the land is left to allow natural regeneration of the vegetative cover. However, throughout Asia, shifting cultivation is coming under increasing population and, in some instances, market pressure, resulting in shortened fallow cycles and resulting resource degradation.

A newly implemented Asia Development Bank funded project in Houaphanh province in the northeast of Laos aims to resolve this problem, assisting farm households to replace shifting cultivation with sedentary farming systems. At present one family cultivates about one ha of upland rice annually and over a 10 year period the farmer cuts down 10 ha of forest. The new system aims to replace the 10 ha used for shifting cultivation with 4 to 5 ha of mainly perennial agricultural production, returning 5 to 6 ha to permanent forest. Food security is being enhanced by increasing rice production through expansion of paddy areas in valleys, adoption of improved production technologies, improvement of water diversion structures, construction of small ponds or reservoirs, and installation of small pump systems. Alternative agricultural activities to provide additional sources of income include: (i) improvement of livestock production using better feeds and veterinary support; (ii) expansion of fish ponds; (iii) improving cash crop production, particularly crops with relatively short production cycles such as ginger, chili, sesame, soybeans, peanuts, and garlic; and (iv) sustainable production and extraction of non-timber forest products.

The transformation is expected to double production of wetland rice and increase ginger, fruit, beef, chicken and fish production even more. Both household food security and cash income of farmers will increase substantially. Natural forestry resources will also be expanded and improved on steeper and more fragile landscapes. It is expected that the lessons from implementation can be extended to the development of other areas of shifting cultivation in neighbouring provinces of Laos and other countries.

Development and introduction of improved technologies should include: (i) improved cropping patterns using crops that contribute to food and cash income; (ii) soil and water conservation and fertility building; (iii) contour planting of trees and shrubs (for timber, forage, fruits and food grains); (iv) mulching and other soil conservation techniques; (v) higher-value agricultural products; and (vi) feeds for livestock. Livestock development is a priority for this system. Advantage should be taken of any opportunities for intensification of village-based, small livestock (chickens, ducks, pigs, etc.) production, as well as large ruminant production. Technologies introduced should provide improved animal health,

[15] Ishihara and Bachmann 2001.

better animal feeding, improved animal husbandry practices and breed improvement. Effective extension and support services will be needed as well as an established animal health service. In some situations technologies can be introduced to improve forage and pasture production for cattle feeding.

General lack of capital is constraining investment in productive activities and rural development in general. Donor assistance should be focused on the improvement of rural financial services and the improvement of farmer access to these services; setting-up community-managed funds etc., with a view to introducing the agricultural community to the use of commercial financial services.

Because of the remoteness of much of this farming system from markets, plus the poor communication and transport networks, the emphasis in agricultural production has to be on low weight and high value products that are easily transported, have a long shelf-life and can be processed locally to add market value. In addition, the development of good rural infrastructure must be actively promoted, not only as a pre-requisite to agricultural development in these areas, but also as a means of creating opportunities for increased off-farm employment, particularly in eco-tourism. Although external assistance may help in building the infrastructure, this will not be sustainable unless the beneficiaries and local institutions participate in planning and construction, as well as contributing to the cost and management of their operation and maintenance.

The Upland Intensive Mixed Farming System has received less attention and benefits from government research and extension services than lowland farming systems for many reasons – remoteness, complexity of system, lack of water resources, a lack of perception of their importance, etc. However, the system represents an important part of the agriculture sector in most countries of the region. The strategic priorities for the future must be to strengthen the capacity of governments to undertake participatory identification of problems, constraints and opportunities for farm development and to provide the necessary support by government or privatised extension and research services in these areas. The complexity and diversity of the system demands that the future priority is for a more holistic, integrated form of research and extension. This should be strongly linked to farmers and be based upon their active participation and should take greater advantage of synergies, consider the whole farm situation and emphasise the conservation of natural resources and protection of the environment.

Skills, knowledge and educational development of farmers are crucial to agricultural development. Programmes of assistance must emphasise participatory analysis of farming systems and opportunity identification, combined with a farmers' field school approach to promoting new technologies that have been shown to result in greater agricultural production and family incomes. Skills and knowledge building must be promoted as an essential component of future development assistance. This must be combined with much improved systems for information dissemination to and access by farmers, particularly because of the remoteness of this system from sources of information.

248

TEMPERATE MIXED FARMING SYSTEM

CHARACTERISTICS OF THE SYSTEM

The Temperate Mixed Farming System covers some 99 million ha in Central-Eastern and Northeastern China, with smaller areas in Korea DPR and Mongolia (see Box 6.9). It contains a total population of 247 million, of which 162 million are classified as agricultural. The climate of the zone is mainly dry subhumid (120 to 179 growing days). The transitional

Box 6.9 Basic Data: Temperate Mixed Farming System	
Total population (m)	247
Agricultural population (m)	162
Total area (m ha)	99
Agro-ecological zone	Dry subhumid
Cultivated area (m ha)	31
Irrigated area (m ha)	12
Bovine population (m)	11

boundary between this system and lowland rice-based system is not easily defined in Central China. Throughout the system, average incomes are low with modest poverty levels. Some 31 million ha are under cultivation, with wheat being the dominant crop. Other major crops include rice, maize, soybeans, sweet potato and rape, as well as citrus and some temperate fruits. Irrigation covers about 12 million ha within the system. The preferred food staple throughout the region is wheat noodles.

There are two main sub-systems: the Loess Plateau Sub-System, involving mixed farming of both summer and winter crops; and the Northern Sub-System, in Northeast China, Korea DPR and restricted parts of Mongolia where the climate only permits cropping during the summer. Both are characterised by rainfall being concentrated in the summer months and by severe frosts in winter, particularly in the northern areas. Average farm size ranges from as little as 0.3 ha in the Loess Plateau of China to several hectares further north, where it gradually blends into the Pastoral Farming System. Average household size is approximately four to five persons.

In the Loess Plateau of China, wheat and rape are the main winter crops; while maize with rice, cotton, soybeans and sweet potato and the main summer crops. Cropping intensity is about 150 percent. Crops are grown under both irrigated and rainfed conditions. Wheat yields averaged about four t/ha in 1999. Yields have risen dramatically since 1970 and even in the last decade have achieved 2.7 percent annual growth.

In the Northern Sub-System (Northeastern China, Korea DPR and Mongolia), because cropping is possible only during the summer, wheat (0.5 m ha in Korea DPR and Mongolia) and other cereals are grown concurrently and compete for cultivated land. Yields are lower in these zones due to adverse climatic conditions, and cereals may be supplemented by cold-resistant crops such as potatoes and cabbage. The higher yields in China are due to crops being grown with high organic and inorganic

---

Box 6.10 A Typical Household of the Temperate Mixed Farming System

A typical wheat farm household with four family members cultivates 0.55 ha of land (60 percent being irrigated) in Shandong Province, China, with a cropping intensity of 140 percent. The land is partially irrigated but the water table is dropping as irrigation for cash crops is expanded. The area, production and yields of the main crops are: wheat (36 percent of the total cropped area, 1.45 tons per annum with a yield of 5.3 t/ha) and maize (25 percent of the area, 1.1 tons per annum with a yield of 5.6 t/ha). Annual production of this farm household for these two main crops totals 2.5 tons; equivalent to 630 kg per capita. Power tillers are used for primary tillage, and additional income is earned through provision of transportation services. The household usually keeps a pig, a goat and some poultry. It has a per capita income of about US$280, which has risen rapidly during the past 20 years, but still remains under the poverty level.

---

fertiliser inputs and intensive pest control practices. In this system, overall cropping intensity is high and scope for expansion of land area is limited.

Livestock are also an important component of the system: particularly cattle for draught power, and pigs, small ruminants and poultry for meat. Some 11 million cattle and 35 million sheep and goats are located in this system and pigs and poultry are widespread. Livestock are reared and managed under extensive conditions in most countries. More intensive production systems are found in China, however, especially for pigs and poultry. In this country, pigs are mostly housed and fed supplementary grain and concentrates.

TRENDS AND ISSUES IN TEMPERATE MIXED SYSTEM

Wheat areas have been declining for the last decade in all countries and this decline is expected to continue in the future. In contrast, wheat yields have been increasing rapidly and overall wheat production is expected to increase, more than offsetting the declining crop area. Areas of maize, however, have been expanding and are projected to increase substantially in the future, provided that production can maintain competitiveness with imported supplies. In the southern part of the system any increase in maize will likely be at the expense of rice production. Overall, maize production is expected to double by 2030 as a result of both increased area and yields. This increase will be a direct consequence of a greater demand for animal feeds. Fattening of store cattle for local markets, using treated cereal straw, is becoming more common, especially in the southern part of the system.

Several specific issues have to be addressed to reduce poverty levels in the Temperate Mixed Farming System. The high crop yields obtained in the intensive production system in China have resulted from very high applications of nitrogen and phosphorus. Further yield increases from increased use of inorganic fertiliser will require a more balanced use of nutrients. Potassium is now a significant limiting factor, but potash fertiliser is fully imported and much more expensive than the locally produced nitrogenous and phosphatic fertilisers. About 40 percent of the crop area in this system is currently irrigated. Some scope exists to expand the existing irrigation systems by increasing the use of surface water and extraction of groundwater from shallow aquifers. However, in some areas over-exploitation of shallow aquifers is already evident from recorded increases in pumping depth.

The system is strongly crop-based and market demand for meat, vegetables and fruits is increasing as urban incomes rise. Farms are expected to diversify to meet this shift in food demand, and this change may be accelerated if world prices for cereals continue to decline. Some conflict is expected in choice of crops based on the competing demands human food and the rising demand for animal feed.

Low population growth rates and migration to cities in China has created labour shortages at crucial times in the farming calendar. This trend is expected to continue. The need for small-scale farm mechanisation is becoming a more important issue. Because of small farm size, family income is low. Farmers will need to grow higher-value crops and increase farm size to increase disposable farm incomes significantly, as well as to expand off-farm income sources.

PRIORITIES FOR TEMPERATE MIXED SYSTEM

Increasing off-farm income represents the most important household strategy for the reduction of rural poverty; with substantial development of agro-processing and other off-farm employment sources. This particular household strategy would be closely followed by diversification and exit from the farming system. There are, however, some prospects for the expansion and intensification of maize production for animal feed. While an 18 percent expansion of irrigated area by 2030 is anticipated in China, the more important future priority, both there and in other countries, is to institute programmes to improve the effectiveness of existing irrigation systems and the efficiency of water use at field level.

Further intensification of crop production will occur as a result of promotion of higher-yielding varieties – particularly hybrid varieties – better balanced use of fertilisers, increased water availability and more efficient water use. It is uncertain to what extent the supply of future production inputs will come from the private or the public sector. Future assistance should promote farm mechanisation and the development of the private sector for provision of goods and services.

Greater emphasis should be given to small-scale intensive livestock production – mainly pigs – and to growing vegetables and fruits, as market demand for these higher-value products will increase with rising urban incomes. Cattle have already been successfully fattened on a diet based on treated cereal straw, but government research and extension services will need to provide the appropriate technical advice and support for this changes in the production system.

STRATEGIC PRIORITIES FOR EAST ASIA AND PACIFIC

The strong economic growth and steady reduction in poverty in China and other regional countries during recent decades is noteworthy. Nevertheless, poor socio-economic indicators in many countries continue to reflect the results of: (i) lack of opportunities for intensification and diversification of farm production; (ii) lack of opportunity for off-farm employment and income for many farm households; (iii) lack of access to financial resources; and (iv) small farm size. This situation is dictated by underlying factors that include: (i) overpopulation; (ii) land fragmentation; (iii) absence of secure land ownership; (iv) deterioration of natural resources; (v) unavailability of information and lack of knowledge; (vi) lack of credit and inadequate supplies of production inputs; and (vii) poor marketing prospects (remote distance, poor infrastructure, small local market demand). Further substantial reduction of poverty can be anticipated if the enabling factors, needed to catalyse rural communities and households to invest their labour, capital and physical resources in agricultural development, are created.

Table 6.4 reflects expert judgement as to the relative importance of each of the five household strategies to reduce poverty within individual farming systems in East Asia and Pacific during the coming decades. As can be seen, the importance of different pathways varies significantly from system to system. In broad terms, lower potential systems are expected to derive a greater proportion of poverty reduction from migration to cities or other areas than do higher potential systems, which are believed to benefit more from diversification and increased productivity. Increased off-farm income is an important pathway for poverty reduction in all systems.

The widespread possibility of gaining access to off-farm income makes this the most important pathway for escape from poverty overall within the region. Approximately 40 percent of poverty reduction expected to derive from this strategy. Diversification of agricultural activities on-farm is the second most important strategy and, together with off-farm income, probably accounts for 70 percent of all development potential on a regional basis.

The specific strategic priorities required to create the enabling environment for strong agricultural growth and further poverty reduction in the region include:

POLICIES, INSTITUTIONS AND PUBLIC GOODS

The economies of many countries in the region (China, Vietnam, Laos, Cambodia and Myanmar) are still, to a significant degree, under state-managed control. These countries in particular still have many policies, regulations and practices that constitute disincentives to the growth of particular commodities, to investment in soil and water resource enhancement, or to higher agricultural input use in general. Future emphasis in assistance will have to be more strongly directed to the adjustment of policies that still cause serious distortions in the macro-economy in

Table 6.4 Potential and Relative Importance of Household Strategies for Poverty Reduction in East Asia and Pacific

Farming System	Potential for agricultural growth	Potential for poverty reduction	Strategies for poverty reduction				
			Intensi-fication	Diversi-fication	Increased Farm Size	Increased off-farm Income	Exit from Agriculture
Lowland Rice	Moderate	Moderate	1.5	3.5	1	3	1
Tree Crop Mixed	High	High	2	3	1	3	1
Root-Tuber	Moderate	Moderate	3	2	1	2	2
Upland Intensive Mixed	Moderate	Moderate	1	3	0.5	3.5	2
Highland Extensive Mixed	Low	Moderate	0	2	0	3	5
Temperate Mixed	Low	Low	1	3	0.5	3.5	2
Pastoral	Moderate	Good	0	1	1	3	5
Sparse (Forest)	Low	Low	0	1	0	3	6
Sparse (Arid)	Low	Moderate	0	1	0	3	6
Coastal Artisanal Fishing	Moderate	Low	1	2	0	5	2
Urban Based	Low	Moderate	1	2	2	5	0
Average for Region			1.1	3.0	0.7	3.3	1.9

Source: Expert judgement.
Note: Total score for each farming system equals 10. Assessments refer to poor farmers only. Average for region weighted
            by agricultural populations of systems derived from Table 6.1.

general and the agricultural sector in particular, and create disincentives for farmers considering whether to invest in agricultural development. Infrastructure is an important driving force for farming systems development, especially when related to water resources management, soil management, transport and markets. An enabling environment for the development of vigorous decentralised government and effective support service industries (such as seed, machinery and agro-processing) needs to be created.

Donor institutions have generally been reluctant to deal with the issue of poor access to credit for individual farmers. Rural banking services and credit institutions are badly in need of restructuring and refinancing. Assistance is critically needed from donors to create greater access by farmers to formal financial services, to improve the functioning of rural financial markets, to stimulate rural savings and community-managed funds, as well as preparing farmers to use commercial financial mechanisms.

TRADE LIBERALISATION AND MARKET DEVELOPMENT

Agricultural development must exploit local and international comparative advantages in a more globalised future economy. The region is already a major exporter of oil palm, rubber and rice, as well as of industrial products. As infrastructure improves, many producers are being exposed to international prices for a wider range of commodities and may well face declining prices for cereals such as wheat and maize as imports become more accessible. Governments must identify and promote production systems that benefit local farmers through exploitation of agro-ecological, and locational, resource advantages. Furthermore, improving per capita incomes are likely to accelerate changes in diet and to increase demand for higher value products (milk, meat, fruits, vegetables, etc.). Diversification into higher value products and adding value to farm produce would increase the overall level and stability of household income. Training and demonstrations of new technologies are required to improve production, post-harvest management, packaging and marketing of these products.

It is generally recognised that agro-industrialisation of rural areas in Asia is an important factor in growth and poverty alleviation. The majority of smallholder agricultural produce is sold through domestic markets, to consumers in rural or urban areas. Opportunities for local level agro-processing should also be promoted to add value to agricultural products, and to create off-farm employment. Thus, in most areas, policies that encourage the development of local entrepreneurs in processing and trade will improve farmers' incomes. This linkage will be particularly important for the Highland Extensive Mixed and Upland Intensive Farming Systems. In these systems, where transport infrastructure is often poor, comparative advantage is likely to be associated with commodities that have a high value to weight ratio.

INFORMATION AND HUMAN CAPITAL

Skills, knowledge and educational development of farmers are a key to agricultural development. Farmers are typically poorly educated, with significant levels of illiteracy in some countries. Most governments do not have strong educational programmes for farmers and access to information is difficult and limited. Skills and knowledge building must be promoted as an essential component of future development assistance, combined with improved systems for dissemination and access of farmers to information. Modern information technology development (computerised networks, local accessing of computer based information, etc.) will become a key component of agricultural development in the future.

The challenge for the future is for government agencies to develop, in participation with the private sector and target communities, computer-based systems for information transfer. This necessarily involves focusing on three major aspects: (i) information generation; (ii) information transfer systems; and (iii) local information access systems. Some interesting initiatives have already been taken in the region to develop information transfer to remote communities without the benefits of basic infrastructure like electricity and telecommunications. Lack of education and literacy amongst villagers in remote locations also provides some impediment to information exchange, but is not insurmountable.

Given the importance of off-farm income as a probable pathway from poverty within the region, and as an engine for rural economic growth, the education of young people should stress the acquisition of vocational skills of value in agro-processing, light manufacture and services such as tourism.

SCIENCE AND TECHNOLOGY

Diversification into higher-value products and adding value by processing, increases overall household incomes and improves income stability. Training and demonstrations of new technologies are required to improve production, post-harvest management, packaging and marketing of these products. Opportunities for local agro-processing should also be promoted in order to add value to agricultural products.

Public-private partnerships could provide the foundation much agricultural research in the future. While the private sector is expected to increase its provision of goods and services to farmers, it is anticipated that governments will still have to provide certain essential support and services to poor small farmers. The strategic priorities for the future should be to strengthen the capacity of governments to undertake participatory identification of problems, constraints and opportunities for farm development. Based on this knowledge, governments should provide the necessary enabling framework for effective extension and research services in partnership with the private sector.

Government research that must keep abreast of private research developments in terms of quality and relevance. The applications of biotechnology in its broadest sense, and genetic engineering specifically, must be evaluated and used where appropriate. Several Asian countries, particularly China, are already important sources of research and knowledge in this area, and this strength should be built upon – albeit with adequate attention to associated risks (see the accompanying case study on biotechnology). Future research must also be more integrated with extension; take greater advantage of synergies; consider the whole farm situation and integrated technologies; and, emphasise efficient and sustainable use of natural resources. The latent potential of farmers for experimentation, adaptation of technologies and farmer-to-farmer extension needs to be more fully exploited. The strategic priorities for agricultural research in the region include better use of water, improved management of soil structure and fertility, and restoring productivity growth in cereals.

NATURAL RESOURCES AND CLIMATE

The basic problem of low incomes rural household in the region is that too many people have only limited access to resources for agricultural production. Technology advances that offer increased efficiency can barely keep pace with diminishing resources as population increases and land fragmentation continue. In this scenario, the socio-economic situation of individual rural households stagnates although overall agricultural output increases. The majority of farmers are quasi-subsistence producers on farms with uneconomically low-volume, low-value production oriented farm units.

Furthermore, in those countries under state-managed control, lack of secure land tenure or ownership is an additional obstacle to agricultural growth. With the land being owned by the state, or allocated on some form of short-term lease, farmers are reluctant to invest in land development. Moreover, without land title, farmers are unable to use land as collateral to access credit and it is not possible to develop an effective land market – a necessary ingredient in land aggregation. Future support is required to assist governments in developing programmes to provide land title and ownership of rural lands to individuals; establish functioning land markets; remove obstacles to land aggregation for fragmented and extremely small holdings; and create local part-time and full-time off-farm employment for farmers on sub-marginal units and for those displaced from the land.

A considerable proportion of the significantly degraded agricultural resource base of the region can be recovered through better management – improved soil management, better utilisation of scarce water resources, and sustainable forest management represent three major thrusts. Along with improved resource management, existing agricultural production needs to be intensified in a sustainable fashion in order to maintain and increase household incomes in the face of declining terms of trade for cereals.

CONCLUSIONS

The East Asia and Pacific region is the most populous of the six developing regions. Despite strong economic growth accompanied by a steady reduction in poverty in some countries, considerable hunger and poverty persist. The foregoing analysis has shown that rural development in the region should concentrate on the basic determinants of economic performance, particularly farm and off-farm rural economic growth. While many policies that emphasise social issues are extremely important, the resolution of these issues in rural areas depends critically on agricultural growth. Strong agricultural and off-farm economic growth, as well as improved household food security, are dependent on a set of enabling factors that create commercial farming systems where surpluses of agricultural products are produced for sale.

Poor members of rural communities require opportunities to increase their labour productivity in farming and to utilise surplus labour in the off-farm sector. Agricultural growth, if equitable, will create beneficial opportunities for all – including opportunities for disadvantaged rural households to become involved in off-farm income generation as suppliers of goods and services, or as primary processors of raw products. Within this overall framework, specific actions directed at poverty-stricken, food insecure and disadvantaged families are necessary.

Although it is impossible, based on the foregoing regional analysis, to prescribe specific national actions, the overall challenge of reducing hunger and poverty in the region demands four inter-linked strategic initiatives:

Increased small farm competitiveness. Increasing the competitiveness of small and poor farmers provides a basis for successful diversification into new higher-value agricultural activities. Components include: improved marketing; better processing; strengthened product standards; expanded access to finance; and integrated technologies for sustainable productivity increases in high value enterprises, as well as traditional staple crops (especially rice, wheat and commodity tree crops).

Improved resource access. Smallholder land consolidation creates larger fields that are better suited to improved technologies and mechanisation to support intensification and diversification. Components include: improved land policies; land titling; land leasing arrangements; and rural credit.

Enabling environment for off-farm employment. Non-farm employment opportunities provide the most important potential for escape from rural poverty in the region. Components include the creation of a favourable environment for off-farm employment in rural areas, the enactment of appropriate policies – with particular emphasis on processing, assembly and tourism – and attention to infrastructure improvement in many systems.

Enhanced human resources. If gains in recent decades are to be carried forward into the future, it is vital that members of small farm households increase their knowledge base and capacity to respond to both changing agricultural requirements and off-farm income generating and employment opportunities. Components include: information and knowledge networks; farmer capacity building; support to entrepreneurship; and training for the younger segments of the population in vocational skills.

257

7

LATIN AMERICA
AND CARIBBEAN

•••

REGIONAL SETTING

CHARACTERISTICS OF THE REGION

The Latin America and Caribbean region covers some 205 million ha and encompasses 42 countries with a total estimated population in 2000 of 505 million. The size of the region, its wide range of favourable ecologies, and its low average population density of 0.25 persons per ha, combined with an urbanisation rate of 75 percent, have led to an extremely high level of biodiversity. According to the United Nations Environmental Programme (UNEP)[1], it contains five of the ten richest countries in the world in terms of biodiversity and 36 percent of the main cultivated food and industrial species. The world's largest unfragmented tropical forest is found in the Amazon basin, and the region possesses 28 percent of the world's forest area – nearly one billion ha in 1994.

This abundance stems in part from the favourable climatic conditions of the region. It possesses 40 percent of the developing world's humid areas, and almost half of its total renewable water resources, but only four percent of the arid and semiarid lands. Some 90 percent of the region's land area is humid and subhumid.

The region contained some 160 million ha of cultivated land[2] in 1999, including 18 million ha equipped for irrigation. This still represents only 18 percent of the estimated potential of the region[3] and it is estimated that no more than one percent of the available water is currently utilised[4]. A further 600 million ha is under grazing and pastureland. The region is globally important in a number of crops and often achieves yields significantly above the developing world average.

---

[1] United Nations Environmental Programme 2000.
[2] Annual plus permanent crop areas.
[3] FAO 2000a.
[4] United Nations Environmental Programme 2000.

With an average GNP per capita of US$3 940 in 1998, it is the wealthiest of the developing regions and also the least dependent on agriculture – only eight percent of GDP was derived from the sector in 1998. As growth in agricultural value added is lower than for industry or services, that share is likely to continue declining. FAO nutritional data indicate that the average diet contains 120 percent of the required minimum daily allowance[5], while the Economic Commission for Latin America and Caribbean (CEPAL) per capita food index for the region rose by 15 percent over the period 1980-1997[6].

Nevertheless, serious problems of equity exist. Not only do the wealthy control one of the highest proportions of resources of any region in the world[7], but there is also a strong urban bias. According to 1997 estimates by CEPAL[8], 54 percent of rural households were classified as poor, against only 30 percent from urban areas. Extreme poverty[9] affected 31 percent of rural households but only 10 percent of urban ones. In total, 47 million rural inhabitants were classified as being in extreme poverty, and a further 78 million are in poverty. Internationally comparable poverty data vary extensively – from fewer than two percent of the population with an income of under US$1 per day in Uruguay (1989 data), to 40 percent in Guatemala and Honduras[10]. Equity problems are particularly evident in respect of land distribution[11].

MAJOR FARMING SYSTEMS IN LATIN AMERICA AND CARIBBEAN

Due to its enormous latitudinal range, varied topography and rich biodiversity, Latin America and Caribbean has one of the most diverse and complex range of farming systems of any region in the world. Sixteen major systems have been defined for the purposes of this book and are briefly described below. These farming systems are summarised in Table 7.1 and all but the Urban Based System are presented graphically in the accompanying Map.

Irrigated Farming System
This farming system encompasses enormous areas of arid lands across Northern and Central Mexico and coastal and inland valley areas of Peru, Chile and Western Argentina. The total land area of almost 200 million ha contains only 7.5 million ha of cultivated land, but almost all is irrigated. Irrigated production occurs in many of

---

[5] FAO estimates that an average food intake of 2 000-2 300 kcal per day is required for average activity.
[6] FAO 1999b.
[7] World Bank data show Brazil to have the highest income inequality in the world (47.9 percent controlled by the top 10 percent of the population), and that 11 of the 20 most inequitable countries in the world are in LAC.
[8] Echevarria 2000.
[9] See Annex 5 for an explanation of extreme or dollar poverty.
[10] World Bank 2000a (Table 2).
[11] Some of the highest GINI (inequity) coefficients for land ownership in the world are found in LAC, reaching over 0.9 in Peru, Paraguay and Venezuela and little less in Colombia and Brazil (Deininger 2000 *pers. comm*).

Major Farming Systems
LATIN AMERICA AND CARIBBEAN

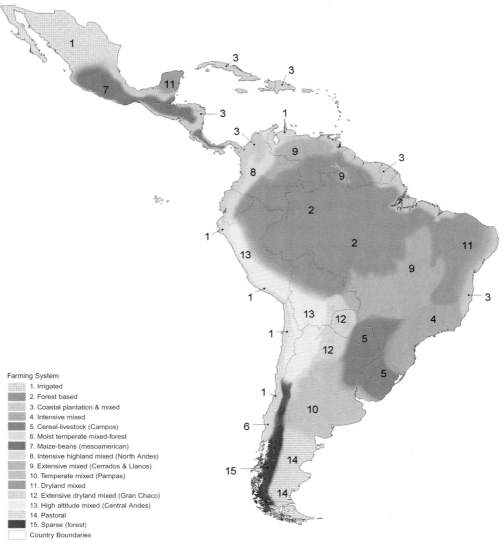

Farming System

1. Irrigated
2. Forest based
3. Coastal plantation & mixed
4. Intensive mixed
5. Cereal-livestock (Campos)
6. Moist temperate mixed-forest
7. Maize-beans (mesoamerican)
8. Intensive highland mixed (North Andes)
9. Extensive mixed (Cerrados & Llanos)
10. Temperate mixed (Pampas)
11. Dryland mixed
12. Extensive dryland mixed (Gran Chaco)
13. High altitude mixed (Central Andes)
14. Pastoral
15. Sparse (forest)
    Country Boundaries

FAO Disclaimer

The designations employed and the presentation of the material in the maps do not imply the expression of any opinion whatsoever on the part of FAO concerning the legal or constitutional status of any country, territory or sea area, or concerning the delimitation of frontiers.

Notes :
Projection = Geographic (Lat/Long)
Map Production - Data Aquisition and Spartial Analysis Team,
UN-FAO/World Bank Global Farming System Study

the other farming systems as well, but always in a minority role. Nevertheless, the Irrigated Farming System accounts for only 40 percent of total irrigated area in the region (18.5 million ha). The presence of irrigation infrastructure allows a relatively high degree of intensification of production – generally commercially oriented – and supports an agricultural population of nearly 11 million. Key products within this system include rice, cotton, fruit, horticulture and vines. Poverty is low to moderate.

Forest Based Farming System
Centred on the Amazon basin and covering over 600 million ha, or 30 percent of the total region, this system comprises scattered indigenous and low-input settler agricultural activity, interspersed with extensive beef and occasional plantation farming – especially towards the margin of the area. Cultivated area is little more than one percent of the total, with negligible irrigation. Population density is very low, with the agricultural population of around 11 million, representing less than 0.02 persons per ha. Poverty is generally low to moderate.

Coastal Plantation and Mixed Farming System
This system covers 186 million ha, and has an estimated agricultural population of 20 million. There are 20 million ha of cultivated land of which 13 percent is irrigated. The system occupies some of the richest agricultural lands in the region, but also includes mangrove swamps and isolated areas of tropical forest. There are two major sub-systems: (a) small-scale family farms with mixed agriculture, in-shore fishing and frequent off-farm employment (e.g. tourism); and (b) large-scale plantations, typically export-oriented and often internationally owned, with intensive production and significant poverty among labourers. Otherwise, poverty is not prevalent.

Intensive Mixed Farming System
Centred on Eastern and Central Brazil, this intensive mixed agricultural system represents the heartland of Brazilian agriculture, and occupies an estimated 81 million ha with an agricultural population of almost 10 million. There are approximately 13 million ha of cultivated land, of which about eight percent is irrigated. Coffee, horticulture and fruit are important products. Poverty levels are relatively low in this system.

Cereal-Livestock (Campos) Farming System
The Campos represent a gradation in moisture, and often soil quality, from the intensive system described above. Covering just over 100 million ha in Southern Brazil and Northern Uruguay, the system has an estimated rural population of about seven million, and is strongly oriented to livestock and rice production. There are an estimated 18 million ha of cultivated land, of which 10 percent is irrigated. Poverty is low to moderate.

Moist Temperate Mixed-Forest Farming System

This system comprises one of the few temperate farming systems within the region and is strongly reminiscent of New Zealand in its topography and climate. It is a small system, comprising only 13 million ha, restricted to the coastal zone of Central Chile. The system has an agricultural population of little more than one million and is characterised by extensive natural and plantation forest (over one million ha) interspersed with dairy, sheep and some crops, such as sugar beet, wheat and barley. Cultivated area is only 1.6 million ha, with negligible irrigation. The agricultural population of the system is estimated at slightly over one million. Poverty is generally low.

Maize-Beans (Mesoamerican) Farming System

Stretching from Central Mexico to the Panama Canal and with an estimated agricultural population of about 11 million – including a substantial indigenous population – this system covers 65 million ha and is historically and culturally based upon the production of maize and beans for subsistence. Although there are 2.4 million ha of irrigation within the system (40 percent; the highest concentration of irrigation outside the irrigated farming system), the historical loss of the better valley lands to non-indigenous settlers and commercial operations has led to extensive and severe poverty and serious land degradation in many areas.

Intensive Highlands Mixed (Northern Andes) Farming System

Covering 43 million ha and with an agricultural population of four million, this system contains two distinct sub-systems, generally differentiated by altitude: (i) the well-developed intermontane valleys and lower slopes – the heartland of Andean coffee and horticultural production; and (ii) the highlands and upper valleys where temperate crops, maize and pigs predominate and where the traditional indigenous culture is strongly established. Total cultivated area is estimated at 4.4 million ha and some 20 percent is irrigated. Poverty is generally moderate in the lower areas, but is extensive, and often severe, at higher altitudes.

Extensive Mixed (Cerrados and Llanos) Farming System

Covering the enormous wooded and open savannah areas of Central-Western Brazil and Eastern Colombia, Venezuela and Guyana, this system encompasses 23 million ha and has an agricultural population of around 10 million. Less than 15 percent is cultivated (31 million ha), and irrigation is almost entirely absent. Only recently starting to become intensively developed, this frontier system offers enormous potential for future agricultural growth in livestock, cereals and soya, among other crops. Poverty is relatively low, although higher among landless immigrants.

Temperate Mixed (Pampas) Farming System

Covering 100 million ha in Central and Eastern Argentina and Uruguay, this system was originally largely devoted to livestock but now contains nearly 20 million ha of

Table 7.1 Major Farming Systems in Latin America and Caribbean

Farming Systems	Land Area (% of region)	Agric. Popn. (% of region)	Principal Livelihoods	Prevalence of Poverty
Irrigated	10	9	Horticulture, fruit, cattle	Low - moderate
Forest Based	30	9	Subsistence/cattle ranching	Low - moderate
Coastal Plantation and Mixed	9	17	Export crops/tree crops, fishing, tubers, tourism	Low - extensive, and severe (highly variable)
Intensive Mixed	4	8	Coffee, horticulture, fruit, off-farm work	Low (except labourers)
Cereal-Livestock (Campos)	5	6	Rice & livestock	Low - moderate
Moist Temperate Mixed-Forest	1	1	Dairy, beef, cereals, forestry, tourism	Low
Maize-Beans (Mesoamerican)	3	10	Maize, beans, coffee, horticulture, off-farm work	Extensive, and severe
Intensive Highlands Mixed (Northern Andes)	2	3	Vegetables, maize, coffee, cattle/pigs, cereals, potatoes, off-farm work	Low - extensive (especially at high altitudes)
Extensive Mixed (Cerrados & Llanos)	11	9	Livestock, oilseeds, grains, some coffee	Low - moderate (smallholders)
Temperate Mixed (Pampas)	5	6	Livestock, wheat, soybean	Low
Dryland Mixed	6	9	Livestock, maize, cassava, wage labour, seasonal migration	Extensive especially drought induced
Extensive Dryland Mixed (Gran Chaco)	3	2	Livestock, cotton, subsistence crops	Moderate
High Altitude Mixed (Central Andes)	6	7	Tubers, sheep, grains, llamas, vegetables, off-farm work	Extensive and severe
Pastoral	3	1	Sheep, cattle	Low - moderate
Sparse (Forest)	1	<1	Sheep, cattle, forest extraction, tourism	Low
Urban Based	<1	3	Horticulture, dairy, poultry	Low - moderate

Source: FAO data and expert knowledge.
Note: Prevalence of poverty refers to number in poverty, not depth of poverty, and is a relative assessment for this region.

cultivated land, although there is only negligible irrigation. The impetus for growth has come from demand for such crops as wheat, soybean and sunflower as well as horticultural production for Buenos Aires and Montevideo. The agricultural population is now estimated at almost seven million, and further intensification of production is expected within the system. Poverty is generally low.

Dryland Mixed Farming System
Due to its location near the coast of Northeast Brazil and in the Yucatan peninsula of Mexico, this large system of nearly 130 million ha has a well-established economic and productive structure and an agricultural population of about 10 million, but faces severe moisture and soil quality constraints. Despite frequent droughts, little more than two percent of the 18 million ha of cultivated land is irrigated. It is a system with extensive and severe poverty among small-scale producers, who exist alongside large-scale extensive ranches, and often depend on seasonal migration and wage labour for survival. Land degradation is a serious problem.

Extensive Dryland Mixed (Gran Chaco) Farming System:
Stretching from North-central Argentina, through Paraguay and into Eastern Bolivia, this system of 70 million ha has only recently been economically developed and still has a rural population of less than two million. Total cultivated area is estimated at under eight million ha, and irrigation is negligible. Unlike the Cerrados and Llanos areas, the growth potential of the Gran Chaco is severely limited by soils and moisture. Extensive poverty is found among the small colonists.

High Altitude Mixed (Central Andes) Farming System
Again divided into two distinct sub-systems, the Central Andean system covers 120 million ha and has a total agricultural population of over seven million. Through most of Peru the system occupies the steep valleys of the high Sierra, while from Southern Peru through Western Bolivia into Northern Chile and Argentina, the altiplano is the predominant landform. Throughout the zone the key characteristics are production at an altitude of more than 3 200 m, a dependence on indigenous grains, potatoes, sheep and llamas, and a very strong indigenous culture. Where altitude and moisture permit, the same temperate crops are cultivated as in the Northern Andes. More than a third of the total cultivated area of 3.1 million ha is irrigated. Poverty is extensive and often very severe in this system.

Pastoral Farming System
As the Pampas extend southwards, they become drier and cooler, merging eventually into the very sparsely populated plains of Patagonia, covering some 67 million ha, where sheep and cattle ranching is the only widespread agricultural activity. Cultivated area is negligible, and there is no reported irrigation in the system. Poverty is low to moderate among the agricultural population of less than one million.

Sparse (Forest) Farming System

At the southern end of the Andes, lower temperatures combined with continued high altitudes, render cultivation generally sub-marginal. The agricultural population which number no more than a quarter of a million (almost 150 ha per person) is largely dependent upon livestock grazing, forestry and tourism for income and cultivate less than 0.5 percent of the land area. Poverty is low to moderate, reflecting the low population densities.

Urban Based Farming System

In common with all other regions of the world, specific peri-urban and intra-urban agricultural systems have developed to serve major conurbations and population centers throughout the region. Focusing on perishable products with high levels of demand but only limited space requirements, these urban-based systems typically include horticulture, poultry and dairy, but off-farm income is usually also integral to the family unit, with many members engaged in agriculture on a part-time basis. An estimated three percent of the agricultural population lives within this system.

REGION-WIDE TRENDS IN LATIN AMERICA AND CARIBBEAN

The following section summarises regional trends with reference where appropriate to the position of the region *vis a vis* all developing countries[12]. After outlining selected projections with regard to population, hunger and poverty, the following section lists some key trends affecting farming systems in the areas of: (i) natural resources and climate; (ii) science and technology; (iii) trade liberalisation and markets; (iv) policies, institutions and public goods; and (v) information and human capital.

Population, hunger and poverty

During 2000-2030, population is expected to increase 40 percent to reach 725 million[13]. This is lower than the overall 47 percent rate projected for developing countries as a whole, but higher, for example, than East Asia. In fact, the rate of regional population growth has declined dramatically in the last 40 years; from 2.8 percent per annum in the 1960s to about 1.6 percent in the 1990s. The proportion of total population living in rural areas[14] is projected to decline from 25 to 17 percent over the next 30 years, leaving rural populations marginally lower than at present (from 128 to 121 million); but significant

---

[12] Unless otherwise stated, historical data is taken from the FAOSTAT statistical system, while future projections are largely extracted from FAO (2000a).

[13] United Nations Population Division 1999.

[14] Rural is defined to exclude cities with a population of more than 50 000 inhabitants, and peri-urban areas with densities of more than 1 000 persons/km2. Thus small towns would be included in the definition of rural.

sub-regional differences are anticipated. The poorer countries are expected to maintain high rates of overall population growth, resulting in an absolute increase in rural populations in such areas as Central America, Bolivia, Paraguay and Haiti. On the other hand, countries such as Argentina and Brazil are likely to experience declines in rural population of 20 percent or more. In general, those countries with projected overall population increases of 50 percent or more to 2030 will see increasing rural populations.

During 2000-2030, the average per capita daily nutrient intake within the region is expected to increase by 10 percent from 2 791 to 3 080 calories, which will maintain average intake in LAC above the developing world average to 2030. This increase in calorie intake is expected to derive principally from meat and vegetable oils (33 percent each) and dairy (18 percent). Roots and tuber consumption is expected to decline. The number of people suffering from undernourishment – currently 53 million – is projected to decline to 32 million by 2030. This represents a drop from 11 percent of the population to 5 percent, but is only half the current international target.

Natural resources and climate

Cultivated land has expanded by 47 percent since 1961, but cropping intensity increased only one percent during this period. During 2000-2030, it is projected to expand a further 20 percent (depending on the evolution of farming systems); one third of the 40-year historical trend rate of 1.76 percent per annum. However, this rate may be underestimated, given the enormous potential for agricultural expansion in the Cerrados, Llanos, Chaco and Amazon basin[15].

During 2000-2030, the irrigated area is expected to increase from 18 million to 22 million ha, but remain constant in relative terms at 14 percent[16] of cultivated land. Irrigation efficiency is low, and only 8.5 million ha of the installed area is thought to be in use. Surface irrigation accounts for almost 90 percent of all irrigated areas. During the period 2000-2030, only minor increases in water use and efficiency are expected.

Over the ten year period 1982/1984-1992/1994, the area under pasture and grazing land increased by a total of three percent in South America and 6.2 percent in Central America to reach 600 million ha[17]. Pasture lands in Guatemala increased by an astonishing 65 percent (albeit from a small base) to 2.6 million ha. At the end of the 1980s, the deforestation rate was estimated at 7.4 million ha per annum, equivalent to 0.8 percent per annum[18]. This rate has since appeared to decline in South America, but accelerated in Central America – to 1.3 percent per annum.

---

[15] This expansion may not be sustainable, however, unless careful resource management practices are followed.

[16] FAO 2000c.

[17] World Resources Institute 2000.

[18] FAO 1995.

Recent experience has shown how vulnerable considerable parts of the region are to climatic variations; including hurricanes in Central America, flooding and loss of fisheries in Pacific South America and drought in Northeast Brazil. Climatic changes discussed in Chapter 1 are likely to exacerbate these risks and even reduce potential yields. However, it is still impossible to predict specific impacts in different geographical regions with any degree of confidence, given that the influence of climatic change is by no means uniform.

Science and technology

In the last 20 years, the value of regional agricultural production has grown at 2.8 percent per annum. However, due to the slowdown in total population growth, and a relatively low income elasticity of demand, the growth in demand for food and raw materials has been declining in recent years and for the next 30 years it is estimated at no more than 2.4 percent per annum. Table 7.2 shows the historical rate of growth of the major crops of the region. The major cereals have all grown strongly in the last thirty years – almost entirely due to yield increases – and the region now accounts for more than one quarter of the developing world's output of maize. Cereal output is expected to continue to expand, albeit at a slower rate than in recent decades. Fruits and vegetables have also exhibited strong growth; the area dedicated to fruit has expanded faster than for any other crop category in this period.

Table 7.2 Trends in Crop Area, Yield and Output in Latin America and Caribbean, 1970-2000

Crop	Harvested Area 2000 (m ha)	Yield 2000 (t/ha)	Production 2000 (m tons)	Average Annual Change 1970-2000 (%)		
				Area	Yield	Production
Wheat	9	2.7	24	0.4	2.1	2.5
Rice	6	3.6	23	-0.1	2.3	2.2
Maize	28	2.7	76	0.3	2.1	2.3
Roots & Tubers	4	12.6	53	-0.1	0.4	0.2
Oilcrops	32	0.5	16	3.1	2.4	5.7
Fibres	2	0.7	2	-3.8	2.8	-1.1
Vegetables	2	14.2	32	1.3	1.8	3.3
Fruits	7	14.2	99	2.8	0.1	2.8

Source: FAOSTAT.

The strongest performing crop category, however, has been the oilcrops, especially soya and sunflower. Production of oilcrops has increased from three million tons per annum in 1970 to almost 16 million tons in 2000 – a rate of growth of almost six percent per annum. Since 1961, more than three quarters of all developing country growth in soya production, and over 40 percent of increased world output, has originated in the region. Growth in output is expected to continue to 2030. Among the major crop categories, only fibres (principally cotton) have show an absolute decline – despite significant yield increases – but this trend is projected to reverse in the coming decades.

Overall crop production growth to 2030 is projected at 1.7 percent per annum Expected strong gains in cultivated area will be associated with a slow rise in cropping intensity – only an 11 percent increase to 2030. During 2000-2030, average crop yields are forecast to grow by less than 50 percent and reflects the greater expansion in cultivated area compared with other regions.

The 356 million cattle within the region constituted 26 percent of the developing world total and have increased by 1.6 percent per annum in the last three decades, faster than developing countries as a whole. In contrast, growth in other species has been slower. However, the rate of increase in all species has declined in the past decade. The cattle population is forecast to grow at 0.9 percent per annum to 2030, while the population of sheep and goats will expand by 0.7 percent per annum. Numbers of pigs and poultry are expected to grow by 0.9 and 1.6 percent per annum respectively.

From 1970 to 1990, agricultural labour productivity increased at about two percent per annum compared with developing country averages of between

Table 7.3 Trends in Livestock Populations and Output in Latin America and Caribbean, 1970-2000

Species	Million Head 2000	Ave Annual Change 1970-2000 (%)
Cattle	356	1.6
Small Ruminants	119	-0.8
Pigs	75	0.6
Poultry	2 396	4.9
Product	Output 2000 (million tons)	Ave Annual Change (%)
Total Meat	31	3.5
Total Milk	60	2.9
Total Wool	0.2	-2.0
Total Eggs	5	4.3

Source: FAOSTAT.

3.5 and 4.5 percent[19]. The slow growth in labour productivity in the region only partly reflects the abundance of land. Growth rates have been particularly low in areas, such as the Andes and Central America, where a higher concentration of small farmers exists.

During the past decade, fertiliser consumption has expanded at the rate of 2.1 percent per annum, to reach 88 kg/ha of nutrient; close to the average rate for the developing world[20]. Fertiliser use to 2030 is projected to increase slowly – at about one percent per annum.

Trade liberalisation and market development

Average agricultural tariffs in 1995 (from 10 to 20 percent) were considerably lower than ten years previously (20 to 60 percent). Nevertheless, the position of the different countries and products varies widely. The region currently accounts for a significant portion of world trade in a number of commodities including: coffee (Brazil, Colombia, Central America); orange juice (Brazil); bananas (Ecuador, Honduras, Costa Rica); table grapes and contra-seasonal temperate fruits (Chile); vegetables (Mexico); cut flowers (Colombia, Ecuador); pineapples (Costa Rica, Guyana), and shrimp (Ecuador, Honduras). Strong growth is foreseen in products that are currently significant in industrialised countries; either due to rising land and labour costs (sugar, cotton, citrus juice, vegetables) or to perceived environmental costs (pork, mushrooms, and possibly chickens).

During 1995-1997, the region had an annual net trade deficit in cereals of 16 million tons and this is projected to double by 2030; a decline in self-sufficiency from 90 percent to 87 percent. However, it is the only developing region with a net positive livestock trade (874 000 tons per annum) and livestock exports are expected to triple by 2030, in contrast to other developing regions. Current net imports of 6.3 million tons of dairy products are expected to grow by 2030, in line with population increases.

The broad shift to the free market in the last decades of the 20th century has freed many constraints on rural labour markets in Latin America (less so in the Caribbean). Consequently, the share of off-farm income in the household livelihoods of poor farmers has been increasing; a trend that is expected to continue to 2030. In more densely settled farming systems, household members work in the local area, whereas in remote or extremely poor areas farm people are often forced into seasonal migration in search of work.

The possibility of a reversal of trade liberalization exists, in which case countries would shift agricultural and food policies towards support for self-sufficiency, including high tariff barriers for basic grains and other staples. The opening up of agricultural frontier lands, which is in great measure a response to the liberalisation

---

[19] Many industrialized countries have shown growth in labour productivity as high as six percent per annum for periods of 20 years or more. Indeed, this is also the case for the Pampas, Southern Brazil, and the low valleys of Colombia.

[20] World Bank 2000f.

of markets, would slow down or even reverse. The shift away from production of basic staples – by small-scale producers in systems affected by poverty – would also be in doubt, since domestic prices for these products could be expected to rise. On the other hand, if trade liberalisation is accelerated, adjustment within farming systems would be even more difficult, poverty would likely increase rapidly and out-migration to urban areas would further accelerate. In fact, poverty figures suggest that this has already been the case since the mid-1990s. However, further trade liberalisation would boost the development of frontier lands and accelerate shifts in cropping patterns towards products still protected in industrial countries, such as sugar cane, cotton, orange juice and tobacco.

Policies, institutions and public goods

Nowhere in the developing world has the logic of structural adjustment and economic liberalisation been carried forward faster, and more profoundly, that in Latin America. Starting with Chile in the 1970s, the region has seen the privatization of large areas of national economies previously under government control; including banking, telecommunications, energy, transport and of particular importance here, agricultural marketing and finance. Ministries of agriculture in many countries – previously often major bureaucracies employing many thousands of staff – were ruthlessly cut back. Services to the sector, such as extension and research, were also significantly reduced. In theory, such reductions should have been met by an increase in the role of the private sector. However, only those products associated with major international commodities, such as bananas, coffee, and citrus, have found it relatively easy to attract private sector research and development. Crops of interest only to smaller producers, or without significant extra-regional demand, have found little private sector support, although several international agencies[21] have maintained programmes related to basic crops – mainly cassava and potato.

It appears unlikely that the trend towards reduced public sector participation in agriculture will be reversed soon, as budgetary constraints limit the ability of governments to assume the enormous recurrent costs – and consequent fiscal deficits – that were once accepted. However, two factors may ease the situation in future. The first is the probable transition of many small producers towards export and market-oriented crops where more private sector interest exists. The second is the mounting evidence that scope exists for effective public/private partnerships in the provision of agricultural support services.

A second major trend that has emerged in the last decades of the 20th century is that of decentralization. Closely linked to the process of structural adjustment, decentralization has often been used primarily as a way of shedding fiscal responsibilities to local or regional levels of government. Nevertheless, the process

---

[21] These include the International Center for Tropical Agriculture (CIAT), the International Potato Center (CIP) and the International Maize and Wheat Improvement Center (CIMMYT).

of decentralization may yet have far reaching impacts on the pattern of rural development within the region, by transferring decision making to levels much closer to the rural poor and affecting the delivery and financing of services to producers. It will also require considerable strengthening of local government and community level capacity in planning, implementation and financial control.

Whether or not the trend towards decentralization will endure through the next three decades is difficult to predict. Real centralization implies a considerable reduction in power at central government level, and may be resisted by existing power structures when and if it is apparent that the process is more than cosmetic. Local elites may also capture a high proportion of the benefits, rendering decentralization ineffective.

Information and human capital

Latin America and Caribbean faces many of the same challenges with respect to information and human capital as other developing regions – perhaps more so, given the market-orientation of the region as a whole. Market requirements are becoming more exacting, technologies are changing more rapidly, and skills development is progressively more vital. Historically, a high proportion of resources within the region has been devoted to secondary and tertiary education, benefiting largely wealthier urban populations. By contrast, rural primary education, communications and information services have been weak or absent. However, in the last three decades there has been a significant improvement in educational attainment in many rural areas, and literacy has increased noticeably, although rural education budgets are still extremely limited.

The transition process being brought about by globalisation will penalise small farmers who are not prepared to respond, and this realization is beginning to influence educational and information priorities at national level. In fact, the privatisation of telecommunications has probably done more to expand information linkages into rural areas than any other policy decision taken in recent years. Privatized energy provision is also accelerating rural electrification, an essential precursor for many modern services. It is likely that wealthier farming systems, such as the Intensive Mixed Farming System in Brazil, will be among the first to benefit from new information technologies, but whether they will reach poor farming households in Guatemala, Haiti or Bolivia in the next few decades remains to be seen.

Selection of farming systems for analysis

Four of the systems delineated above have been selected for more detailed analysis – using selection criteria based largely upon the prevalence of poverty, population and growth potential – are described in more detail in the following sections of the Chapter.

Within the region there are three farming systems clearly associated with extensive and often severe poverty, namely:

- Dryland Mixed Farming System of Northeast Brazil and Yucatan;
- Maize-Beans Farming System of Mesoamerica; and
- High Altitude Mixed Farming System of the Central Andes.

An additional farming system was also selected, as it represents one of the major agricultural frontiers left in the developing world, namely the:

- Extensive Mixed Farming System of the Cerrados and Llanos.

EXTENSIVE MIXED (CERRADOS AND LLANOS) FARMING SYSTEM

CHARACTERISTICS OF THE SYSTEM

The Extensive Mixed Farming System covers about 230 million ha, of which some 190 million ha, known as the Cerrados, are in Central Brazil, and a further 40 million ha – the Llanos – extend across parts of Guyana, Southern Venezuela and Eastern Colombia. The total system population of 24 million is approximately 40 percent agricultural[22]. The zone has a

Box 7.1 Basic Data: Extensive Mixed (Cerrados & Llanos) Farming System	
Total population (m)	24
Agricultural population (m)	10
Total area (m ha)	233
Agro-ecological zone	Moist subhumid
Cultivated area (m ha)	32
Irrigated area (m ha)	0.4
Cattle population (m head)	60

subhumid tropical climate (rainfall from 1 000 to 2 000 mm per annum) with a clearly defined dry season, although the Llanos tend to be more humid than the Cerrados. Natural vegetative cover ranges from open grassland through woody savannah to gallery woods along rivers.

Historically, the frontier savannah areas – with their isolation from the cities of the coast, acidic nutrient-poor soils, and lengthy dry seasons – were judged suitable only for extensive ranching. At the beginning of the 1970s only three percent was under cultivation. Since then, however, growth has been rapid, especially in the better soils of the Cerrados. Upland rice is often the first crop to be planted, and is still dominant in Llanos. In the Cerrados, however, soybeans and maize have now assumed greater importance. Total cultivated area within the system is currently estimated at over 30 million ha, including permanent crops. However, an estimated 40 million ha of the Cerrados have been severely degraded by poor land management. These are predominantly areas established

---

[22] The proportion of non-agricultural population within the system is higher than may be expected due to the presence of Brasilia, which lies within the system.

in the early years of Cerrado settlement, using upland rice and *Brachiaria* sown simultaneously.

Large farms (larger than 500 ha), often with absentee owners, have traditionally dominated the Cerrados and Llanos and still account for approximately ten percent of holdings. The vast majority – an estimated 70 percent of all production units in the Cerrados and probably higher in the Llanos – still have ranching as their primary activity. This accounts for 40 to 45 million ha of pasture and 60 million head of cattle across the farming system.

Despite the predominance of ranching, there are a growing number of large mixed and arable farms in the Cerrados zone, which comprise many of the 50 percent of holdings that fall within the 10 to 100 ha size range (see Box 7.2). These mid-size units tend to employ considerable seasonal labour. Already the Cerrados account for some 20 percent of the national output of beans – a major staple in Brazil – while coffee production is expanding in the East. Other significant contributions to national agricultural output from the Cerrados include 34 percent of soya production, 21 percent of maize and 21 percent of rice. The importance of agriculture is, however, much more restricted in the Llanos. Although still less than one percent (0.4 million ha), the use of irrigation is expanding.

Box 7.2 A Typical Household of the Extensive Mixed (Cerrados & Llanos) Farming System

The 50 ha family-operated farm in Northern Goias State, in the heart of the Cerrados, was created and registered some 20 years ago, and may well have been purchased from a large rancher with a long-established presence in the region. A large portion of the farm is still dedicated to grazing a herd of 40 beef cattle, but annual cropping of beans (4 ha), maize (4 ha) and rice (two ha), plus vegetable production for family use, are important activities. Fertilizers have generated reasonable crop yields, but soil hardpan formation is becoming an increasing problem. The family of six relies almost exclusively on the farm for their income, as there is little regular off-farm employment available. Casual labour may be hired at peak harvest periods. Marketing and the purchase of inputs is one of the bigger problems faced by the family as the nearest town is 40 km away, and the roads are in poor condition, especially during the rainy season. It is thus not feasible to produce perishable products. Because of the isolation, education and health care are serious concerns for the family. Poverty is not a major problem.

The role of medium-sized farms appears to be growing in importance in both the Cerrados and the Llanos. Evidence from the Llanos indicates that in the period from 1961 to 1997, holdings over 1 000 ha fell by more than a third, while the number of holdings under 20 ha also declined. Similarly, fewer than 10 percent of holdings in the Cerrados are under 10 ha, and there is evidence from some states that the number has declined since 1970, suggesting land consolidation is underway.

Studies of agricultural potential for the Cerrados estimate total land area suitable for cultivation in excess of 100 million ha. The Llanos, with more serious soil suitability problems, could provide perhaps an additional 10 to 15 million ha. This represents three times current cultivated land use. The rapid expansion of agriculture within the system has, however, caused considerable soil degradation and a reduction in native biodiversity.

The overall level of poverty in the system is much less severe than in the semiarid Dryland Mixed Farming System which borders the Cerrados. Two-thirds of the farms are owned, while only a small percentage are rented. The number of landless labourers emigrating into the Cerrados is increasing, however. Some degree of bankruptcy among farmers has also been recorded.

The historically low population density in the Extensive Mixed Farming System has meant that infrastructure development has been limited, and costs for transportation and storage have been relatively high in comparison to more settled agricultural areas. The high cost of inputs, low soil nutrient levels, and low land prices, is reflected in low land productivity. Yields of major crops tend to be lower than national averages (80 to 90 percent for soya and maize, but as low as 50 percent for rice in the Cerrados). Investment in education, training and other government services within the system has been poor.

TRENDS AND ISSUES IN EXTENSIVE MIXED (CERRADOS AND LLANOS) SYSTEM

The current growth of the Extensive Mixed Farming System is expected to continue and even accelerate over the coming years, although growth rates will be closely linked to market access and demand for soya, beef, cereals and other crops. Total cultivated area can be expected to approach 70 million ha by 2030, or over 100 million ha including pasture. Livestock will no longer be the dominant activity. Land speculation may become a problem. Data from 1995 for the Llanos zone already indicate a 12 percent annual turnover of farm properties; considerably higher than the national average of 3.5 percent for Venezuela as a whole. The structure of farms within the system in the future will have a major impact on the nature of development. If ownership stays predominantly with the large haciendas, considerable poverty may develop within the system. If, however, land distribution becomes more equitable – as current trends suggest may be happening – this is unlikely. Intensification could also be expected to occur more quickly.

Considerable investment can be expected in transportation systems, storage facilities, social infrastructure, and processing – partly financed by the private sector. These changes are expected to reduce transaction costs, increase farm income, facilitate diversification and expand off-farm employment (attracting still more immigrants to the system). Given the current rate of population growth and migration, it is expected that the total population of the system will double in the next 30 years. However, agricultural populations will probably increase at a slightly slower rate.

Good potential exists for agricultural diversification into such activities as acid-soil tolerant fruits (pineapple and passion fruit), mango and avocado. Dry-season food crops such as pigeon pea and pearl millet are also expected to expand in the Cerrados. Both of these categories may be attractive, especially to smaller producers. However, as cropping intensities rise, increasing demands for irrigation water will require effective planning and if this is poorly managed, could lead to conflict.

The key trend for annual cropping in the Cerrados is likely to be the adoption of no-till cultivation methods. Already practised over several million ha, it is expected to grow rapidly in the future. The main advantages of this system include: (i) more timely sowing; (ii) improved yields; (iii) earlier harvesting that permits a second (cover) crop; (iv) conservation of soil organic matter; and (v) reduced production costs. However, not all experiences with no-till agriculture have been successful. Inappropriate herbicide application, lack of suitable technologies for smaller farmers, and poor training of extensionists have all caused problems.

Field level research undertaken by the Brazilian Agricultural Research Corporation (EMBRAPA), indicates that substantial gains in crop and livestock yields are technically feasible over the next thirty years if environmentally sustainable production approaches are widely adopted. Maize and field bean yields have the potential to increase by over 100 percent (to 5.5 t/ha and 3.2 t/ha respectively), rice by 75 percent (to 2.8 t/ha) and soybean by 40 percent (to 3.5 t/ha). Meat off-take from beef cattle would increase by a projected 300 percent, reaching 0.2 t/ha per annum. The projected increases would derive exclusively from improvements in production systems, not improved varieties, while the strong increases in annual livestock of-take per ha assume the recovery of large areas of degraded pasture land.

In summary, key issues facing the frontier savannah farming system over the next 30 years include:

- The distribution of farm sizes and ownership within the system, and the impact of that distribution on poverty and production intensification;

- The creation of a wide range of infrastructure to support the accelerating economic development of the zone;

- Achievement of further agricultural expansion without damaging the relatively fragile soils of the savannah zone; and

- The ability to reverse degradation of large areas of poorly managed pasture lands.

PRIORITIES FOR EXTENSIVE MIXED (CERRADOS AND LLANOS) SYSTEM

The main strategies for poverty reduction in this system are intensification of production – coupled with improvements in infrastructure – and an increase in farm size among smaller producers. Secondary sources for poverty reduction are enterprise diversification and increased off-farm income. In order to respond to the challenges described above, a series of priorities are indicated. These include the development of mechanisms to promote the expansion of small to medium sized production units, together with strengthened technical assistance services to smaller producers, tax regimes favouring holdings under 100 ha, financing for land acquisition, and the promotion of co-operative and other forms of joint services for input and output marketing. New agro-industries and post-harvest operations (at family, co-operative and corporate level) should be facilitated in order to create new demand opportunities and off-farm employment.

It is important to validate and disseminate information on intensified integrated production systems and diversification options – especially for smaller farmers – including effective water use, no-tillage methods and integrated crop-livestock systems. To be effective, this requires improved communications with farmers and their participation in adaptive research and trials. Efforts should be focused on restoring the estimated 40 million ha of degraded pasture lands – larger than the current total cultivated area – in order to channel agricultural growth to existing areas and reduce pressure for clearance of new savannah lands.

Specific interventions can be expected to change significantly over the next 30 years. However, innovative technologies and approaches already exist for reversal of degraded pasture lands (see Box 7.3). While mainly tested on large holdings, these approaches are also relevant to smaller producers and have resulted in dramatic increases in sustainable stocking capacity.

Box 7.3 Achieving Sustainable Productivity Increases in the Extensive Mixed Farming System[23]

The tendency to operate non-rotational systems of production, whether livestock or crop-based, has contributed to serious degradation of soils over as much as 40 million ha of the system and is causing concern in terms of pest and disease problems. Research and field trials have clearly shown the significant benefits arising from mixed crop-livestock production systems. The introduction of soybean, other crops and undersown pasture species into ranched areas (typical for large farms), can permit land recovery and subsequent higher stocking densities on a rotational basis, while stocking of dual-purpose cattle in smaller holdings which previously have been largely crop-based can also bring benefits.

---

[23] Spehar 2000.

As moisture availability in the system varies, different crop combinations prove optimal. These include many crops that are still little known in the savannah context, such as castor beans, pearl millet, grain amaranth, kenaf, pigeon pea and quinoa. The integrated production systems tested have reversed soil degradation and achieved significant yield increases. Field data indicate that beef production can increase 300 percent (on a per ha basis) across the system, while maize and beans outputs rise over 100 percent. Net average incomes per ha for participating farmers have increased from US$200 to US$350. While larger farmers may need little support for investment, the adoption of mixed cropping technologies among smaller farmers requires assistance. The agricultural potential of the system justifies increased field work in applied research, seed multiplication and integrated pest management systems. Potential may exist for utilisation of these technologies in the Llanos and also in the West African savannahs.

DRYLAND MIXED FARMING SYSTEM

CHARACTERISTICS OF THE SYSTEM

The Dryland Mixed Farming System includes two principal areas within Latin America: (i) the Northeast of Brazil, comprising about 20 percent of the country or 110 million ha; and (ii) the Yucatan peninsula of Mexico, extending into the Northern Peten zone of Guatemala, covering about 17 million ha. The agricultural population of the system is estimated at

Box 7.4 Basic Data: Dryland Mixed Farming System	
Total population (m)	27
Agricultural population (m)	11
Total area (m/ha)	127
Agro-ecological zone	Dry – moist subhumid
Cultivated area (m ha)	18
Irrigated area (m ha)	0.4
Cattle population (m head)	24

about 500 000 in Yucatan and almost 11 million in Brazil (see Box 7.4). As much as half of the rural population of Brazil live within this system[24]. Annual precipitation in Northeast Brazil varies from 400 to 600 mm in the drier west of the Brazilian system, to 1 000 mm in the East. In the Yucatan, the average range is 600 to 1 500 mm. In both regions, soils are mainly shallow and stony with areas of low forest vegetation and elevations are low to moderate. Good quality agricultural land is scarce and there are few erosion control measures. About 18 million ha of the semiarid area are subject to severe desertification in Northeast Brazil.

The long dry season, frequent droughts and uncertain patterns of precipitation typical of the system, make farming a highly uncertain process for the vast majority of producers without access to supplemental irrigation. In both zones, more than

[24] This farming system boundaries has been defined to exclude the heavily urbanised coastal zone of Northeast Brazil.

80 percent of farmers practise semi-subsistence production (see Box 7.5). Crop failure – especially in maize and rice – is common if rains are late. In Yucatan, shifting cultivation is a traditional subsistence practice of the Mayas that is still widely used today. This form of agroforestry is a succession of two components: the cultivation phase (*milpa*) where maize, beans and squash are grown together, and the resting phase (*acahual*) where wild brush and trees take over and replenish the soil. Cultivation traditionally lasts two or three years and fallow between five and twenty years, depending on soil, vegetation and land availability.

Land distribution is strongly bimodal. In Northeast Brazil, there are about two million farmers within the system, cultivating an estimated area of 15 million ha. However, more than half (59 percent) have holdings of less than five ha and account for only 6.1 percent of the total arable area (another 22 percent have holdings from 5-20 ha). At the other extreme, only 8.2 percent have holdings over 50 ha, but these account for 61 percent of all land[25]. Larger holdings are concentrated very heavily on maize (often for feed), sugar cane towards the coast, and livestock – with 49 percent of farmers registered as producing beef, 55 percent dairy and 40 percent poultry.

In the Yucatan, each *ejidatario*[26] usually has between three and eight ha under cultivation with an average 4 to 4.5 ha. Total sown area in Yucatan in 1995 was 1.1 million ha. Just over half (58 percent) of Northeast Brazilian farmers are owners, although this is skewed towards the larger landholders. Sharecroppers and tenants account for a further 17 percent, and the remaining 25 percent are informal occupants.

Box 7.5 A Typical Household of the Dryland Mixed Farming System

With a holding of 3.5 ha in Piauí State in Northeast Brazil, the family of seven produces mostly beans (1.5 ha), maize (one ha) and cassava (0.5 ha) under a rental or share cropping agreement with a local landowner. Yields are low, and reflect the poor soil quality, lack of soil moisture and low input use (no seed is purchased). Given the high proportion of output going to the landlord, available money is better spent on other things and only one-third of family income comes from cultivation activities. Most farming tasks fall to the wife and children, as the husband is often working off-farm, either as a local labourer or in employment involving seasonal migration. A recent period of labouring on a coastal sugar estate has allowed the family to enjoy the luxury of a milk cow which, together with the two goats, is fed on crop residues and roadside vegetation. There are also a few chickens. The family has never received a visit from an extension officer and the rudimentary schooling and health facilities often stop functioning due to lack of operating budget.

---

[25] Instituto Brasileiro de Geografia e Estatistica 1996.

[26] An *ejidario* is a member of a community managed, state-owned ejido, or area of land, that bestows inheritable user rights, but not ownership, to its members. Since 1992, however, liberalisation of legal controls on *ejidos* has meant that more and more ejidarios have converted their use rights into private ownership.

Small producers within the farming system have become poorer in the last few decades. More than 50 percent of rural families in Northeast Brazil live in chronic and severe poverty, with an average family income of only US$366 per annum (compared with a national average of US$938, and US$1 744 for the south)[27]. Farmers normally do not use improved seed, fertilisers, pest and disease control or mechanisation. Crop yields reflect this low level of technology and inputs. Average yields across the system are: maize (one t/ha); beans (0.45 t/ha); cassava (9.9 t/ha); and, rainfed rice (1.59 t/ha). Nevertheless, Northeast Brazil accounts for more than 30 percent of national production of beans and cassava[28]. In the 1996 Census, 20 million ha of native pasture and 12 million ha of improved pasture were recorded for the northeast, only about 15 percent of which was found on holdings of less than 50 ha. These pasture areas are thought to have increased significantly since the census.

Irrigated agriculture is poorly developed; partly as a result of shortage of water availability, partly due to poor soil conditions, and partly because of investment requirements beyond the reach of most small producers. In Yucatan, there were only an estimated 47 000 ha of irrigated crop production in 1995 – less than 5 percent of the total cropped area – while in Brazil the total is under 400 000 ha. By contrast, there are abundant water conservation measures in place, including reservoirs, retention barriers desalinisation, etc., but none work well during periods of severe drought. Frequently, the installed technologies are not understood by those they are supposed benefit.

Infrastructure throughout the marginal drylands system is poorly developed. Public services such as health and education are only available in some locations and are generally insufficiently funded to be operated effectively. Poorly maintained and unsurfaced roads and a low degree of market development add to the problems facing economic progress in the region.

In Yucatan a crisis has arisen, as increasing population pressure has forced a reduction in the fallow period of the shifting agricultural production pattern. As a result, insufficient time is given to the *milpa* land to recover its fertility after the cultivation period. Yields, and the ability to resist drought, have been reduced, lowering levels of food security in rural communities. The rapid growth of tourism in the coastal zones of Yucatan, and its consequent demand for labour, has also had a profound direct impact on the structure, makeup and economic status of the farming system. Many families have migrated permanently to the state's new coastal cities such as Cancun and Cozumel[29]. A similar pattern of migration is also occurring in the Brazilian northeast. Because of the marginal nature of the area and the recurrent droughts faced by producers, the rural population has become very dependent on periodic government assistance. Since

---

[27] Instituto Brasileiro de Geografia e Estatistica 1996.
[28] Superintendency for the Development of the Northeast 1999.
[29] Torres 1997.

no long-term solution has been developed, this population represents a migratory time-bomb, with some estimates placing the number of potential migrants at 8 to 13 million.

TRENDS AND ISSUES IN DRYLAND MIXED SYSTEM

The key sectors that offer potential for regional income growth are tourism, services and agro-industry. By year 2030, the productive structure of this farming system will probably be more concentrated than today, as many sub-marginal producers will have left. There is a low probability that the system will be able to finance its own development, so it will continue to depend on government resources. Total population is projected to grow at one percent per annum. Income distribution will continue to be highly skewed and any decrease in poverty will rely heavily on government action programs.

The operating capacity of public institutions, including the research and extension sector, is expected to increase. However, improved response to small farmer needs, and expanded co-operation with the private sector, is unlikely to occur unless significant measures are undertaken to restructure the organisation and management of research organisations. On the other hand, the organisation and democratisation of society will be stronger.

Drought effects are likely to be aggravated over the years, as climatic instability increases and degradation of natural resources reduces the capacity of the system to resist long dry periods. The impact will be high, further degrading soils and vegetation and increasing population outflow. These negative effects will be mitigated by growing irrigation activities – with an expected 0.5 million ha of new irrigated land. Much of this irrigation will be devoted to the production of tropical fruit for export, creating nearly an estimated 300 000 jobs. A key constraint is the widespread perception that lack of water is purely a result of limited natural resources. In reality, it arises largely from inequitable land distribution, inappropriate technologies, and poor resource management. Land degradation in sub-marginal holdings further exacerbates the problem, although opportunities do exist for low water-demand production systems (e.g. cashew).

Yucatan faces a particular challenge with respect to the sustainability of shifting cultivation practices. Technical changes within the *milpa* system are limited to the introduction of external inputs such as herbicides, improved varieties and, to some extent, fertiliser. Crop diversification, or changing the cropping cycles on the same *milpa*, are possible adaptations. However, if fallow periods continue to decline, the only possible outcome will be serious soil and vegetation degradation and drastically lower yields. This may well happen, unless out-migration occurs at a faster rate than population growth. Other important issues to be considered are:

- reform of the existing system of agricultural land to permit consolidation of holdings and increased efficiency;

- control of desertification in the driest areas; and
- using ecotourism potential to create employment opportunities.

PRIORITIES FOR DRYLAND MIXED SYSTEM

In contrast to other regions of the world that have already made the transition to modern agricultural practices, the Dryland Mixed Farming System has failed to undertake the necessary changes to stimulate a broad and equitable process of agricultural and socio-economic development. Even major advances in technology will not permit a poor agricultural population of 10 million people to escape from poverty over the next 30 years, given existing resource constraints. If farm populations can be reduced, and a more equitable land distribution achieved, then the possibility exists for increased earnings for those remaining – together with a halt to the ever-increasing degradation of the natural resource base.

Two major strategic approaches to poverty reduction can thus be proposed: (i) alternative livelihoods, principally through exit from agriculture within the system; and (ii) increased off-farm incomes. In addition, agricultural growth through increased farm size, diversification, and some intensification of production will contribute to the reduction of poverty.

Provision of alternative livelihood opportunities to sub-marginal farm families within the region would include incentives for the creation of agro-industry and other rural occupations, such as training of workers and tax benefits. Assistance in relocating sub-marginal farmers to areas of agricultural expansion (i.e. the Cerrados) is also important; possibly including compensation for exit from currently occupied lands and access to finance to buy land in expansion areas. A further element in this strategic approach is the provision of skills training and infrastructural improvements to facilitate the movement of people (especially youth and women) into regional urban areas.

The second strategic approach consists of providing those remaining on-farm with the potential for increased earnings through land purchase and diversification into higher value crops (possibly directed at the tourist sector). This may exclude many renters who have no initial land base from which to expand. Experience in a number of countries has shown, however, that financing land purchase costs alone is not enough. Any programme of this type must also address: (i) on-farm investments and working capital requirements; (ii) dissemination of technologies that improve productivity in relation to moisture constraints – including development and dissemination of drought resistant varieties and species and encouragement for the replacement of maize; and (iii) zero-tillage technologies appropriate for small producers; small-scale irrigation where feasible.

Introduction of farming practices that reverse the degradation of the natural resource base should also receive a high priority. These practices include: (i) the expanded utilisation of legumes and fodder crops (e.g. *Mucuna pruriens* and *Canavalia ensiformis*); (ii) zero or limited grazing systems for small-stock; and (iii) greater attention to the potentials of native vegetation. Land use planning should also be given priority to improve the identification of areas under risk. Meteorological research leading to specific drought forecasting all over the region would also be valuable.

In addition to these major strategic approaches, public financing must be shifted away from emergency drought relief and similar programmes into activities that provide hope for future avoidance of these conditions.

MAIZE-BEANS (MESOAMERICAN) FARMING SYSTEM

CHARACTERISTICS OF THE SYSTEM

The Maize-Beans (Mesoamerican) Farming System extends over an area of approximately 65 million ha. It occupies mostly upland areas from the Panama Canal to the highland plateaux of Guatemala and Central Mexico. The system is distinguished by: (i) the significant proportion of indigenous population[30]; (ii) the central role, both agriculturally and culturally, of maize and beans; (iii) the small size of

Box 7.6 Basic Data: Maize-Beans (Mesoamerican) Farming System	
Total population (m)	77
Agricultural population (m)	11
Total area (m ha)	65
Agro-ecological zone	Dry – moist subhumid
Cultivated area (m ha)	6
Irrigated area (m ha)	2
Cattle population (m head)	14

holdings – typically under five ha and in El Salvador, less than two ha[31]; (iv) the high degree of on-farm consumption of production (over 65 percent in Honduras)[32]; and (v) the importance of seasonal migration of wage labour to lowland agricultural and coffee estates. Coffee, and intensive small-scale irrigated vegetable production (in areas close to roads and urban centres), are important income sources and often critical in determining the degree of poverty within a community.

Cultivated land may extend as high as 3 500 m above sea level in the Guatemalan highlands, but the majority is between 400 and 2 000 m, with a precipitation from

---

[30] Indigenous people account for 66 percent of total population in Guatemala and 29 percent in Mexico, but are lower in other Central American countries. Within the system itself, the proportion can be estimated at 60 to 80 percent.

[31] Comité de Acción para el Desarrollo Social & Económico de Centroamerica/European Commision 1990.

[32] Comité de Acción para el Desarrollo Social & Económico de Centroamerica/European Commision 1990.

1 000 to 2 000 mm per annum. There is extensive irrigation, much of it under the control of larger farmers, although small-scale systems play an important role in horticulture. Most soils are of volcanic origin, and relatively fertile, but on slope lands tend to be thin and subject to erosion[33]. FAO studies from the 1980s estimated severe erosion on as much as 45 percent of all land in El Salvador and 25 to 35 percent in Guatemala[34]. Forest cover was severely reduced during the 20th century, leaving large areas of contiguous forest only in inaccessible areas and in National Parks. A distinctive sub-system in Central Mexico[35] shares the cultural and agronomic elements of the main system, but is agro-ecologically different, consisting of high altitude plateau (2 000 to 3 000 m elevation) with lower temperatures and poorer soils.

The system has an estimated agricultural population of some 11 million people, half of them in Mexico[36]. This ranges from about 50 percent of national agricultural population in Guatemala to less than 20 percent in Honduras, while arable area within varies from 40 percent (El Salvador) to 10 percent (Panama) of national totals[37]. In 1989, it was estimated that there were 1.4 million producers of basic grains in Central America[38], the vast majority of whom would be included in the system.

Large-scale estates, frequently in excess of 100 ha, are interspersed throughout the system. Often controlled by absentee landlords or corporations, these estates have traditionally been dedicated to the commercial production of coffee and beef although more recently rubber, cut flowers and foliage production have increased in importance. In addition, commercially-operated family farms created by European settlers are clustered in the more fertile valley areas of the system, and often produce vegetables and dairy products as well as coffee. Most indigenous producers control their family parcels under customary arrangements but lack legal title, rendering access to formal credit sources very difficult. (see Box 7.7).

Yields tend to be low; with maize averaging 1 to 2 t/ha[39]; by contrast average maize yields in Sinaloa State, where irrigation is widespread, reach 6 t/ha while system yields of beans (0.6 to 0.9 t/ha) are lower than the Mexican national averages of over 1 t/ha[40]. Nevertheless, small-scale indigenous producers are important contributors to national output of these crops. In 1999, over 50 percent of the area sown to maize in Mexico was within the system boundaries. In total, some

---

[33] FAO 1999a.

[34] MAG/FAO/CIP/IICA 1996, p.63.

[35] Comprising much of the states of Hidalgo, Tlaxcala, Guanajuato, Queretero, and Mexico.

[36] Instituto Nacional de Estadistica Geografica e Informatica 1995.

[37] MAG/FAO/CIP/IICA 1996.

[38] Comité de Acción para el Desarrollo Social & Económico de Centroamerica/European Commision 1990.

[39] Yields in the altiplano area of Central Mexico tend to be higher (from 2 to 2.5 t/ha) reflecting proximity to urban markets.

[40] Secretaria de Agricultura, Ganaderia, Desarrollo Rural, Pesca y Alimentación 1998.

Box 7.7 A Typical Household of the Maize-Beans (Mesoamerican) Farming System

A farm household in Quiché Department, Guatemala might have traditional control of a total of 3.5 ha, some 1.5 ha of which are dedicated to maize, and 0.75 ha to beans. A low yielding second harvest may be possible on part of the holding, depending on soils and slope. Coffee, the principal cash crop, occupies less than 0.5 ha, while tree fruits and vegetables for household consumption and possibly local sale perhaps a further 0.5 ha. The household occupies the remaining space. If the household is wealthy, or receives remittances from abroad, it may have a cow for milk and draught, plus some chickens. The household head could well be an indigenous woman, especially where there has been armed conflict or extensive out-migration. When there is a male head of household, he will often be seasonally absent providing income from wage labour on the coast. Input use is low (although normally will be used for the coffee) and there will be no access to formal credit, although itinerant buyers may advance funds to regular clients. There may be a primary school within reach, but probably no year round access by road to the community.

---

6 to 7 million ha of maize are harvested annually within the system[41]. The importance of the system is even more pronounced for coffee, which requires altitudes over 500 m for proper development and fruiting. Almost all regional coffee production derives from the mesoamerican system area. However, large coffee estates account for much of that output.

Extensive poverty is present throughout the system, reaching levels as high as 80 percent in the Guatemalan Departments of Huehuetenango and Quiché. A regional average of 60 percent was estimated by IICA in 1991[42]. Malnutrition is also widespread, especially in the period before harvest. Returns per unit of land tend to be greater – but population densities much higher and holding sizes smaller – in areas where coffee production is practised. Food insecurity is exacerbated by significant variability in coffee prices from year to year.

Public infrastructure is sparse or completely absent away from local administrative centres, especially in those areas where there has been prolonged armed conflict in recent decades (Chiapas in Mexico, Guatemala, El Salvador and Nicaragua), and many indigenous communities are several hours from the nearest road. Similarly, the availability of education, health care and other services is minimal. To compensate, many indigenous communities have high levels of social cohesion, enabling community mobilisation for a wide range of tasks. Community controlled forest areas are also common, but tend to be very fragmentary.

---

[41] Secretaria de Agricultura, Ganaderia, Desarrollo Rural, Pesca y Alimentación 1998.
[42] FAO 1999a.

TRENDS AND ISSUES IN MAIZE-BEANS (MESOAMERICAN) SYSTEM

Fragmentation due to inheritance and other causes has increased the number of holdings and decreased the average size over recent decades. The number of holdings with maize in Guatemala more than doubled, from 321 000 to 667 000 between 1964 and 1996, (however not all may be within the system)[43]. This is faster than the rate of population increase. Although urbanisation rates are also increasing, projections indicate no significant decline in rural populations in Mexico and Central America over the next 30 years. This suggests that pressure on access to land – an underlying cause of so much of the civil conflict in the region in the last 20 years – will continue.

With so little unexploited land available, existing trends are likely to continue: (i) exploitation of ever steeper slopes; (ii) intensification of traditional production systems; and (iii) diversification of production. Expansion onto steep slopes will generate only short-term gains, as underlying soil structure is difficult to maintain and erosion will increase. In addition, increasing climatic variability resulting in torrential rainfall and flooding, is already believed to be responsible for major damage to many degraded areas. This trend will probably intensify.

The positive relationship between population density and yield levels in Central America[44] suggests that yields of both maize and beans are likely to increase over time, perhaps by 50 to 100 percent. However, a downward trend in farmgate prices for basic grains is likely to increase pressure on semi-subsistence farmers. Falling international prices, which are projected to decline even further over at least the next ten years[45] and trade liberalisation, have eroded the degree of protection previously enjoyed by national producers. Although major advances in maize yields may well occur in industrialised countries in the future, the reliance of farmers on self-produced seed, plus widespread soil limitations, would likely limit the benefits to system farmers.

Increased diversification will offer some compensation. National urban populations with increased incomes will demand more high value products, and improved technologies in post-harvest handling will continue to expand speciality markets in industrial countries. Many of these products are labour intensive and can be well suited to family labour. Diversification has already occurred in horticultural and fruit production in peri-urban and other favourable areas throughout the mesoamerican system and will likely accelerate over the next 30 years.

Four principal development household strategies are thus foreseen for small producers within the mesoamerican system. Firstly, those with favourable resource

---

[43] Comité de Acción para el Desarrollo Social & Economico de Centroamerica/European Commisión (1990), p. 17 for 1964-1979 data; 1996 data from: Unidad Sectorial de Planificacion Agropecuaria y de Alimentación (1996).

[44] In 1985 Panamá, with a population density of 28 persons/km^2 recorded average maize yields of 0.93 t/ha while El Salvador, with a population density of 265 persons/km^2 recorded 1.84 t/ha. Other Central American countries fell between these points.

[45] World Bank 2000e.

endowments (including the possibility of irrigation), location, and human capital will probably emerge from poverty as specialist suppliers of export-oriented products, despite their small holding sizes (see Box 7.8).

Other cases of diversification into intensive horticultural and fruit production include sweet onions in Nicaragua and chilli peppers in Belize. Maize and beans will continue to be grown for household consumption only, but perhaps with dramatically higher yields, as this group will have the resources to adopt new technologies. However, it is not believed that this strategy will ever represent a viable option for more than a relatively small percentage of mesoamerican system smallholders – perhaps 15 percent or less.

Secondly, a larger proportion of smallholders are likely to continue to rely on the farm for their basic sustenance, but turn increasingly to off-farm employment as a means of earning the income needed to finance basic household expenses (medicine, education, clothes, etc.). This income may also finance greater input use,

---

Box 7.8 Private Sector Support for Small Farmer Diversification [46]

The key role of the private sector in supporting diversification and income generation among indigenous smallholders in the highlands of Guatemala demonstrates the potential for effective co-operation between the private sector and traditional farmers. Although snow peas and broccoli were pioneered in the early 1970s by agribusinesses, within 10 years production of these perishable commodities had shifted entirely to smallholders. Despite little if any external assistance, by 1996 these crops had grown to support more than 21 000 indigenous families through an estimated US$33 million in additional annual gross income; equivalent to US$1 500 per family. More than 2 500 further jobs are estimated to have been created in associated post-harvest and marketing activities. Expansion is continuing, as new non-traditional crops such as raspberries gain importance. High labour requirements and the need for intensive management leads to average crop areas of only 0.24 ha per family, ensuring dispersion of benefits, and demonstrating that smallholders can achieve a competitive advantage for this type of product.

It is argued that the rapid expansion of smallholder production, and the high proportion of final price (47 percent) accruing to the producers), is a direct result of the competitive market created by the many small and medium-scale marketing enterprises active in the non-traditional field. The success of these enterprises, in turn, owes much to generally supportive government policies, and in particular, to a dynamic business support organisation (GEXPRONT). This contributed significantly to reducing the barriers to entry for small enterprises, resolving key marketing bottlenecks and, more recently, brokering private-sector support to producers in applied research and extension. These results suggest that support for the private sector, if leading to more open markets and improved efficiency of operations, may be an effective strategy for supporting diversification among small producers.

---

[46] Abstracted from Case Study 5, Annex I.

raising yields. The growth of export-oriented production on the part of commercial farmers and pioneer smallholders will create employment opportunities, both in agribusiness, as well as in services. Expanded tourism may also offer a source of employment.

A third path will consist of families who abandon their holdings and move to urban centres. It is likely that, over the next three decades, this exit strategy will be followed by a sizeable proportion of the rural population, reaching perhaps as high as 20 to 25 percent for areas such as El Salvador where population densities are high.

The fourth path comprises those who neither benefit from the new developments nor migrate in search of work. This group will account disproportionately for the extension of cultivated area on steep slopes, risking severe environmental and human loss from flooding and landslides in search of increased production. Agricultural output will bring declining real income as relative returns diminish and with few resources to purchase inputs, yields will stagnate or decline. Poverty will worsen for this group, perhaps dramatically. Unfortunately, they are also likely to be the largest group, and may account for more as many as half the population in some zones.

Throughout the system, public infrastructure and services are likely to continue to improve, especially as a result of significantly expanded post-conflict rural investment programmes in countries such as Nicaragua, El Salvador and Guatemala. Private sector and civil society participation in rural areas is also expected to increase in importance.

PRIORITIES FOR MAIZE-BEANS (MESOAMERICAN) SYSTEM

The system is characterised by extensive and often severe poverty. Yet focusing attention on increasing yields of traditional products can produce limited poverty alleviation at best. The problem facing producers is not one of insufficient foodstuffs, but rather the need for higher cash incomes to meet household needs. Where no alternative sources of cash exist they are forced to sell output that would otherwise be consumed within the household, hence creating secondary malnutrition.

For those producers occupying degraded or fragile slope land and unable or unwilling to return such land to forest cover, the priority must be to promote more sustainable patterns of production that can be readily adopted with few resources, and can provide rapidly realisable benefits in output or labour use. Specific interventions include: (i) permanent high value crops; (ii) reduced tillage; (iii) higher plant populations; (iv) contour cultivation; (v) improved varieties, (vi) live barriers; (vii) intercropping; (viii) dispersed tree cover; and (ix) mulching. The benefits of these technologies and the feasibility of their adoption have been clearly demonstrated by a number of innovative projects within the system.

However, while such practices can both increase yields and lead to more sustainable use of natural resources, they will have only limited impact on increasing household incomes unless integrated into diversification and marketing programmes, and can only be seen as part of any solution.

Diversification offers the greatest potential rewards but, even among those who can make the transition, support will be needed. The private sector is best equipped to provide this, as entrepreneurs understand most clearly the needs and demands of the market. Nevertheless, a crucial role remains for Government in ensuring that the business environment is appropriate for small farmer-private sector interaction. Important measures include: (i) ensuring a competitive environment for enterprises, with low barriers to entry and controls over monopoly powers; (ii) promotion of farmer associations and small enterprise groupings, that can act as effective channels for financing, technical assistance and management training; and (iii) increasing the participation of producers and traders in the setting of policies and negotiation and monitoring of trade agreements. The development of land markets would accelerate the transition, permitting producers to buy-out less successful neighbours and form the nucleus of a commercial family farming sector.

Off-farm employment and other rural employment may initiate an upward spiral of employment, earnings expenditure, and increased demand for goods and services among those unable to diversify production. Investment by medium and large scale agro-industries, assembly plants and tourism can be promoted by offering non-financial incentives. These could include: (i) public infrastructure provision in zones where companies are establishing operations; (ii) extension and organisational assistance to contract suppliers; (iii) training of company staff; and (iv) assistance in dealing with municipalities in land acquisition, local taxation, etc.

The reduction of rural poverty among those unable to diversify production or obtain off-farm employment must focus on facilitating a successful exodus of people from these areas. Empirical evidence strongly suggests that the poorest segments of the population do not migrate as much as wealthier rural inhabitants; they lack the resources to do so[47]. An appropriate strategy would be to tackle this problem on two fronts – providing resources for migration and attempting to increase the probability of successful absorption at their destination. Start-up capital for migrants might be provided through: (i) payments for the transfer of customary land rights to groups interested in conservation and biodiversity, thus taking sub-marginal land out of circulation; and (ii) financing the purchase of land rights by more successful small producers. Literacy and vocational training is also important for would-be migrants and their families, to provide basic employment skills.

---

[47] Inter-American Development Bank 1999.

HIGH ALTITUDE MIXED (CENTRAL ANDES) FARMING SYSTEM

CHARACTERISTICS OF THE SYSTEM

The High Altitude Mixed (Central Andes) Farming System extends over 121 million ha from Cajamarca in Northern Peru, through Bolivia into Northern Chile and Northeast Argentina (see Box 7.9). An estimated 40 percent of the territory of Peru and Bolivia falls within the system boundaries, as well as smaller portions of Chile and Argentina. In the north a series of interwoven ranges dissected by longitudinal valleys make up the Peruvian Sierra. Further south, at about latitude 14° South, the Andes divide into two major ranges, enclosing the plateau or *altiplano* of Peru, Bolivia and Northern Chile and Argentina. This vast treeless area of land is composed of undissected tableland above the level of 3 500 m and is characterised by interior drainage. Some of the agricultural land reaches 4 500 m[48]. Precipitation is concentrated within a single wet season of variable length and ranges from 150 mm in the western ranges to 1 000 mm per annum in the eastern ranges. Although the soils, as well as their capability for agricultural production, are extremely diverse their fertility is typically low. All the lands in the system are affected by severe soil erosion.

Agro-ecologically the zone is extremely complex[49]. The great variation of soil types and the frequent sharp changes in altitude are accompanied by dramatic changes in temperature, humidity and rainfall. An aridity gradient exists from east to west across the Central Andes as well as from north to south along the length of the chain. Annual mean temperature varies greatly with altitude. Mean daily temperature is generally below 10°C and frost is common, especially during the dry season.

Apart from altitude, other key features that characterise the Central Andean High Altitude Farming System are the overwhelmingly indigenous population, the virtual absence of large holdings – unusual in Latin America – and the low levels of external input use. Most of the system was originally part of the Inca Empire and has retained strong cultural elements inherited from that period, which have changed only superficially. Poverty within the system is extensive. In 1997,

Box 7.9 Basic Data: High Altitude Mixed (Central Andes) Farming System	
Total population (m)	16
Agricultural population (m)	7
Total area (m ha)	121
Agro-ecological zone	Semiarid – dry subhumid
Cultivated area (m ha)	3
Irrigated area (m ha)	1
Cattle population (m head)	9

---

[48] The latitude limit to potatoes cultivation is 4 200 m at latitude 15° South.

[49] More than 60 biotic zones of the 103 found in the world are represented in the Central Andes and *Altiplano* near Titicaca Lake.

68 percent of the total rural population of Peru fell below the national poverty line and this proportion is believed to be higher for Bolivia, although recent data are not available.

According to the 1994 Census, almost 60 percent of holdings in the Peruvian Sierra were under 3 ha with 1.5 to 2.5 ha cultivated (often in scattered parcels), while in the *altiplano* they reach 15 to 20 ha, with 1.5 to 2 ha cultivated. These small cultivated areas, combined with the poor productivity of such high altitude arid lands, result in endemic poverty, widespread soil degradation and erosion, and out-migration has become an important element of the system. There is an extensive flow of permanent and seasonal migration to the recently opened land on the eastern side of the Andes and to the Amazonian lowlands beyond. Nevertheless, despite out-migration, it is estimated that the rural population within the system grew by 1.6 percent per annum during the period 1960-1990 – this growth rate is expected to decline in future. The most densely populated areas of this farming system are the Peruvian Sierra with about 0.3 inhabitants per ha and the Bolivian *altiplano* where in certain parts, such as the areas surrounding La Paz, Cochabamba and Potosi, it can reach 0.4 inhabitants per ha. The remaining arid and subarid parts of Chile and Argentine are very sparsely populated. The average rural population density for the whole farming system is 0.06 persons per ha (17 ha per person).

The cultivated area within the system is about 3.1 million ha and represents as much as a third of the national cultivated area of Peru and Bolivia. An estimated 1.2 million ha are irrigated, mostly in the arid western section in Peru. On the basis of statistical data from 1994, an estimated 1.2 million farms in Peru[50] and 0.6 million in Bolivia[51], fall within the system. The total number of farms for the entire system would be over two million. Legal rights over property and other resources are not commonly established. In the Peruvian Sierra, approximately one-third of holdings are legally owned, while two-thirds are held under customary arrangements. There is almost no formal land rental, although there may well be informal arrangements. The agricultural population of some 7 million people, three-quarters of them in Peru[52], rely on a subsistence-based mixed production system including potatoes, pre-Colombian Andean crops (e.g. quinoa and chenopodium) and barley, maize, and lima bean. Sheep are important in the Peruvian Sierra, while the camelidae (llama, alpaca) dominate further South. Guinea pigs are also of major importance at higher altitudes. The potential for irrigation is reasonable. However, given the topography of the system, much of the water only becomes available on the lower flanks of the western ranges.

In the Peruvian Sierra, typical land use patterns distinguish three major production systems according to altitude: (i) the valley floor where corn, quinoa,

[50] Instituto Nacional de Estadistica e Informatica 1996.

[51] Muñoz 1999.

[52] The system rural population is estimated at 40 percent of total rural population in Peru and 45 percent in Bolivia.

chenopodium and potatoes are grown. Where water is available, small-scale traditional irrigation systems may make horticultural production possible; (ii) the intermediate slopes, where drier western terraces are dedicated to barley and grains and the better eastern slopes are dominated by tuber cultivation; and (iii) the high hills where the cultivation of more frost-resistant crops is combined with pastoral activities.

In the *altiplano* sub-zone further to the south, the land use pattern chiefly depends on the gradient of rainfall. In the most humid areas agriculture is widespread, while under drier conditions extensive livestock production predominates. In some of the arid and semiarid areas, such as the 'Valles Altos' of Bolivia, extensive degradation of soils has caused major changes in prior production patterns, as traditional crops such as maize have become infeasible.

Average system yields are constrained not only by agro-ecological conditions but also by the limited use of external inputs and the low productivity of family labour. In the Peruvian Sierra, less than 10 percent of smallholders are estimated to use purchased seed, but nearly 70 percent use organic fertiliser of one form or another. Maize yields typically do not exceed 1 t/ha, with quinoa yielding 0.85 t/ha and potatoes 10 t/ha. Other cereals (wheat, barley) average approximately 1 to 1.2 t/ha, but these yields may reflect the participation of larger producers. Further south, in the *altiplano* sub-system, yields drop further: potatoes from 4 to 5 t/ha; quinoa 0.6 t/ha and wheat and barley about 0.6 to 0.7 t/ha.

During the mid-1980s and the beginning of 1990s, structural and sectoral adjustment programmes caused major changes in national economies. Food production grew at annual rates of three percent and five percent for Bolivia and Peru respectively[53] while agricultural exports expanded at an even higher rate; eight percent and nine percent respectively for the same two countries. Food imports also rose, but at a lower rate, resulting in a net improvement within the domestic agricultural sector. Nevertheless, the evidence suggests that most of these gains have been captured by the modern agricultural sector, bringing little benefit to the producers of the high altitude system. The modern agricultural sector has also been the beneficiary of most public resources devoted to the rural areas, including the development of improved agricultural technologies. The system is characterised by a widespread lack of basic infrastructure in such areas as education, health, roads, and markets. In Bolivia, the proportion of overall public resources devoted to the agricultural sector has not been consistent with the contribution of this sector to the economy. Agricultural GDP was 16 percent of the national total in 1999 but the sector received only six percent of the total public budget. The allocation of resources to the agricultural sector is more equitable in Peru, where both expenditures and agricultural GDP are around 7 percent.

[53] The growth rate was calculated for the period 1985-1996 for Bolivia and 1990-1996 for Peru.

TRENDS AND ISSUES IN HIGH ALTITUDE MIXED (CENTRAL ANDES) SYSTEM

Over the next 30 years, rural populations within the system are not expected to fall significantly. Pressure on access to land will persist as declining real prices for agricultural products drive producers to expand their cultivated areas and increase stocking levels. The low productivity explains the apparent contradiction between the low population/cropland ratio and the persistent high pressure on land. The widespread soil erosion occurring on the slopes of the Peruvian Sierra and the *altiplano* will likely worsen without substantial changes in cropping patterns and natural resource management practices. Strong economic growth nationally, and in the lower valleys and Amazonian lowlands in particular, may accelerate out-migration. Although historically a relatively abundant resource, labour may join humidity, soils and slope as a limiting factor of production if this occurs.

The evolution of land tenure and landholding distribution during this period is an extremely complex matter. It is expected to be mainly influenced by whether or not adequate land registration, financing, and market development for land will be achieved, requiring considerable legislative institutional reform[54].

Although crop yields are low by regional standards, the adoption of available improved technologies requires levels of input use that are not feasible for most producers under current circumstances. In fact, natural resource degradation and possible labour shortages will increasingly challenge current production levels. Also, opportunities for crop diversification are more limited than in other zones, although expansion of irrigation and protected cultivation under plastic tunnels may provide limited opportunities.

The best opportunities for many producers may lie in improved community organisation to benefit from the potential for added value in existing products. Stronger marketing linkages to end-users (supermarkets, institutions, and restaurants) and the processing of raw materials (milk, potatoes and grains) could significantly increase family earnings, while speciality products such as quinoa and camelidae wool may provide profitable export opportunities.

Key issues that will have to be addressed if poverty reduction is to be achieved and economic growth promoted within the system, include:

- Unsustainable natural resource management practices, resulting in soil degradation and erosion;
- Low prices for agricultural outputs;
- Lack of off-farm employment and income generating opportunities;
- Low factor productivity, especially with respect to labour and land;
- Inadequate public sector investment in infrastructure and agricultural services.

---

[54] The present regulation of the land market was established in Peru by the land reform of 1953, which remains popular among small farmers, but restricts the consolidation of holdings.

PRIORITIES FOR HIGH ALTITUDE MIXED (CENTRAL ANDES) SYSTEM

The extreme agro-ecological conditions, fragmented landholdings, poor soils and lack of off-farm employment opportunities have resulted in extremely high poverty levels within the Central Andean high altitude system and render the sustainable development of the system both a necessity and challenge. Soil degradation on the hillsides in the Peruvian Sierra and in the *altiplano* compromises the long-term potential for land productivity[55]. Although poverty is recognised as a dominant force affecting soil dynamics in the mountainous areas, the manner in which it influences production systems is complex. Erosion control projects implemented within the system have had only limited success, and must recognise that purely technical responses will fail to resolve the problem. Instead, they must be better integrated with the creation of wider economic opportunities for small famers, while recognising the limitations imposed by low labour productivity and fragmented holdings.

The concentration by small-scale producers on low value commodities for domestic markets has left them exposed to stagnant demand and with consumers who are unwilling to pay higher prices for such aspects as varietal improvements, post-harvest handling or packaging. Yet a number of the products grown within the system have significant potential for international specialist and niche markets. Anecdotal evidence suggests that major increases in prices can be achieved by tapping into these markets for llama and alpaca wool, quinoa, speciality potato varieties and similar products, especially if the potential exists for origin-labelling or control. Fair trade agreements may also offer income increasing opportunities, but are inherently limited in scale. Diversification for export markets will require improved producer organisation to co-ordinate and bulk volumes required for export shipments; as well as efficient input supply mechanisms (including finance). Technical assistance would be needed to ensure adequate quality control, develop post-harvest handling and packaging, and establish effective market linkages.

Off-farm income, particularly related to agro-industry, can contribute significantly to rural development in small-farm areas. Agro-industry often induces rapid technical change among participating small farmers, contributes to demand for local production[56] and creates off-farm employment (see Box 7.9). However, the imperfect functioning of markets has traditionally inhibited a broad expansion of small-farm oriented agro-industry. This is particularly true in relation to rural credit[57], land markets, insurance for agriculture activities, information, technology and specialised inputs. Agro-industries have developed a number of strategies

---

[55] Morales and Knapp 1987.

[56] Well documented in CEPAL, FAO & GTZ (1998).

[57] Export-oriented agroindustries frequently require products with higher input levels and costs than traditional crops.

Box 7.9 Farmer Organisation for Income Generation, Off-farm Employment and Increased Value Added to Production[58]

The grassroots rural dairy processing industry that has sprung up in the highland areas of the Peruvian Sierra demonstrates the potential for generating added income among poor farmers in the Central Andean Farming System. Although conventional agribusinesses play a major role in processing and supplying dairy products, a multitude of small farmers spread over the highland still produce and sell their products on a traditional basis. In 1987, in the Sierras of Chuquibamba District, Peru, a group of 57 farmers, with the support of an NGO, decided to construct their own small-scale dairy plant. Mainly oriented to supply the neighbouring urban areas with cheese and yoghurt, production evolved rapidly from 91 t in the beginning to 639 t per annum in 1996. This experience was emulated by other communities and individuals across the region. From 1991 to 1995, 16 additional dairy plants were established in the region, showing classical 'clustering' within a single district. At present, the 17 plants combined process almost 11 000 t of milk per annum and provide an estimated US$6.6 million additional annual gross income to 1100 farmers, equivalent to US$0.33 per person per day, an improvement of 17 percent over current family incomes. An estimated 155 further direct and indirect jobs have been created. The investment required to create a job has been as low as US$1 400 per worker.

Although this case highlights many positive aspects and promising perspectives for poverty alleviation among small farmers, a more comprehensive analysis is needed to ascertain the long-run viability of these rural small-scale dairy plants and their competitiveness in liberalised markets for dairy products. The intervention of NGOs has been critical in this experience through the provision of technical and financial assistance, as well as in upgrading human capital among the peasants, but is probably too limited for large-scale replication. To insure the long-term growth of these small farmers' income generation initiatives, improved public policies and services are essential.

to compensate for the effects of these imperfect market, including the provision of farmer credit, technology and inputs, as well as renting of land from small producers[59].

Although it is difficult to develop recommendations for such programmes and policies outside the context of a specific activity, they would generally include the reduction of information costs and improved market linkages for producers in order to move toward assured market access and financing of production costs. The framework should include a strategy to strengthen technical assistance. The reduction of transactions costs arising in the first stage of the linkage between the

[58] de Grandi 2001.

[59] A very innovative link between farmers and agro-industry has been established in the Ica Valley of Peru. Here a tomato paste processor rents land from local farmers, who work on their own land, but as employees of the processing plant.

industry and farmers[60] is important, including rapid, simple and enforceable arbitrage mechanisms to resolve the conflicts that often arise between farmers and agro-industry in their transactions. Facilitating access to credit and removing legal and market constraints affecting small farmers with regard to enlarging their landholdings, are also of great importance. Similar priority should be accorded to reducing the costs of training - both to farmers and to agro-industry – as well as to supporting farmers' organisations.

Increased land and labour productivity is a further priority area, as the High Altitude Farming System of the Central Andes is characterised by very low factor productivity. Average smallholding size is relatively large by the standards of many farming systems, but the very poor returns to land and labour leave producers with little benefit for their efforts. While low productivity is in part a result of unfavourable climatic and soil fertility conditions, it can be argued that the current system fails to utilise effectively those resources that are available. Priority must be given to participatory research and extension on adapted crop varieties for this high altitude zone (short season, drought tolerant, etc.). It is worth noting that successful trials have been made in promoting indigenous technologies – such as the use of large earth planting beds dissected with deep trenches that reduce frost damage by avoiding settling of cold air on growing plants – and more work would be worthwhile in this area.

It is important to accelerate the regularisation and registration of farm ownership, the lack of which seriously hinders land market development and provide strategic support to land buyers – mainly information and notary services – including identifying of available land and the provision of more readily-accessible mortgage facilities.

The achievement of productivity increases is closely related to public investment in infrastructure and services, in improving human capital within the farm population through education and health care, provision of specific government programmes to promote the development of the agro-industrial sector, as well as the completion of the reforms in factor[61] markets. The conditions to achieve these objectives do not yet appear to have been met. At the root of any strategy for rural development is the premise that macroeconomic stability and more appropriate relative prices, are not sufficient by themselves to bring about large-scale agricultural productivity growth. These must be complemented by government support, in particular in the form of more effective government investments in agriculture. Greater emphasis should therefore be placed on adequate public resource allocation to agriculture through suitable budgetary adjustments.

---

[60] Agro-industries generally prefer to be linked to the commercial sector, as transactions costs are lower than those incurred in the small farm sector.

[61] Land market reform is unlikely in the medium term future as the necessary preparatory steps (as undertaken in Mexico as part of their land reform process) still have not been started in Bolivia and Peru.

STRATEGIC PRIORITIES FOR LATIN AMERICA AND CARIBBEAN

The following strategic priorities derive from the analysis of the four selected farming systems supplemented by expert knowledge of the other systems. It is believed that the conclusions with regard to poverty reduction and agricultural growth presented below will be broadly relevant across the region as a whole[62]. There is considerable scope for reduction of agricultural poverty in Latin America and Caribbean, through production intensification, diversification (including value added), expansion of farm size, off-farm employment and exit from agriculture[63]. Table 7.4 indicates the relative importance of each of these strategies as factors in reducing poverty within individual farming systems in Latin America during the coming decades.

As can be seen, the importance of different household strategies varies significantly from system to system. In broad terms, lower potential systems derive a greater proportion of poverty reduction from farming system exit – migration to cities, abandoning farms for employment in the off-farm economy or moving to another farming system – than do higher potential systems, which tend instead to derive more benefits from productivity increases.

Across all systems except the most remote, it is expected that diversification will be a major source of agricultural poverty reduction. Diversification would include a shift into higher value non-traditional crops as well as added-value activities, such as grading, packaging, and on-farm processing. Increased off-farm employment and income generation is also believed to be generally important. However, strategies such as the expansion of farm size among small farmers is important as a source of poverty reduction in only a few cases.

Expected sources of poverty reduction have implications for the specific interventions in each of the five principal categories outlined in the introduction to this book. Each of these categories is briefly examined below:

POLICIES, INSTITUTIONS AND PUBLIC GOODS

Three key strategic areas are likely to dominate governmental and institutional roles within farming systems in Latin America over the next 30 years: (i) improving access to land and – to a lesser extent – water, in farming systems with extensive poverty and among poverty groups in more wealthy systems; (ii) promoting alternative occupations for the agricultural poor who do not have access to

---

[62] There is also poverty reduction and growth potential within the Forest Based System, covering the majority of the Amazon basin and adjacent humid areas. Clearly major economic growth – including agriculture - can be expected to occur within this system over the next 30 years. However, serious natural resource and political constraints render its development highly controversial.

[63] See Chapter I for a discussion of these household strategies for escape from poverty.

Table 7.4 Potential and Relative Importance of Household Strategies for Poverty Reduction in Latin America and Caribbean

Farming System	Potential for agricultural growth	Potential for poverty reduction	Strategies for poverty reduction				
			Intensi-fication	Diversi-fication	Increased Farm Size	Increased off-farm Income	Exit from Agriculture
Irrigated	Moderate	Low	4	3	1	2	0
Forest Based	Moderate - high	Moderate	3	3	2.5	1	0.5
Coastal Plantation & Mixed	Moderate	Moderate	2	2	1	3	2
Intensive Mixed	Moderate	Low	3	2	3	1	1
Rice-Livestock (Campos)	Moderate - high	Moderate	3	2	2	1	2
Moist Temperate Mixed-Forest	Low	Low	3	3	0.5	2.5	1
Maize-Beans (Mesoamerican)	Low – moderate	High	1.5	2	1	2.5	3
Intensive Highlands Mixed	Moderate	Moderate	2	2.5	1	2	2.5
Extensive Mixed (Cerrados)	High	Low 1/	4	2	3	1	0
Temperate Mixed (Pampas)	Moderate	Low	3	2	0	2.5	2.5
Dryland Mixed	Low	High	0.5	1.5	1	3	4
Extensive Dryland Mixed	Moderate	Moderate	3	3	2	2	0
High Altitude & Altiplano	Low	High	1	2.5	0	2	4.5
Pastoral	Low	Low	0	1	0	3	6
Sparse (Forest)	Low	Low	0	2	0	5	3
Urban Based	Moderate	Low	2	3	0	4	1
Average for Region			2.4	2.1	1.5	2.1	1.9

Source: Expert judgment.
Note: Total score for each farming system equals 10. Assessments refer to poor farmers only. Average for region weighted by agricultural populations of systems derived from Table 7.1.
1/ But considerable poverty reduction potential exists for those migrants entering the system from other areas.

sufficient land and water to escape poverty; and (iii) strengthening public goods in rural areas. In all these areas government must inevitably play a major role, although preferably working in co-operation with civil society and private sector groups.

In many farming systems, a small minority of large farmers occupy large areas of land, which are often utilised only at relatively low intensities, while most producers are confined to smallholdings which are increasingly less viable. Civil conflict has often been a direct result of this situation. For the Maize-Beans (Mesoamerican) and Dryland Mixed Systems (arguably less so for the Central Andean System), poverty levels are directly related to problems of access to, and control of, natural resources – primarily land. Effective land policies is also important in frontier areas (e.g. the Extensive Mixed system) where in-migration from neighbouring poverty systems could lead to conflict. Key strategic priorities include: (i) improved functioning of land markets, through acceleration of cadastral and titling procedures, conflict resolution mechanisms, and changes in land tax structures; (ii) land banks to buy both marginal and large holdings and resell land with the objective of consolidating smaller commercial holdings; (iii) fiscal disincentives to under-utilised holdings and incentives for sale to land banks; and (iv) supported exit for sub-marginal producers including, where feasible, negotiating the purchase of traditional rights to land.

A vital aspect of policy reform is the enforcement of legislation prohibiting illegal seizure of lands and other resources. This applies not only to powerful interests capturing state land, but also to small producers illegally occupying private lands and colonists entering indigenous community lands. Where such risks are perceived to exist, land may not be put on the market or offered for rental due to the fear of attracting squatters. This has become a major issue in recent years in the coastal zone of Guatemala, for example.

Despite the opportunities that may exist for diversification and increasing output value among small-scale farmers, there will inevitably be many marginal and sub-marginal farmers who simply lack the human, financial, locational and natural resource assets to benefit from these opportunities. Two broad alternatives exist: local off-farm employment and outmigration.

Off-farm employment offers a major route for escape from poverty in severely constrained farming systems. Policies, institutional support and public goods can all play a major role in promoting such employment. Natural resource-based industries offer employment opportunities, but the disadvantages of locating facilities in rural, compared with urban, areas must be overcome. National and local governments can co-operate with the private sector in the design of integrated programmes in which larger potential employers (agro-industries etc.) would be offered incentives to offset the perceived advantages of urban operations. Support measures might include: (i) improved infrastructure in the area of the plant and its suppliers, perhaps together with a long-term commitment from the employer to part-finance maintenance; (ii) provision of training for future staff of the employer;

(iii) supply organisation among raw material providers (crops, livestock, etc.); and (iv) the creation of rapid, transparent and binding dispute arbitration and settlement mechanisms for suppliers and the employer.

To promote the development of small-scale enterprises, key interventions would include: (i) simplification of small enterprise registration and approval procedures; (ii) assistance in preparing realistic business and investment proposals; (iii) training in simple accounting and administrative procedures; (iv) more rapid and flexible financing of investments; (v) priority in providing basic services (e.g. electricity, telephone, water, etc.); and (vi) encouragement and resource provision to associations representing small scale rural enterprises.

Out-migration has been the traditional response for those who are not able to participate in diversification or off-farm employment activities. In recent years, the focus has been exclusively on retaining the rural population in situ, and discouraging out-migration. Yet, if little potential exists for substantial increases in quality of life within the system, this retention policy must be questioned. Indeed, it is timely to identify and implement measures to ensure that any process of out-migration is a positive one, both for those migrating and for those remaining within the system. These would include innovative measures, such as targeted out-migration incentives, to increase the human and financial capital of migrants and thus ensure better economic possibilities in the future. Such incentives could involve providing capital to departees who hand over control of lands currently occupied to the financing agency. Where these lands are sub-marginal for agricultural purposes they would be passed to conservation authorities for reforestation and watershed protection measures. Otherwise, land banks would finance their acquisition by more successful neighbours, thus contributing to land consolidation.

Training – particularly of women and young people – in vocational skills of direct relevance to off-farm employment or migration, needs considerable strengthening throughout the region. This should be seen as second in importance only to basic primary education, as a social service in rural areas.

One key area of public goods is infrastructure. Although infrastructure is increasingly accepted as a largely private sector activity, such areas as rural roads, electrification and water capture and distribution for irrigation will have to remain public goods, and are critical for diversification and intensification activities in many areas. The withdrawal of the state from many rural institutional activities (banking, extension, marketing) renders strengthened support and oversight capacity for civic and private institutions essential.

TRADE LIBERALISATION AND MARKET DEVELOPMENT

The liberalisation of trade and markets is probably the dominant force governing the evolution of farming systems, and thus rural hunger and poverty, within the region. Imported products increasingly compete in national markets, often undercutting local producers – at least in easily-served urban markets. A rapid transition to free market conditions will increase the prevalence of poverty in the short term, as producers face declining prices for traditional products and difficulties in the transition to new higher-margin products. Those systems with severe poverty are most seriously affected, as they often lack the human, financial and technological resources needed to adjust. In the longer run, trade liberalisation should also create opportunities for market development and diversification, although not all system participants are likely to be able to benefit from such changes.

Governments have legitimate roles with respect to markets and trade. However, experience has shown that many direct state-supported interventions merely impede the transition process while providing little real benefit to poor farm households. Instead, the most effective strategy is often to establish the conditions for an active and competitive private and civil sector in rural areas as outlined in the previous sub-section (see also the Maize-Beans [Mesoamerican] Farming System case study). Apart from creating an environment that is supportive of small business establishment and growth (see previous sub-section), such a strategy would comprise interventions to assist farmers to organise themselves to respond to new opportunities, including: (i) training group leaders in commercial management and administration; (ii) providing information, genetic material and technical assistance to promote the adoption of new crops; (iii) promoting value-added activities (selection, packaging, processing) through technical and financial assistance for quality standards, brand creation and targeted marketing; and (iv) improving access to financing for required investments.

One traditional area of public intervention has declined in many farming systems as a result of restructuring and decentralization: setting and enforcing market-related norms and standards. Activities in areas such as weights, measures, quality standards, disease monitoring and tracking, and phyto-sanitary controls are all vital public functions if market and trading systems are to function effectively.

INFORMATION AND HUMAN CAPITAL

Accelerated rates of change appear inevitable in traditional systems, and the process will require both improved information and human resources. Provision of information by the public sector involves substantial recurring costs and is frequently irrelevant to real market needs, so the service is best provided by private sector buyers and traders, or through trade or producer associations. Typically, the most effective support that Government can offer for information dissemination is the improvement of communications channels, whether they be cellular telephone networks, open licensing of local radio stations, or simply improved access roads to rural areas.

Human resource development should focus on vocational training, and numeracy. Literacy may not necessarily be the first priority. Not all rural inhabitants are farmers, and agricultural training should be only one possible training alternative, alongside skills such as sewing, mechanics, welding, cooking etc. These skills may be particularly important for future out-migrants (especially young people) in helping them to find employment at their destinations. Training should also be able to address the needs of specific employers in rural areas (whether agro-industry or non-agricultural) as a way of removing disincentives to rural enterprise operations.

Over a thirty year period, the use of new communications technologies, such as the Internet, may revolutionise the transfer of information and skills to poorer rural communities. However, considerable infrastructure development, as well as profound changes in government thinking about services and service provision, will be needed before the promised revolution can occur.

SCIENCE AND TECHNOLOGY

A number of pioneering projects have shown that a range of technologies already exist that can contribute to improved natural resource management and drought tolerance. These include (i) increasing soil organic matter content e.g. by legumes (*Mucuna pruriens* and *Canavalia ensiformis*); (ii) no-tillage cultivation, multi-cropping and small-scale irrigation linked to terracing on lower slopes and in semiarid areas; and (iii) vegetative barriers, contour protection, permanent crops and agroforestry on steeper slopes. The zero or controlled grazing of livestock, especially goats, when combined with fodder crops and trees, is another promising technology improvement, as is the integrated management of fragile savannah soils.

However, significant changes are needed in the field of applied agricultural research. Greater use must be made of participative approaches to areas such as improved varietal selection and field trials of new potential diversification crops. Achieving this will require considerable restructuring of national research organisations in many LAC countries, with particular emphasis on disbursement mechanisms for research grants and on staff training in participatory methods. Responsiveness of the research system to market demand must be increased. Although hybrid genetic material would be acceptable for diversification, it is likely that material capable of on-farm multiplication would be a prerequisite for traditional crops.

Increased research is required on short-season and drought-tolerant crops suitable for small producers, and in particular on technologies that increase labour productivity in systems with high levels of poverty. To increase the ability of smaller producers to compete effectively in growing international markets, research will also be needed in such areas as: (i) adapting existing and future post-harvest technologies to the needs of smaller producers; (ii) appropriate IPM and organic cultivation practices and tools (e.g. biological controls); and (iii) field testing of new varieties/species and determining optimal agronomic practices.

NATURAL RESOURCES AND CLIMATE

Many regional farming systems are experiencing increasing levels of natural resource degradation. In the absence of primogeniture or active land markets, fragmentation of holdings is a natural consequence of population growth over time. Without appropriate policy incentives or technologies to increase yields and improve soil fertility, the result is soil mining and expansion of cultivation into sub-marginal areas. Predicted population increases in 'poverty' systems – such as the Maize-Beans (Mesoamerican) System and the High Altitude Mixed (Central Andes) System – will only exacerbate these pressures. Frontier systems with lower population densities face a different set of constraints. Settlement in these systems has been historically sparse due, in part at least, to limitations in agricultural potential. Poor management practices can result in widespread damage and degradation to the natural resource base, as already recognised in the Cerrados (Extensive Mixed Farming System).

Although the solution to these problems may lie partly in interventions described in other sub-sections – including increased off-farm incomes – specific responses appropriate to densely populated systems do exist. Among these, the development and implementation of effective, community-level natural resource management plans is extremely important. Such interventions must include technical assistance and incentives for adoption, plus an emphasis on demonstrating rapidly realisable benefits from watershed improvements, forestry and other resource management activities. Other promising interventions centre upon moisture conserving technologies in dryer areas to combat the droughts and desertification (e.g. North-east Brazil and Central Andes), and effective watershed protection (Mesoamerica and Northern Andes). Both impacts are likely to become more common as a result of global climatic changes and risk reduction mechanisms will need to be strengthened.

For frontier systems, intervention priorities include the development of a detailed knowledge base on natural resources and their characteristics within the system, and the linkage of this knowledge base to planning tools and appropriate resource management approaches. This would be backed by research on the development of crop varieties adapted to limitations of frontier zones (e.g. aluminum tolerance, post-harvest characteristics), and dissemination of results. Of fundamental importance, however, are land settlement and development policies which encourage appropriate patterns of land use, through the use of instruments such as land taxes (regional and municipal); land grants; facilitated credit for investment or working capital; and, eligibility for support services (marketing, extension, veterinary services, etc.).

Larger farms are clearly better equipped in terms of resources to adjust to the new economic realities, but it should not be assumed that larger farms are always more competitive. The experience of Guatemala, for example, has shown that smallholders can be more efficient than commercial farms with respect to labour-intensive crops. All farming systems have potential for competitive production by small farmers, as well as for increased off-farm income generation, although the proportion achieving these goals will vary substantially from system to system. Where agro-ecological conditions are favourable and markets easily accessible, for example in the Coastal Plantation and Mixed Farming System, a relatively high proportion of smallholders may be able to follow these strategies. However, where agro-climatic conditions and tenure patterns impose severe constraints, fewer producers may be able to make the transition, and system exit assumes greater importance. This is likely to be the case in the High Altitude Mixed Farming System of the Central Andes and the Dryland Mixed Farming System of Northeast Brazil and the Yucatan.

Due to its abundant water and largely tropical and sub-tropical climate, the region is well endowed with high potential farming systems. However, many of the frontier areas – such as the Extensive Mixed Farming System of the Cerrados and Llanos, or the Forest Based System of the Amazon – possess fragile soils with nutritional limitations. And although development strategies will clearly be influenced by the agronomic potential of the system involved, the key role of land distribution in the region renders these differences less significant than in many other parts of the world. Even in high potential systems, improvements in yields or cropping intensity of traditional crops would have only a limited potential to reduce poverty among small farmers. By contrast, diversification and increased off-farm employment comprise essential strategic approaches for small producers in both high and low potential systems.

CONCLUSIONS

The Latin America and Caribbean region offers a sharp contrast between extensive frontier areas with low population densities and a high future growth potential, and established densely-populated systems – many with extensive poverty. Yet these two extremes share a number of common challenges that define a clear strategic focus for the region over the next thirty years, and although it is impossible based solely on the foregoing regional analysis to prescribe specific national actions, the overall situation demands a clear strategic focus for agricultural development and poverty reduction based on three, inter-linked, regional initiatives:

Sustainable resource management. Sustainable management of natural resources and the reversal of resource degradation are of prime importance, both in established high population systems and in rapidly growing frontier areas. However, a clear positive impact on producer incomes is essential if widespread adoption is to occur. Components include: dissemination of proven technologies for smallholders, notably green mulching, small-scale no-till, vegetative barriers, terracing and zero grazing; expanded attention to the selection, testing and dissemination of varieties appropriate for small producers, with an emphasis on permanent and tree crops; financing producer out-migration from unsustainable lands to permit reforestation; promotion of off-farm employment opportunities, so as to reduce pressure on densely populated areas; and, improving knowledge of frontier area lands and their fragile soils.

Improved resource access. A fundamental precondition for development in the region is improved access to – and control over – land by poorer rural populations. Components include: strengthened cadastral, titling and registration services; dispute resolution services; land banks financing consolidation of smallholdings, as well as purchase, breakup and resale of larger holdings; improved management measures for communally owned lands, including protection from invasion and colonisation; and, taxation policies that provide incentives for sustainable land use.

Increased small farm competitiveness. It is essential to increase the capacity of the smaller producers within farming systems, to respond adequately to trade liberalisation and market development. Components include: training of farmer groups in commercial management and administration techniques; improved technologies for high value production; reduced barriers to entry for small enterprises, as well as the strengthening of enterprise associations; the facilitation or part financing of the development of rural market-related infrastructure such as roads, communications and market facilities; and provision of incentives for relocation of agroprocessing and other enterprises to rural areas – including training of personnel, infrastructure provision and technical support to contracted producers.

8

GLOBAL CHALLENGES, POTENTIALS AND PRIORITIES

...

Widespread and severe household food insecurity occurs in many farming systems and this is expected to remain a major concern during coming decades. Indeed, available projections[1] point to a probable failure to meet the commitments made by the international community at the 1996 World Food Summit and in the Millennium Declaration to halve hunger and poverty by 2015. In all regions, poverty and household food insecurity are more prevalent and more severe in rural areas than in urban areas. Futhermore, food insecurity and poverty are interrelated. Poor households lack the purchasing power to ensure adequate nutrition, while food insecurity in itself causes poverty. Malnourished people, because of reduced intellectual and physical capacities, often suffer more illness, and have lower labour productivity and weak educational achievements. Whilst there is an urgent need for transitory measures to safeguard minimum nutritional and livelihood standards (e.g. safety nets), long-term programmes are required to support a sustainable process of pro-poor economic growth and development.

In this Chapter various ways of closing the hunger and poverty gap, which exists between current projections (a business as usual scenario) and the international development goals of halving hunger and poverty by 2015, are examined. The Chapter commences by grouping the 72 farming systems identified in the six regions into eight broader categories. The relative importance of household strategies for escaping from poverty is then examined in relation to each category, in terms of: intensification; diversification; increased operated farm size; increased off-farm income; and exit from agriculture within the farming system. In order to shed further light on strategies for poverty reduction, the farming systems are then re-grouped according to: (i) resource potential, and (ii) agricultural intensity (as an indicator of access to services).

Secondly, a global strategy for hunger and poverty reduction is defined, focusing on five areas; the reform of the policy and institutional environment, measures

---

[1] FAO 2000a.

related to efficient markets, improving the availability of information and human capital, effective technology deployment and the application of sustainable natural resource management.

SYSTEM CATEGORIES, ENDOWMENTS AND HOUSEHOLD STRATEGIES

FARMING SYSTEM CATEGORIES

The 72 farming systems identified in the six developing regions can be grouped into eight major categories (see Chapter 1 and Annex 2), based on the characteristics described in Chapters 2 to 7, in order to facilitate comparison and integration of individual system priorities into an overall global strategy for poverty reduction. These eight system categories, are: (i) irrigated farming systems; (ii) wetland rice based farming systems; (iii) rainfed farming systems in humid (and subhumid) areas; (iv) rainfed farming systems in steep and highland areas; (v) rainfed farming systems in dry or cold areas; (vi) dualistic farming systems with both large-scale commercial and smallholder farms; (vii) coastal artisanal fishing mixed farming systems; and (viii) urban based farming systems. Except in the case of the dualistic category, these system types are dominated by smallholder producers.

The quality of underlying resources varies widely between farming system categories and differences can be noted even within a single farming system. Farming systems endowed with irrigation or humid climates normally have higher agricultural potential than systems in dryland areas. In addition, access to agricultural services – especially markets – has a major influence on the development opportunities of a farming system. Figure 8.1 shows the relationship of seven of the eight system categories in terms of these two important variables.

The domains of each system category are relatively large because of the heterogeneity of their constituent farming systems and differences between farm household environments within a single system. In this connection, dualistic systems would tend to cover the entire Figure and thus were omitted.

As can be seen from Figure 8.1 (and as discussed in earlier chapters), the irrigated, wetland rice based and, to a lesser degree, rainfed humid system categories tend to have relatively high average household resource endowments. However, their access to agricultural support services and markets varies markedly – from poor (towards the upper left corner of the Figure, e.g. Gezira Irrigation Scheme in Sudan) to good (in the upper right, e.g. Lower Nile Valley irrigation areas in Egypt).

In contrast, often because of poor infrastructure, rainfed highland farming systems have restricted access to services but resource endowments can vary from fairly good (in the upper left corner, e.g. Upland Intensive Farming System in China) to poor (in the lower left corner, e.g. High Altitude Mixed Farming System

Figure 8.1 Categories of Farming System by Resource Endowment and Access to Agricultural Services

Household Resource
Endowment

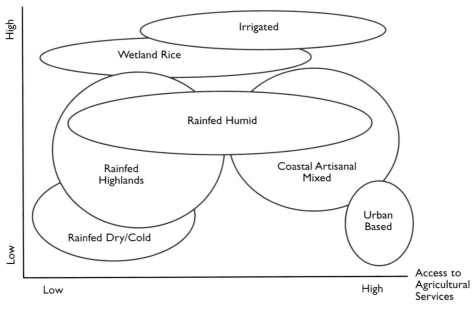

Note: Dualistic farming system category extends across much of the Figure and so is not displayed.

in the Central Andes). Rainfed farming systems in dry or cold areas tend to have poor resource endowments and poor access to services (e.g. Pastoral Systems in all regions). On the other hand, Coastal Artisanal Farming Systems often have good access to services but the underlying resource base varies, placing the domain of this system on the right hand side of the Figure. Finally, Urban Based Farming Systems typically have good access to markets, but their resource base is typically quite restricted.

The eight categories of farming system are further compared in Table 8.1, which shows the areas of total land, cultivated land and irrigated land, agricultural population and market surplus. The six irrigated and rice based wetland systems[2] contain an agricultural population of nearly 900 million people with some 170 million ha of cultivated land, of which nearly two-thirds is irrigated. There are three major classes of smallholder rainfed farming system (in humid, highland or dry/cold areas), which together contain an agricultural population of more than

---

[2] One irrigated farming system in Eastern Europe and Central Asia has relatively large farms and, for the purpose of the present discussion, is included in the category of dualistic systems.

Table 8.1 Comparison of Farming Systems by Category

Category characteristic	Small-holder irrigated schemes	Wetland rice based	Rainfed humid	Rainfed highland	Rainfed dry/cold	Dualistic (large/small)	Coastal artisanal fishing	Urban based
Number of Systems	3	3	11	10	19	16	4	6
Total Land (m ha)	219	330	2 013	842	3 478	3 116	70	n.a.
Cultivated Area (m ha)	15	155	160	150	231	414	11	n.a.
Cultivated/Total (%)	7	47	8	18	7	13	16	n.a.
Irrigated Area (m ha)	15	90	17	30	41	36	2	n.a.
Irrigated/Cultivated (%)	99	58	11	20	18	9	19	n.a.
Agric. Population (million)	30	860	400	520	490	190	60	40
Agric. Persons/Cult (p/ha)	2.1	5.5	2.5	3.5	2.1	0.4	5.5	n.a.
Market Surplus	high	medium	medium	low	low	medium	high	high

Source: FAO data and expert knowledge.
Note: Cultivated area refers to both annual and perennial crops. n.a. Not available.

1 400 million people with around 540 million ha of cultivated land. Dualistic systems comprising farms of mixed size contain a further 190 million farm people with a cultivated area of 11 million ha. Finally, two further minor classes of smallholder system – four coastal artisanal fishing mixed and six urban based systems – contain a combined total of about 100 million people. These eight categories of farming system are described in the following paragraphs.

The three smallholder *irrigated farming systems* are dependent on large-scale irrigation schemes dominated by small-scale farming. Although this category contains only about 30 million women, men and children who farm about 15 million ha of irrigated land, it is important for national food security and export earnings in many countries. Although huge investments have been made in large irrigation schemes, most still face the challenge of improving water use efficiency in coming decades. In addition, many are now facing financial difficulties; notably in Sub-Saharan Africa, Eastern Europe and Central Asia. Environmental sustainability is also a concern in a number of cases[3]. Outside the context of large-scale schemes and wetland rice systems, small-scale irrigation supplements the livelihoods of many millions of rainfed farm households, and is considered an integral part of the particular farming system in which it is located.

[3] Box 2.6 recounts the poor water management, input supply and yields in the Gezira scheme. It is also expected that some of the large scale schemes in Eastern Europe and Central Asia which are not viable will be reduced in size or even closed.

The three *wetland rice based farming systems* of East and South Asia, which include a substantial proportion of irrigated land, support an agricultural population of around 860 million. Although bunded rice cultivation is the distinguishing characteristic of these systems, a wide range of other food and cash crops are produced and poultry and livestock are raised for home consumption and sale. These systems depend on the monsoon, but nearly 60 percent of the cultivated land is equipped with irrigation facilities. Relatively little grazing or forest land remains – almost half of land is under annual or permanent crops – and these systems suffer from intense human pressure on the natural resources base, with 5.5 persons per ha of cultivated land. There is a moderate degree of market surplus; these systems underly national food security in most Asian countries.

The 11 *rainfed humid farming systems* are based on smallholder cultivation of root crops, cereals or tree crops. They often contain an important component of livestock and support an agricultural population of approximately 400 million. There is little irrigation. Pressure on land is typically moderate – only 2.5 persons per cultivated ha on average – although there are some areas of intense pressure. There is a moderate, but varying, degree of market development and substantial opportunities for further development.

The 10 smallholder *rainfed highland farming systems* in steep and highland areas contain an agricultural population of more than 500 million. In most cases these are diversified mixed crop-livestock systems, which were traditionally oriented to subsistence and sustainable resource management. However, these days they are characterised by intense population pressure on the resources base, which is often quite poor – averaging 3.5 persons per cultivated ha, aggravated by heavy grazing pressure on the four-fifths of the land which is not cultivated. Given the lack of road access and other infrastructure, the level of integration with the market is often low.

The 19 smallholder *rainfed dry/cold farming systems* in dry or cold low potential areas, cover an enormous land area – around 3.5 billion ha – but support a relatively modest agricultural population of around 500 million. These lower potential systems are generally based on mixed crop-livestock or pastoral activities, merging eventually into sparse and often dispersed systems with very low current productivity or potential because of environmental constraints to production. Market development in these extremely low potential areas is limited.

The 16 *dualistic farming systems* are characterised by significant contrast, i.e. a mix of large, often commercial, farms together with smallholder farms. This category contains an agricultural population of nearly 200 million and more than 400 million ha of cultivated land in a variety of ecologies, and exhibits diverse production patterns. Such systems are prevalent in Eastern Europe, Central Asia and Latin America, but can also be found in Africa. All except one are predominantly rainfed systems – the exception being the Irrigated Farming System in Eastern Europe and Central Asia, which is dominated by medium and large farms.

Four *coastal artisanal fishing mixed farming systems* have been defined[4]. The crop component of these systems is important for household food security, but the principal livelihood is inshore fishing, with a rapid growth in aquaculture in many parts of the world. Because of infertile soils crop yields are often low. The few areas with fertile soil often face serious risks of storms and floods – as occurs around the Bay of Bengal. Many systems include some tree crop production (e.g. coconut and cashew) and small livestock, especially goats, and poultry.

Six *urban based farming systems* have been identified, that are dynamic, market-driven systems, typically focused on intensive, high-value horticultural and animal production. Urbanisation is increasing everywhere and these farming systems will assume even greater importance in the future.

The analysis of the eight global categories of farming systems suggests significant differences in the relative importance of the strategies available to poor households for reducing poverty and hunger. Derived from expert judgement, Table 8.2 shows the relative importance of these household strategies – which also correspond to rural development strategies on a wider scale. The relative potential impacts suggest an optimal mix of strategies, required for closing the gap between the 'business as usual' projections of slow poverty reduction and the goal of halving hunger and poverty by 2015 in each of the major farming systems.

Table 8.2 Relative Importance of Different Poverty Reduction Strategies by Farming System Category

Poverty Reduction Strategies	Small-holder irrigated schemes	Wetland rice based	Rainfed humid	Rainfed highland	Rainfed dry/cold	Dualistic (large/small)	Coastal artisanal fishing	Urban based
Intensification	3.4	1.7	1.9	0.9	1.5	2.8	0.7	1.3
Diversification	2.9	3.4	2.7	2.7	2.3	2.0	2.5	2.7
Increased Farm Size	1.2	0.9	1.7	0.6	0.9	2.0	0	1.7
Increased off-farm Income	1.9	2.8	2.2	3.0	2.2	1.8	4.2	3.6
Exit from Agriculture	0.6	1.2	1.4	2.8	3.1	1.3	2.6	0.8

Source: Expert judgement.
Note: Scores for each farming system add to 10.

The *irrigated farming systems* have relatively low incidence of poverty and hunger, and are fortunate in having good prospects for halving existing poverty. It is judged that three-quarters of the reduction is poverty will be derived from farm improvement (intensification, diversification and increases in operated area). Fully

[4] The Coastal Plantation and Mixed Farming System in Latin America has been characterised as a dualistic system.

one-third will be derived from production intensification – because growing conditions are so favourable in these schemes, productivity increases will arise from improved water, soil fertility and crop management – and diversification, often involving export cash crops with established marketing channels, will provide a further 30 percent. Nevertheless, increases in off-farm income, from both local and seasonal migration, are expected to contribute nearly 20 percent of aggregate reduction of poverty.

The *wetland rice based farming systems* will be developed largely through farm improvement, which will contribute some 60 percent of the reduction of poverty – notably through diversification of crop, livestock and fish production. As one aspect of diversification, local processing of farm produce will also add value and income. Intensification is also important (especially in countries such as Cambodia and Myanmar), although less so than the expected one-third contribution from the increase in non-farm income. The importance of off-farm income reflects the strength of the rural off-farm economy in China, which accounts for nearly half of the farmers in this system category.

The *rainfed humid farming systems* depend, to a significant degree, on all five household strategies for the halving of poverty. Among these strategies, diversification will contribute more than one-quarter of poverty reduction and increased off-farm income slightly less than one-quarter. In these crop-livestock systems, livestock will play a major role in diversification; and small scale farmer managed irrigation will contribute to both intensification and diversification.

The *rainfed highland farming systems* offer fewer prospects for farm improvement, which accounts for about 40 percent of poverty reduction. The driving forces for poverty reduction will be increases in off-farm income and emigration (exit from agriculture), which both contribute about one third. Diversification, especially to high value products with relatively low transport and marketing costs, will also contribute significantly to poverty reduction.

The *rainfed dry/cold farming systems* have a similar pattern of poverty reduction to the highland systems, because of their low agricultural potential and the poor marketing infrastructure. Livestock and irrigation development will play important roles.

The *dualistic farming systems* will derive poverty reduction from all five household strategies, with more than two-thirds arising from farm improvement. Both intensification and diversification will be supported by irrigation and market development. Increases in operated farm size will contribute around one-fifth of aggregate poverty reduction.

The *coastal artisanal fishing* mixed farming systems are heavily dependent on increased off-farm income for poverty reduction, with substantial contributions from diversification and exit from agriculture.

The *urban based farming systems* also depend for poverty reduction on increased off-farm income and diversification, with significant contributions from intensification and increased size of business.

IMPLICATIONS OF FARMING SYSTEM RESOURCE ENDOWMENTS

Both existing livelihood levels and the potential for future improvement depend upon the quality and availability of natural resources[5]. The resource base of a farming system is best conceptualised as the average resource endowment of typical farm households, measured according to their productive potential when using existing technologies. With few exceptions, all farming systems can be classified in this manner, by taking into account both average farm size and the quality of natural resources. When approached in this way, resource potential can be viewed as a continuum running from systems situated in arid areas to those located in fertile, irrigated conditions.

Examples of farming systems in low potential areas are: (i) the Agro-Pastoral Millet/Sorghum System in Africa; (ii) the Rainfed Mixed System in South Asia; and (iii) the High Altitude Mixed (Central Andes) System in Latin America. Farming systems in high potential areas include: (i) all Irrigated Systems; (ii) the Cereal-Root Crop Mixed System in the moist savannah of West and Central Africa; (iii) the Tree Crop System in East Asia and Pacific; and (iv) the Extensive Mixed (Cerrados and Llanos) System in Latin America. A summary of the contrasting characteristics of high and low potential farming systems situated at the two opposite ends of the spectrum is presented in Table 8.3.

Table 8.3 Comparison of Farming Systems by Resource Potential

Characteristic	High potential	Low potential
Number of Systems	26	25
Agricultural Population (million)	1 450	290
Cultivated/Total Area (%)	14	6
Irrigated/Cultivated Area (%)	29	11
Agricultural Persons/Area Cultivated (pers/ha)	2.8	1.0

Source: FAO data and expert knowledge.
Note: Cultivated area refers to both annual and perennial crops. An additional nine systems were of indeterminate or mixed resource potential, e.g. urban systems; and 12 systems of medium potential.

More than 60 percent of the agricultural population of developing regions – or around 1 450 million people – live in systems with relatively *high potential* for increased productivity from the viewpoint of resources. Farming systems in higher

---

[5]
Jazairy et al 1992.

potential areas have greater average population densities and generally enjoy better economic and social infrastructure than low potential areas. However, these areas are not without constraints: in fact, many environmental and socio-economic factors impede agricultural development and extreme fragmentation of holdings may also be a problem. Moreover, contrary to popular wisdom, a significant proportion of the world's poor and hungry people is also found in areas with higher potential.

Farming systems in *low potential* areas with low or erratic rainfall and poor soil fertility, tend to have relatively few agricultural development opportunities, and farmers may be more concerned with minimising risk than maximising food production or profit. Low potential areas tend to face higher risks, particularly in the distribution and amount of water available for farming needs. Other natural disasters, such as locust attacks, may also be important. Unfortunately, the range of options open to smallholders for livelihood improvement from off-farm employment in these low potential areas is also more restricted than in high potential areas as a result of limited market development.

Poverty reduction in low resource potential systems therefore, often depends upon seasonal or permanent migration to seek employment as labourers in wealthier systems, or to urban areas. The need for alternative livelihoods is striking: exit from agriculture contributes almost one half of the poverty reduction potential and increased off-farm income around one quarter. In both cases, a substantial proportion of seasonal and permanent migration will be long distance and sometimes across national boundaries. Nevertheless, intensification, diversification and increased farm or herd size together contribute about one third to aggregate poverty reduction, largely centred on livestock or irrigation development. Relationships between household improvement strategies and resource potential are encapsulated in Table 8.4 below.

Table 8.4 Relative Importance of Different Poverty Reduction Strategies by Farming Systems Resource Potential

Characteristic	High potential	Low potential
Intensification	1.9	0.9
Diversification	3.1	1.4
Increased Farm Size	1.2	0.9
Increased off-farm Income	2.5	2.4
Exit from Agriculture	1.2	4.4

Source: Expert judgement.
Note: Scores for each farming system add to 10.

Farming systems in the *high potential areas*, by contrast, depend principally on diversification and off-farm income for poverty reduction, and together these factors contribute nearly 60 percent of the improvement potential. Intensification will also make a substantial contribution, but may be constrained by land fragmentation in some cases. The linkages to poverty reduction resemble those for the irrigated, wetland rice based and rainfed humid systems. Overall, high potential systems offer the principal hope for expanded food production in the future, and will thus justify a considerable proportion of rural investment funds targeted at expanding global food production.

IMPLICATIONS OF AGRICULTURAL INTENSITY AND ACCESS TO SERVICES

Within the range of farming systems there is a gradation in the level of production intensity which is closely related to access to agricultural support services (see Table 8.5). *Low intensity systems* – including agro-pastoral, pastoral and sparse agriculture systems – support 350 million people but have scattered populations, extensive land use practices, low levels of input use and little market surplus. These systems tend to coincide with the low resource potential areas discussed above.

Table 8.5 Comparison of Farming Systems by Level of Intensification

Characteristics	Low intensity	Medium intensity, food-oriented	Medium intensity, market-oriented	High intensity
Number of Systems	27	20	6	17
Agric. Population (m)	350	950	100	1140
Cultivated/Total Area (%)	5	21	17	28
Irrigated/Cultivated Area (%)	9	14	10	54
Agric. Persons/Area Cult. (pers/ha)	1.0	2.1	1.0	4.8
Market Surplus	low	medium	high	medium

Source: FAO data and expert knowledge.
Note: Cultivated land refers to both annual and perennial crops. Two systems were omitted from this classification.

Medium intensity farming systems have evolved into two distinct sub-types – food oriented and market oriented – depending on the forces involved. Where population pressure on resources has been the dominant factor, systems have

316

adjusted towards intensive food crop production – including root crops, plantains and cereals – often within a mixed crop-livestock system. Systems of this type cover more than 2 000 million ha and support an agricultural population of about 950 million people; they include many of those systems most associated with rural poverty. A moderate level of market development is evident, associated with higher intensity of external input use and greater intensity of land use.

The second sub-type – market-oriented medium intensity – contains fewer systems and development has been driven principally by the existence of readily accessible market opportunities, whether local (typically horticultural) or international (often based on tree and industrial crops). With an agricultural population of only 100 million people, these systems are less important in terms of poverty reduction than they are in terms of export earnings.

High intensity systems will be a major factor in increasing global food security. These include irrigated and wetland rice systems (where more than 50 percent of the cultivated land is irrigated), as well as systems with reasonable resources and infrastructure. Despite a high population pressure of almost five persons per cultivated ha, and small average farm sizes, these systems have an advanced level of market development with significant external input use and a substantial amount of irrigation – allowing them to generate a surplus for sale to urban areas and export markets.

The relative importance of potential strategies for poverty reduction by system intensity is shown in Table 8.6. *The low intensity farming systems* resemble, from the viewpoint of sources of reduction of poverty, the farming systems in the low potential areas (see above). Whilst farm improvement (intensification, diversification and increase in farm size) will account for around 40 percent of poverty reduction, the greatest driving forces are exit from agriculture and increase in off-farm income.

Table 8.6   Relative Importance of Potential Strategies for Poverty Reduction by Level of Intensity of Farming System

Characteristics	Low intensity	Medium intensity, food-oriented	Medium intensity, commercialised	High intensity
Intensification	1.2	1.7	2.7	1.6
Diversification	1.5	2.8	2.3	3.3
Increased Farm Size	1.3	1.1	1.2	0.9
Increased off-farm Income	2.1	2.5	2.5	2.8
Exit from Agriculture	3.9	2.0	1.4	1.4

Source: Expert judgement.
Note: Scores for each farming system add to 10.

317

The *food-oriented medium intensity farming systems* will depend for poverty reduction almost equally on farm improvement and alternative livelihoods (increased off-farm income and exit from agriculture). Logically, among the farm improvement group, diversification away from an emphasis on food production will be the most important source of poverty reduction. The commercial medium intensity farming systems resemble the food-oriented systems, except that farm improvement will contribute around 60 percent of poverty reduction. Interestingly, both intensification and diversification will play important roles.

The *high intensity farming systems* resemble the commercial systems, except that diversification will be relatively more important, and intensification relatively less important, presumably because substantial intensification gains in the high intensity systems have already been realised. Farm improvement will contribute around 60 percent of poverty reduction, but off-farm income is also expected to play a major role in poverty reduction.

OVERALL IMPORTANCE OF DIFFERENT HOUSEHOLD STRATEGIES FOR POVERTY REDUCTION

While the above depiction is inevitably a simplification of reality, it provides an insight into the components of a global strategy that are likely to be most fruitful for poverty reduction within any given type of system, and hence can indicate approaches – whether national or international – that will most strongly justify investment. Farm improvement will be, overall, the most important source of poverty reduction; and for higher potential systems, at least, the main engine whereby the international development goals of halving hunger and poverty will be realised. Within farm improvement, on-farm diversification will be the most important source of poverty reduction, while intensification has an important contribution to make in a more restricted range of systems. Nevertheless, intensification and diversification often proceed in parallel. Among alternative livelihoods, off-farm income will be the most important source of poverty reduction, with a contribution nearly as large as diversification. The following paragraphs examine the roles of each of the five strategies with respect to poverty reduction.

Further *intensification* of existing production patterns will be a significant source of poverty reduction in four farming system categories (see Table 8.2), and will be dominant in the development of irrigated and dualistic farming systems. It is of medium importance in rainfed humid and wetland rice systems and of relatively minor significance in two other system categories. As might be expected, it is of medium importance in high potential systems overall yet, counter-intuitively, is a higher priority in commercial medium intensity farming systems than in food crop or low intensity farming systems.

Diversification is rated as being an important means of reducing poverty in all categories of farming system. On-farm diversification entails an increasing emphasis on non-traditional cash crops – particularly vegetables, fruits, spices and colorants, livestock products and aquaculture – especially those that are labour intensive. In addition, agro-processing and other post-harvest activities that add value, are judged to be a promising development avenue. Diversification is expected to be most successful in high intensity farming systems in areas of high potential.

The opportunity to *increase farm size* seems to be a significant option only for poor households in rainfed humid farming systems, where pressure on land is only moderate and land development potential is good, and especially in dualistic farming systems. Most other categories of system have little short-term opportunity for expanding agricultural areas and any increase in farm size will depend on farm land consolidation. Nevertheless, highly intensive systems in East Asia and, to a certain extent South Asia, have reached such small average farm sizes that some land consolidation may be essential if production intensification programmes are to be effective. Some potential to expand the operations of poor urban based farm households also exists.

The existing trend to *increased off-farm income* is expected to continue, particularly among poorer farmers. The future exploitation of this source of income is anticipated to be a key source of poverty reduction in all systems, but is of particular importance in the highland system category, as well as in rainfed systems in dry and cold areas. Because of excessive land division and fragmentation caused by high population density, land resources available to farmers are often too restricted to support viable modern farming techniques. The ultimate solution for many families is to move away from farming and seek alternative employment, often through migration to larger urban areas, but sometimes by relocating to frontier areas (e.g. the Extensive Mixed System in Latin America or the Cereal-Root Crop Mixed System of West Africa). This strategy of *exit from agriculture* within the system is important in low potential areas as a whole, especially where few opportunities exist for supplementing household income with local off-farm employment. It is expected to be particularly prevalent in the rainfed humid, highland and dry/cold categories of farming system, as well as in the coastal artisanal fishing category.

Although exit from agriculture is more significant for low intensity systems, the regional analyses suggest that other household strategies are relatively little affected by the level of intensity of the farming system. Intensification, diversification, increase in farm size and off-farm income are all classified as having the same degree of importance at all four levels of intensification. Nevertheless, it is expected that diversification and increased off-farm income will generally be easier to achieve in high intensity systems, due to improved market and service development, while increased farm size may well be feasible only in lower intensity systems[6].

---

[6] It should be remembered that increased farm size refers to small farmers only. More intensive systems may see larger farmers expanding as they buy out sub-marginal producers, but offer little potential to smaller producers.

Table 8.7 Principal Regional Initiatives for Poverty Reduction

Sub-Saharan Africa	Middle East and North Africa	Eastern Europe and Central Asia	South Asia	East Asia and Pacific	Latin America and Caribbean
Sustainable resource management	Sustainable resource management	Improved resource access	Improved water resource management	Increased small farm competitiveness	Sustainable resource management
Improved resource access	Improved irrigation management	Re-oriented agricultural services	Strengthened resource user groups	Improved resource access	Improved resource access
Increased small farm competitiveness	Re-oriented agricultural services	Expanded market development	Re-oriented agricultural services	Enabling environment for off-farm employment	Increased small farm competitiveness
Reduced household vulnerability	Enhanced human resources		Improved rural infrastructure	Enhanced human resources	
Responding to HIV/AIDS	Rationalised agricultural policies				

Source: Regional strategic initiatives presented in Chapters 2 to 7.

A GLOBAL STRATEGY FOR REDUCTION OF HUNGER AND POVERTY

The principal regional initiatives highlighted as a result of the analysis of farming systems and presented in the preceding chapters, are summarised in Table 8.7. Although the titles of the initiatives may be similar, the actual components of the identified initiatives vary across the regions. The initiatives can all be related to the five broad areas of focus employed throughout the book: (i) policies, institutions and public goods; (ii) trade liberalisation and market development; (iii) information and human capital; (iv) science and technology; and (v) natural resources and climate.

POLICIES, INSTITUTIONS AND PUBLIC GOODS

There is a strong case for policy reform at national and global levels in order to support the sustainable development of farming systems. Reforms would include the creation of conducive macro-economic frameworks and expanded investment in public goods and services, in order to compensate for various market failures in research, infrastructure, etc. Many countries have embarked on reforms that have led to a less interventionist public sector, thus opening new opportunities for the provision to farmers of a wider range of services from multiple sources. What is needed now is to ensure that policies and institutions underpin smallholder development, as well as expanding the capacity of private sector service suppliers. This focus is particularly relevant to Africa and to Eastern Europe and Central Asia.

Most reviews of policies and institutions suggest that governments should complete the withdrawal of direct public support from viable commercial farming and privatise associated services, such as seed production and marketing. Nevertheless, it is clearly in the public interest that governments should continue to ensure reliable access by the small farmer sector to relevant public goods, as well as promoting the sustainable use of natural resources. Government efforts should be devoted to clear cases of public goods supply; including roads, education and health services, and research and extension facilities addressed to the needs of poor farmers and marginal areas (see Box 8.1). They should also concentrate on the enforcement of regulations (e.g. fair trade, food standards) with a particular emphasis on avoiding barriers to entry for new participants.

Some success has been achieved with the outsourcing of public service and infrastructure provision to private firms, NGOs and universities, thereby achieving

Box 8.1 Public and Private Roles in Research for Small Farmers

The role of the private sector in agricultural research is expected to continue to expand. Commercial products and services related to plant breeding, pesticides, veterinary products and farm machinery are likely to remain the main foci. Some of the results of this private sector research will be relevant to small farmers in developing countries. In some cases, there may be opportunities for public-private sector partnerships, sharing research costs while making the resulting technologies available to farmers in developing countries on affordable terms. For instance, small-scale irrigation or no-till technologies might find a small but lucrative market among smallholders and gardeners in high-income countries, whilst similar technologies could have wide applicability among poor farmers. Nevertheless, there remain many critical research areas in which the public sector will have to take the lead. These include integrated natural resource and watershed management, true-breeding improved varieties, IPM, and raising smallholder labour productivity. Given the long gestation period for most agricultural innovations, research priorities that will respond to small farmers' needs for new technology 20 to 30 years hence should be identified now, and the appropriate roles of public and private sectors determined. Finally, there needs to be a new willingness to invest in research that will benefit not the farmers of today but a next generation of women and men.

efficiency gains. This type of innovation must include a strong element of local participation, which is critical for monitoring the private provision of such goods and services. Farmers' organisations and the private sector can play a key role in many areas, such as seed multiplication and varietal development (see Box 2.5 on Community-Based Seed Supply Systems). In addition, exporters' associations can often implement phytosanitary inspection. Moreover, research priorities and budgets can be managed through competitive bidding and public-private cost-sharing arrangements.

The five most important priority thrusts in reducing hunger and poverty, concerned with improvements to policy, institutional and public goods, are seen as:

- Establishing equitable, secure, transferable and flexible resource user rights;

- Providing sustainable infrastructure to poorly serviced areas;

- Supporting small-scale farmer managed irrigation schemes;

- Continuing agricultural policy reforms and strengthening meso-level institutions; and

- Strengthening targeted safety nets.

Establish equitable, secure, transferable and flexible resource user rights

The efficient and sustainable utilisation of both individual and common property resources requires clear, enforceable and transferable user rights; as well as functioning markets for those rights, plus taxation policies which encourage efficient resource use. Advisory services need to acquire more insight into the specific mechanisms whereby access to land, water, grazing rights, forest areas and other natural assets, are managed by communities.

The recognition of customary land rights – especially rights to common property resources – is critical to ensuring their productive and sustainable use in many systems with low population density. It would also permit communities operating under traditional land rights systems to arrange commercial relationships with agribusiness groups. Existing legislation, in attempting to protect such customary rights, often hampers arrangements for contracts and other legal agreements on land use[7]. Finally, poorly functioning or restricted land markets contribute to land fragmentation and ever decreasing average farm sizes. This is starting to become a significant contraint in the more intensive systems, and projected gains in production intensity, as well as diversification, are likely to be impeded if land market functioning is not facilitated.

In countries that have inherited dualistic agrarian systems, positive changes in land access can be encouraged through phasing out of subsidies to large-scale commercial farmers, as well as by applying fiscal disincentives to non-productive use of land. Development of land markets can often be advanced through the

---

[7] Tanner 2001.

recognition of informal land rental and sharecropping transactions, facilitation of financing for land purchases and effective measures to protect women's (especially widows') access to land.

Provide sustainable infrastructure to poorly serviced areas

The rate at which farming systems develop towards market-based models is closely correlated with the availability of infrastructure. Road access and electrification have been particularly important in this regard and communications are of growing importance. Improving farmers' access to basic economic and social infrastructure reduces transaction costs. Agricultural knowledge underpins the improvement of farming systems and is usually associated with demand for improved educational services. Therefore, increased investment in rural infrastructure, especially when focused on transport and low cost communications for small-scale farmers, should be a high priority for governments.

With regard to the provision of infrastructure, the main problems in the past have been: (i) urban bias in public expenditure; (ii) inability of local governments to generate enough revenue for operation and maintenance; and (iii) lack of consideration of community priorities and participation in at the planning stage, leading to a passive dependence on government. Because of limited public investment capacity, careful targeting of infrastructure development is crucial in order to meet the needs of poor smallholders.

The reduction of poverty is often most difficult in areas of low potential where agricultural growth prospects are limited and where low population densities increase the per capita cost of service and infrastructure provision. As a consequence, relatively little public investment has been made in these areas, but the social justification is particularly high since private sector interest is difficult to attract.

Support small-scale farmer managed irrigation schemes

In most situations, policies for the development of water resources should give priority to small-scale, farmer managed irrigation, which is usually more sustainable and cost-effective than large-scale schemes. Moreover, rehabilitation of existing schemes should generally take precedence over construction of new schemes. In either case, the establishment of secure land and water rights and the building of effective user-driven local management institutions is an essential complement.

For existing large-scale schemes, the main thrust should be to make them more sustainable and competitive by encouraging greater farmer participation in their management, reducing O&M overheads and improving the efficiency of water supply and use. These changes involve the formation or strengthening of water users' associations, as well as reinforcing farmers' skills in business and on-farm water management.

Continue agricultural policy reform and strengthen meso-level institutions

Many developing countries have already been through a process of structural adjustment. The priority is to complete policy reforms already started by governments (especially in Eastern Europe and Central Asia), but at the same time, to safeguard poor rural communities and families whose vulnerability is often accentuated by adjustment measures – at least during the process of transition. This latter aim may require a combination of targeted short-term measures to assure access to adequate food, as well as structural steps to improve livelihoods through raising the productivity and risk bearing capacity of small farmers. In many systems, population pressure already exceeds theoretically sustainable levels and the main challenge is to identify alternative livelihood opportunities – either inside or outside the area. In some cases this may involve encouragement of out-migration, facilitated through appropriate skills training, capital endowment and the establishment of efficient land markets.

The reduction of biases against agriculture and rural development, particularly those that disadvantage the poor, is an important element of policy. Some of these biases have their origins in the goal of providing cheap food to cities; others are related to natural resource preservation and can have the effect of limiting access to resources by the poor more than the rich – one example is the case of forest regulations in the Highland Mixed Farming System in South Asia. It is not only policies *per se* that disadvantage the poor, but also the way in which they are implemented, as this takes place at the local level in a manner that often favours the powerful and discriminates against the poor.

Improved techniques must be developed to facilitate the assessment of risk in relation to policy and investment decisions, particularly in the light of the expected increase in climatic variability. All too often risk is not explicitly considered as a critical factor in small farmer decision making. Yet a wide range of decisions – including the choice of crop research priorities, the planning and provision of water and irrigation infrastructure, and the formulation of policies affecting land management – are all significantly affected by variability and risk. In addition, uptake of new technologies by small farmers is often inversely correlated to the perceived risks of adoption.

There is an increasing recognition that many traditional farming systems incorporate features that: (i) permit participants to reduce or share risks; (ii) make efficient use of resources; and (iii) resolve potential conflicts over resource allocation, while at the same time ensuring the long-term sustainability of limited natural resource endowments. This has been especially the case with pastoral and dryland farming systems, where attempts to replace traditional practices with new production technologies have often failed dismally, leading to increased poverty and breakdowns in existing resource management systems.

Little progress has been made in creating effective insurance mechanisms for small farmers producing in such difficult environments, and further work is needed on risk mitigation mechanisms that combine low per capita costs, acceptability to participants, and effectiveness in cushioning unpredictable shocks. A degree of insurance can, however, be built into farming systems, through diversification, inter-cropping, crop-livestock integration and the use of crop varieties resilient to stress conditions.

Strengthen targeted safety nets

As noted in the next section, the process of market-based development is likely to increase poverty – at least in the short to medium term – among many farm households. Governments have legitimate social responsibilities towards these households that transcend market functioning, particularly with respect to the protection of disadvantaged citizens (children, women, refugees, and those suffering from disasters). Even though social support programmes may raise issues of dependency, the problem of malnutrition and hunger must be addressed as a matter of urgency. Government intervention can complement market functions, on both humanitarian and economic grounds, instead of attempting to replace markets through general price supports, subsidies or tariffs. This complementarity could be achieved by providing carefully targeted support – for example through food security programmes in which communities are engaged in participatory planning to ensure adequate nutrition for all members. It could also involve adjustments in access to land and water resources, strategic changes in production systems (e.g. the addition of backyard vegetable production), and improvements in feeding habits and sanitation. Food assistance (e.g. school meals, food for work to create new infrastructure and productive assets such as small-scale irrigation) for vulnerable groups who are unable to translate their food needs into effective demand, is also of great importance, and can be designed to stimulate local markets.

TRADE LIBERALISATION AND MARKET DEVELOPMENT

At present, the movement towards reduced barriers to international trade is well established, although the pace of change is uncertain. This process will affect all but the most isolated producers in farming systems throughout the developing world. However, the type of changes induced – and their impacts on production, poverty and food security within individual systems – will depend on a variety of factors; most notably resource availability and market environment, future advances in technology (preservation techniques, transport, communications, etc.) and changes in consumer demand.

Evidence from a number of systems (Maize-Beans Farming System in Mesoamerica, Maize Mixed Farming System in Eastern Africa in the 1980s, and the Lowland Rice Farming System in East Asia) demonstrates that smallholder farmers can participate successfully in market-driven growth and significantly increase household income. Nevertheless, those farmers unable to adjust, due to a lack of resources or an unfavourable policy and institutional environment – such as are now evident in the Maize Mixed Farming System in Southern Africa – will remain dependent on traditional staples for cash income. As such, they face long-term declining incomes as reduced trade barriers and new technologies reinforce the downward trend in international prices of major food commodities.

Based on the analysis of farming systems in each of the developing regions, the five most important global priority thrusts concerned with maximising benefits from trade liberalisation and market development in order to reduce hunger and poverty, are seen as:

- Ensuring trade liberalisation is a two-way street;
- Focusing smallholders on labour-intensive or niche products;
- Satisfying household food security needs during transition;
- Fostering competitive business, especially small rural enterprises; and
- Supporting agricultural market development.

Ensure trade liberalisation is a two-way street

Although trade liberalisation is beneficial, even when enacted unilaterally, it is undeniable that those benefiting from reduced barriers to entry for agricultural products are principally urban populations, while those that benefit from reduced barriers to exports are principally agricultural producers. The considerable barriers still remaining to the entry of major categories of agricultural goods to markets in areas such as Europe, North America and Japan, mean that trade benefits to developing countries have so far largely been in the first group – reduced prices for urban consumers – thus threatening traditional producers with increased poverty as a result of a combination of lower prices for food staples and continuing barriers to diversification.

While it is true that trade barriers in industrialised countries have been reduced for many agricultural commodities, these have often been for products with only limited domestic production or those where the developed world has a strong technological comparative advantage. Protection levels for products such as sugar, where tropical countries may have a strong comparative advantage, are still high. Furthermore, the perception exists – fairly or otherwise – that the industrialised countries are quick to use a range of escape clauses related to phytosanitary, environmental or policy matters to justify extraordinary controls on the import of agricultural products that may threaten domestic business interests. Small developing countries simply do not have the expertise, financial resources or global political clout to seriously challenge these controls. Where complaints are made – as in the case of the European Union controls on banana importation – the perception is that settlements are arranged to meet the needs of the industrialised world, leaving developing country plaintiffs on the sidelines.

This imbalance, which is also apparent beyond agriculture in such areas as textiles, is contributing to a profound unease among many developing country governments concerning the wisdom of liberalisation and may ultimately result in a backlash against the entire globalisation process that goes beyond street protests at major economic fora. The breakdown of the globalisation process would be a great pity, as real long-term benefits are possible for even small-scale producers in developing countries, but a world economic order built on a structure and process that are widely perceived as unfair will not be durable. International agencies, and in particular governments of industrialised countries, must recognise the seriousness of this risk and act to reduce perceptions of inequality in the design and conduct of multilateral trade agreements.

Focus smallholders on labour-intensive or niche products

Although smallholders will inevitably wish to continue producing staple crops for food security and cultural reasons, major urban markets will generally find cheaper supplies from larger high-technology producers – often in other countries. However, as demand for specialist foods grows, and new post-harvest technologies improve product quality and extend the life and durability of perishable items, small producers will have increasing opportunities to achieve attractive cash incomes through the production of specialised products where diseconomies of scale exist (labour intensive and niche horticultural products, fruits, spices, ornamentals, organics etc.). Small farm size is not an impediment to accessing these types of markets, which are expected to grow rapidly in importance, especially if farmers can combine forces through voluntary associations. Even producers who are geographically isolated have the potential to participate in these opportunities, through a focus on very high value-to-weight products (colorants, extracts, essential oils, etc.).

The transition to market oriented production of competitive products is seen as a crucial step in rural economic development and poverty reduction. Not only are incomes generated in those households directly engaged in production, but employment is also created in packaging, transport and related marketing activities, as well as in service provision to successful producers.

Satisfy household food security needs during transition

The restructuring of farm activities to benefit from new market opportunities requires access to a minimum level of resources – natural, human and financial – as well as the ability to accept a certain level of risk in the transition process. In many systems, only a minority of small producers can meet these conditions without significant external assistance. However, with their example, as well as the assistance of larger producers who are often pioneers in innovative production and marketing of crops, the later entry of other, less well endowed, producers is more feasible. The activities of pioneers, whether large or small, is also often important in creating indirect employment and demand for supporting services.

However, if the number of potential pioneers is too restricted there may be insufficient output to create a critical market volume for these products and the development of market-oriented production may fail. Farming systems with a high level of chronic and widespread poverty will often face this barrier. Not only will producers be more concerned about family survival than cash generation, but local buyers and service providers will be few and the establishment of market mechanisms more difficult. Assisting the transition to market-oriented production in systems with high poverty-levels may, therefore, be possible only once food insecurity is reduced, and a minimum level of cash flow is available through the sale of surpluses from traditional crops.

In these systems, attention will need to be focused first upon increasing output of food staples, improved family nutrition, and food security. This will require further investment in appropriate genetic material, food storage structures, natural resource management and education. Careful consideration may also need to be given to the feasibility of facilitating the reduction in rural populations through the provision of skills training and other programmes to assist successful outmigration.

Foster competitive business, especially small rural enterprises

There is ample evidence that direct public participation in marketing operations is generally ineffective and may even yield negative returns. Experience has shown that market development occurs most easily where private individuals – both producers and traders – play a leading role in determining the functioning of markets. From the perspective of small producers who have very limited market power, a competitive market environment in which a number of buyers are active, is crucial. Small producers appear to benefit most strongly from the presence of small traders, processors and other buyers. Such small-scale players are usually unable to control prices in the way that larger enterprises can, and they are also more willing to purchase in small quantities from isolated locations. They may even be members of the same community in which the producer lives.

Helping develop a favourable marketing environment for small producers often means supporting small-scale entrepreneurs through such areas as financing, information, and simplification of bureaucratic procedures which only larger enterprises can manage. It also involves the improved provision of public goods (see previous section). Associations of small traders, processors and exporters can also provide important support to small entrepreneurs, reducing barriers to entry and ensuring that their needs are taken into consideration when developing or reviewing sectoral policies.

This is not to say, however, that larger agribusiness enterprises are necessarily a negative influence, especially if operating in a competitive environment. The contributory role of larger farmers and processors as pioneers, sources of technical advice and credit, buyers from outgrowers and as sources of wage labour, should not be forgotten. Small-scale traders – especially in the case of export crops – must generally sell-on their product to larger enterprises in the regional or national capital. In this situation, farmers' associations can play a role in helping small producers deal more equitably with larger enterprises by increasing volumes and strengthening their bargaining power.

Support agricultural market development

Although governments have little direct role in market operations, the transition of farming systems to market-oriented production can be greatly assisted through the creation of an appropriate enabling environment, including: (i) appropriate rural infrastructure, especially roads, electricity and telecommunications; (ii) commitment to a stable and balanced exchange rate; (iii) establishing and enforcing market standards for both inputs and outputs; (iv) avoiding taxation of agricultural output, focusing instead on under-utilised assets or income; and (v) monitoring and enforcement of trade agreements that have an effect on smaller producers.

Given the importance of agro-industry as a potential source of demand for rural production – and its potential to create employment – market development can also be assisted by removing disincentives to the location of processing and related operations in rural areas. Financial incentives tend to encourage short-term responses from agribusiness that result in unsustainable investments and withdrawal of operations once financing (or tax breaks) cease. However, governments can encourage sustainable rural investment through matching private investment with public infrastructure provision, training of employees, assistance to contracted suppliers, the reduction of red-tape required for investment, and by ensuring favourable long-term fiscal policies.

Finally, the public sector can support strengthened contractual arrangements between producers, intermediaries and processors. Such agreements may be for simple delivery of products, or may include co-operation throughout or in parts of the production process. Market development will be seriously impeded if these contractual arrangements are poorly defined or inadequately protected under law. Conflict resolution procedures need to be low-cost, timely and seen as fair by both parties, while enforcement of contracts should be guaranteed.

INFORMATION AND HUMAN CAPITAL

Three important global priority thrusts, concerned with enhancing the benefits of agricultural information dissemination and use and developing human capacity, have been identified to reduce hunger and poverty:

- Ensuring wide availability of agricultural information;
- Providing broad, systems-oriented agricultural training, especially for women; and
- Strengthening off-farm vocational skills, especially for youths.

Ensure wide availability of agricultural information

Globalisation, urbanisation, and the accelerating pace of technological change, are all increasing knowledge requirements within farming systems in all regions. New

Box 8.2 Narrowing the Digital Divide

Remarkable progress has been made in information technology (IT) links between regions, countries, villages and farmers. The following examples illustrate some of these efforts at village and regional level.

The Chennai, India-based M.S. Swaminathan Research Foundation has established information networks in nine villages in West Bengal, India. Each village runs its own 'info-shop' – the network terminus – and pays the electricity bills and communication costs. Where there is no electricity and no communication lines, new technologies have been introduced. For example, the project has established a minimalist communications network linking the phoneless Veerampattinam fishing village with the city of Pondicherry, by using solar panels for electricity generation and wireless transmission systems. Four times a day, a local volunteer checks the Web and broadcasts information (crop prices, weather forecasts, etc.) through a village public address system.

Kampung Raja Musa is a community that is being used as a test case to extend IT into rural areas in Malaysia. Two kiosks have been established in its community hall, containing touchscreen computers. Guided by icons, villagers can access a database that covers subjects like dressmaking, farm management, how to market produce, how to deal with government bureaucracies, etc. Video clips assist users in obtaining information, so terminals are accessible to illiterate people. In addition, PCs have also been installed to provide access to the Web and email services for the community.

Internet connectivity in Africa is being supported by several regional initiatives. Most internet connectivity lies in OECD countries, and to improve information access in Africa it is first necessary to increase the number of users with access to the web. Although the initial wave of users will be urban and professional, the second wave could be rural and agricultural. In Latin America a series of IFAD projects established a regional web-based network for the exchange of experience. This network allows the sharing of project implementation experience and also of the performance of technologies in different settings, from which farmers can learn.

approaches must be developed to support information flows between farmers and formal knowledge sources – such as research institutions and markets – as well as horizontally among farmers themselves. Small farms do not generally have the same degree of access to agricultural technology and market information as large farms. Thus, public investment in the dissemination of agricultural information is of particular relevance to small-scale farming systems. In some regions, information technology systems are already being adapted to respond to the information needs of small farmers (see Box 8.2), but further public support will be required before the full potential of information technology systems can be exploited, especially in remote areas and where poverty is prevalent. The need is to develop effective mechanisms for information generation, transfer and use by beneficiaries.

More thought must also be given to the long-term sustainability and relevance of agricultural information systems, which generally require significant levels of operating resources. There is little evidence that users are willing to pay enough to make such services self-supporting, while pressure on government recurrent budgets often means that services descend to 'least-cost' solutions once external financing is withdrawn. This all too often results in out-of-date information that is of little relevance to the real needs of the users (e.g. market price information is given for international markets because it is available free, while data for nearby markets are omitted because they are too expensive to collect).

Provide broad, systems-oriented agricultural training, especially for women

Training and capacity building involve the empowerment of community members, enabling them to identify problems in a systems context, to analyse causes and effects, to assess options and to arrive at well-informed decisions in order to prepare to take responsibility for their own future by assuming ownership of the development process. This often requires the assistance of professional facilitators to ensure that all groups in the community have a chance to express their views, to help find appropriate technical solutions, formulate and implement community action plans, monitor results and assess outcomes. The implication of this approach is that extension services must reorient their operations by basing them on facilitative rather than prescriptive techniques; with community participation forming the keystone in determining priorities and testing possible solutions. This will involve the adoption and adaptation of participatory diagnostic tools and experiential learning methods. An essential concomitant is the formation and strengthening of common interest or resource user groups, that will strengthen the problem-solving capacities and self-reliance of rural communities. Implementation is likely to involve partnerships between governments, private sector or NGO service providers, civil society organisations and community-based groups.

With the decline in public resources for research and extension, many systems are chronically short of personnel who possess skills related to systems analysis, participatory methods and qualitative analysis techniques. The percentage of female professional staff is also deficient in most cases. To ensure that training of agricultural support professionals is broadened – particularly in systems concepts and participatory practice – the curricula of agricultural training institutions should be revised and continuing efforts made to recruit and train more women officers.

Strengthen off-farm vocational skills training, especially for youths

The farming system analyses presented in previous chapters clearly indicates that not all farm households can expect to escape from poverty through agricultural activities. In fact, a major percentage of youths will participate directly in off-farm income generating activities or exit from agriculture; few will remain employed solely in agriculture throughout their lives. Governments must strengthen vocational training aimed at alternative employment, whether within a rural setting or through migration to urban areas. In addition, schooling for younger rural children also needs strengthening, particularly at primary and secondary levels.

SCIENCE AND TECHNOLOGY

Most of the growth in food production during the past three decades has resulted from the adoption of productivity-boosting technology in areas of high agricultural potential – particularly those with relatively high and reliable rainfall or equipped with irrigation. A major challenge in the coming decades will be to generate technologies that contribute to increases in agricultural production and improvements in livelihoods in lower potential areas. For the longer term, there must be concerns about the heavy reliance of intensive agriculture on technologies that have inherently limited sustainability. 'Factory' livestock farming systems are faced with enormous problems of organic waste disposal and are increasingly seen as sources of food safety problems. Inappropriate fertiliser application is leading to nitrate pollution of surface and groundwater resources, while the uncontrolled use of pesticides is creating enormous health and environmental hazards. Equally worrying is the progressive narrowing of the genetic breadth of farm crop and animal species.

The technical foundations for 'modern' agriculture can no longer be taken for granted and there is a need to search for more sustainable strategies towards intensification. This task is urgent, given the limited extent to which thinking has been focused on more sustainable technologies for high-intensity farming, and the very long gestation period required to develop and disseminate new methods. The analyses of farming systems in this document suggest a number of important characteristics of technologies suitable for poor farmers. They also suggest some areas for technology development that offer opportunities for poverty reduction (see Box 8.3).

Five important global priority thrusts, concerned with targeting science and technology, have been identified to reduce hunger and poverty:

- Focusing technology through participatory research and development;
- Increasing land and labour productivity in high potential areas;
- Increasing labour productivity in low potential areas; and
- Promoting the adoption of biotechnology with safeguards.

Focus technology through participatory research and development
Except in regions where the Green Revolution has taken place, there are few opportunities for widespread dissemination of new agricultural technologies in the

---

Box 8.3 Promising Areas for Pro-Poor Technologies

Ideal pro-poor technologies are characterised by increased long term sustainable productivity, labour intensity, suitability for women, adaptability to seasonality, stability and resilience, compatibility with integrated and diversified systems, low external input requirements, and ease of adoptability. Promising areas include:

- Biological nitrogen fixation;
- Integrated plant nutrient management;
- Water use efficiency and water harvesting;
- Integrated soil and water management;
- Conservation agriculture;
- Agroforestry and permaculture;
- Horticulture and other minor crops;
- Medicinal crops and spices;
- Biomass production;
- Managed carbon sequestration;
- Customised crop varieties;
- Integrated intensive farming systems;
- Integrated pest management;
- Energy crops;
- Gender selection in animals; and
- Genetic resistance to animal diseases.

---

form of predetermined packages. Each farm differs in terms of its resource endowment; especially in the relation between land and labour resources, degree of access to input and output markets, and vulnerability to risk. Each household also differs in terms of needs and objectives; particularly in the extent to which farmers see production as contributing mainly to family food security as opposed to cash income. The need, therefore, is for participatory approaches to research and development that can engage farmers in diagnosing problems and in identifying possible solutions adapted to their particular circumstances. These approaches can also help to inform researchers of priority areas for investigation and enable them to better understand farmers' viewpoints and perceptions, thereby increasing the relevance of research.

Increase land and labour productivity in high potential areas
Technology does not move forward at an even pace. The major productivity gains made in rice and wheat, particularly in the 1970s and 1980s, have given way to a

slower rate of growth in the last decade and it is still not clear how this trend towards stagnation can be reversed. Nevertheless, a number of important technological breakthroughs appear to be on the horizon – including 'golden rice' and biological nitrogen fixation in non-legumes – that can be expected to have a significant impact on farming practices within the next three decades. In the meantime, substantial gains are possible from raising average yields towards the levels obtained by the best farmers, even under current technologies (see Box 8.4).

Box 8.4 Yield Gaps and Declining Productivity Gains in Rice Production[8]

The Green Revolution of the 1960s enabled rice production to rise to meet the demands of a rapidly growing world population. The average annual growth rate (AGR) in yield ranged from 1.7 to 2.3 percent over the period from 1960-1990. In the 1990's, however, rice yield AGRs have declined to only one percent and reports of actual declines in yields are being received from countries such as Thailand, India and the Philippines. The reasons for these declines are still not yet fully understood.

Over the next 30 years productivity growth must once again be accelerated to ensure food security and poverty alleviation, especially in Asia and Africa, either by lifting average yields closer to the current yield ceiling or by raising the ceiling itself. It is probable that the theoretical maximum paddy yield is not very different from that of wheat, at 20 t/ha per crop. However, yield gaps of as much as 60 percent are observed in national production systems, offering a considerable potential in this direction as well. While one component of such gaps arises from underlying natural resource and environmental constraints, a significant proportion derives from management practices. Recent studies have generated the following recommendations:

- Maintain balanced nutrient applications;
- Make all stakeholders aware of the potential dangers of excessive intensive cropping;
- Incorporate yield stabilising traits in varieties;
- Build-up levels of organic matter in the soil;
- Conduct fewer but more appropriate long-term experiments with more detailed, interdisciplinary measurements and observations;
- Monitor yield and productivity trends continuously, with due regard to multiple products;
- Develop location specific varieties and technologies, such as an integrated crop management approach like the *Rice Check System* used in Australia;
- Intensify technology transfer activities using successful models such as contiguous area demonstrations;
- Reduce post harvest losses; and
- Improve linkages between research, development, extension services and farmers.

[8] Abstracted from Case Study 1, Annex 1.

It should also be remembered that there are traditional systems – older rice-based systems for example – that have remained highly productive because of skilled labour and management, despite continuous cropping for centuries. Nevertheless, decreasing average farm size and fragmentation of holdings is becoming an increasingly important constraint to development in a number of key Asian systems.

Different sets of technologies offer opportunities for growth in areas with high labour to land ratios, where there are often attractive options for the labour intensive production of high value commodities. A variety of high-value enterprises should be considered. Organic products offer one alternative (high value, high labour). Parts of many high-density systems are becoming peri-urban, providing good market potential in spite of population pressure – especially for vegetable growing and related agro-processing, small-scale dairying, small ruminant fattening and poultry production. Moreover, within these areas the abundant labour may be advantageously used to improve the productive capacity of land; for example through terracing or drainage.

Increase labour productivity in low potential areas

Areas of low agricultural potential often face more serious labour availability constraints than those related to land availability. Where productive activities have to be dispersed (e.g. transhumant herds, scattered production plots, food gathering), and where the functioning of the household requires lengthy journeys for basic inputs such as firewood or water, labour can rapidly become a key factor limiting output. Such limitations are sometimes exacerbated by out-migration or civil conflict, as has been the case in the Central Andean High Altitude Mixed Farming System or in many parts of Africa. Research on production technology has traditionally focused upon maximising returns to land rather than labour; replacing labour with capital only in more intensive systems (e.g. two-wheeled tractors in intensive rice systems). Yet there are good opportunities for improving labour productivity in many systems; examples include altering the time of land preparation from wet to dry season by using of cover crops to control weeds, by investing in draft power and by simple improvements to hand tools such as punch planters.

Where shortage of labour constrains production and incomes and there is easy access to more land, there is considerable interest in labour-saving technologies such as zero tillage and the use of draft animals for cultivation and haulage. Given the right stimulus, rural families will often convert labour resources into productive assets. Other opportunities for cutting cash expenditures without losing output include substitution of mineral nutrients by those from organic sources and changing from pesticide-based pest control systems to IPM.

Promote the adoption of biotechnology with safeguards.

Biotechnology offers a great potential for the customisation of new varieties of cash and food crops to specific farming systems and problems, if adequate safety standards are applied and provided that the new materials are affordable (see Box 8.5). The customisation of varieties, particularly those that can cope with abiotic stresses prevalent in low potential areas, has the potential to benefit poor farmers throughout the developing world.

To the extent that the lead in biotechnology applications will lie with the private sector, deliberate measures will have to be taken at the international level to create incentives for expanded research on themes relevant to poor farmers in developing countries – whose needs would otherwise be by-passed. Such measures could include international public funding for biotechnology research and development

---

Box 8.5 A Biotechnology Strategy for Poor Farmers[9]

International biotechnology initiatives geared toward the benefit of the poor are scattered among bilateral agencies, donors, private foundations and multilateral organizations. Pooling these resources to focus on priorities that address the specific needs of poor farmers is desirable. A global strategy which incorporates opportunities for partnerships among stakeholders – focusing on the needs of poor farmers and food consumers – offers considerable potential benefit for developing countries. Components of this strategy might include:

i) *Technology transfer.* Although most biotechnology research is currently conducted by the private sector in developed countries, a number of technologies offer potential benefit to poor farmers in developing countries. International organizations can assist these countries to identify and negotiate access to technologies on favourable terms, thus facilitating partnerships between developed and developing country and improving developing country capacity in biotechnology. An inventory of currently available technologies of potential use to developing countries would be a useful step. Since subsistence farmers are not in direct competition with industrial agriculture, these initiatives allow developing countries an easy entry to adopt the technology from the bottom-up.

ii) *Technology development.* Currently, most developing countries are taking advantage of technological spillovers from developed countries. It is crucial to assess what are the missing technologies that need to be developed specifically for developing countries and which offer potential for improving the food security. This can be done by assessing local constraints that cannot be solved by conventional means. It is recommended that developed countries increase their development assistance to biotechnology-related activities. There have been excellent studies and surveys done by ISNAR on national and regional institutional capacity, including priority setting and constraints to production, both infrastructural and biological. At FAO, an inventory for available technologies, including those in the pipelines, is being developed. It is important that these data be consolidated for regional and national project design. It would also promote better co-ordination of international and national initiatives.

---

[9] Abstracted from Case Study 2, Annex I.

focused on improving the performance of tropical food crops as well as livestock. There is also a need for safeguards and regulations to reduce risk to indigenous genetic materials from contamination, and to guard against further erosion of genetic resources of farm crops and livestock. The regulatory mechanisms, including regional agreements and risk assessment protocols, need to be put in place as a matter of urgency in order to permit safe movement of useful genetic materials into and within developing regions.

NATURAL RESOURCES AND CLIMATE

Increasing pressure on the use of scarce land and water resources, accelerating environmental degradation, and the possibility of climatic change are challenging the sustainability of farming systems in all regions, even those with low population densities. Four important global priority thrusts have been identified, concerned with achieving more sustainable and productive use of natural resources and minimising adverse climatic effects:

- Focusing on the sustainability of natural resource use;
- Recapitalising soil fertility;
- Improving water resources management; and
- Increasing capacity to respond to climatic changes.

Focus on the sustainability of natural resource use

There is now a heightened awareness, among both the public at large and farmers in general, of the need to conserve and productively manage natural resources. Public interest in industrialised countries assigns a high priority to the maintenance of natural resources for future generations and to reducing global environmental damage. This provides the main justification for international public funding towards the development and promotion of methods that maintain or enhance natural capital and increase global environmental benefits (e.g. increased carbon sequestration through higher soil organic matter levels, reduced production of greenhouse gases and less pollution of international waters, etc.).

Declining productivity and farm incomes on degraded lands have highlighted the need for farmers to improve the management of natural resources. Improved land management can be stimulated by the promotion of practices that not only generate environmental benefits, but also rapidly yield tangible returns. Thus, public research and extension should focus on measures that increase farm incomes whilst also conserving and enhancing the condition of natural resources. These measures are typified by minimum tillage technologies and integrated plant nutrient management, which simultaneously reduce production costs while improving *in situ* retention of moisture and raising soil fertility, thereby raising yields, reducing yield variability and cutting erosion.

In many situations, conservation agriculture, involving reduced tillage, offers promising possibilities for increasing labour productivity and the efficiency of input use while simultaneously reducing moisture stress. Conservation agriculture has been promoted in a number of farming systems, and its performance in Latin America – and more recently in Africa – has been promising.

Recapitalise soil fertility

The loss of soil fertility, with associated stagnation of productivity, cuts across most farming systems in all regions. The loss is particularly acute in irrigated wheat and rice-based farming systems, some rainfed farming systems (e.g. the Maize Mixed Farming System in Africa) and highland farming systems (e.g. the High Altitude Mixed (Central Andes) Farming System). Because of declining commodity prices, exchange rate adjustments and reduced subsidies, application of mineral fertiliser on staple crops has frequently become unprofitable and its utilisation by small farmers in most developing countries has fallen sharply. Farmers have not yet fully compensated for this loss through greater use of organic sources of nutrients, more balanced use of nutrient applications or adoption of soil conservation practices to minimise erosion. As the greatest concentration of nutrients occurs in surface soils, the degradation and loss of topsoil can severely reduce yields. The cost of investment in preventative measures is far less than the costs and time required to restore the original level of soil fertility once erosion has occurred.

Priority initiatives to rectify the current situation include: (i) greater use of green manures, enriched fallows and other sources of organic materials, including composting; (ii) expanded use of biological nitrogen fixation; (iii) better integration of crops and livestock; (iv) wider adoption of inter-cropping systems; (v) expansion of silvo-pastoral systems, especially on steeper slopes; and (vi) improvement of fertiliser import and distribution facilities and services with a view to reducing the farmgate price of fertilisers.

Most of these initiatives place little reliance on external inputs – and hence on input supply and financing services – and some have the advantage of enabling farmers to increase the productivity of their land through converting labour resources, which often have low opportunity cost in the off-season, into productive assets. This type of investment can play a extremely important role in building-up soil fertility, improving land management (e.g. terracing steep hillsides, draining bottomlands) and intensifying land use (e.g. planting tree crops, building fishponds). The creation of a policy environment that gives smallholders confidence in the future of farming, including reasonable security of land tenure, is an important trigger for this sort of initiative.

Improve water resources management

Although the adverse consequences of water shortages are more evident in some regions than others, water supply constraints are important in specific farming systems in all parts of the developing world, e.g. the marginal drylands of Latin America or the agro-pastoral systems of Sub-Saharan Africa. In most cases, the rising demand for water for domestic and industrial purposes associated with urbanisation will greatly intensify the competition for available fresh water. Where farming systems are rainfed, strategies must focus on improving the capture of rainfall and the utilisation of soil moisture. Possible measures include: (i) making minimum and no-tillage technologies accessible to small farmers, as done successfully in Brazil; (ii) providing true-breeding, short-season crop cultivars and drought resistant fodder species that can maintain livestock populations through dry periods; and (iii) expanding water-harvesting efforts for small-scale capture and utilisation of run-off, as pioneered successfully in such countries as India and Niger.[10]

Poor water use efficiency is often the result of water being considered a low value or free public good. For irrigated farming systems, changes are needed in the key areas of water and rural energy pricing policy and strengthening local management of irrigation infrastructure; both of which are important elements in increasing the technical efficiency of water use.

Increase capacity to respond to climatic changes

Changes in the frequency of extreme climatic events – whether it be temperatures, precipitation or atmospheric events – and shifts in agro-ecological conditions including those triggered by rising sea levels are likely to alter farming practices fundamentally in some vulnerable areas, such as coastal areas, semiarid zones and steep lands. Droughts, floods and hurricanes or typhoons are all expected to become much more frequent.

A better understanding of the probable nature and impact of climatic changes is urgently needed, and appropriate adjustments of agricultural policies and projects are required to mitigate adverse effects. The development of watershed protection and anti-desertification measures is likely to take on a greater urgency. It is also necessary to establish a greater capacity, both nationally and internationally, to respond effectively to damaging weather events, such as floods and droughts, to minimise their long-term impact on resource management and rural livelihoods.

---

[10] See Case Study 4, Annex 1.

9

CONCLUSIONS AND
WAYS FORWARD

...

This book has examined trends and challenges facing farming systems in the six developing regions of the world and has proposed strategic priorities for poverty reduction, increased food security and agricultural growth. Since half the total population of developing regions – and a majority of the hungry and the poor – are farmers and their families, the successful implementation of these recommendations would represent a substantial contribution towards the achievement of the international development goals of halving hunger and poverty by 2015.

This final Chapter begins by highlighting the key findings presented in Chapter 8. It then considers the implications of the proposed priorities for the roles of key stakeholders. Various ways to extend these analyses, at global and national levels, are then suggested. The Chapter ends with a closing note that attempts to distil the essential changes in development practice which would arise from adopting these recommendations.

HIGHLIGHTS OF FINDINGS

SOURCES OF AGRICULTURAL POVERTY REDUCTION

Some of the most abject poverty in the world is concentrated in farming communities. Many farm women, children and men depend on a precarious balance of multiple livelihoods, in which hunger is a daily fact of life and where access to basic services, education, health and water supplies is even more difficult than for the urban poor. Contrary to conventional wisdom, a majority of poor farm families live in areas with medium to high rainfall and significant agricultural development potential. Although there is also considerable poverty in dry and remote areas with low agricultural development potential, they support many fewer people than the more intensively farmed areas. Most commonly, the world's rural poor are concentrated in areas where population density is high and farms are

341

small, growing food crops at a low-to-medium level of intensity. Often, off-farm income represents an important source of household livelihood.

The analysis presented in Chapters 2 to 7 showed how changes in population, markets, technologies, policies, institutions and information flows are simultaneously placing new pressures on, and opening new opportunities for, the smallholder farming community. Where land is available, population growth and market demand are fuelling an expansion of cultivated area; although not always into areas appropriate for sustainable agriculture. In most places, however, land is scarce and incentives for good resource management are absent; soils are being depleted, holdings are shrinking and farmers are sliding deeper into poverty. Increasingly, farm families are being forced to resort to seasonal, and ultimately permanent, migration in search of alternative livelihoods. On the other hand, where support structures exist and policies promote effective resource management, small farmers are successfully intensifying and diversifying production, enhancing their resource base and increasing off-farm income through family employment in local agro-industries.

The improvement of farm household livelihoods that would be necessary to meet the international goals of halving poverty and hunger by 2015 could be derived from five main sources, which correspond to the predominant farm household strategies for escaping hunger and poverty, as shown in Box 9.1.

Box 9.1 Household Strategies for Hunger and Poverty Reduction

- Intensification of existing patterns of farm production;

- Diversification of production, including increased market orientation and value added post-harvest activities;

- Increased operated farm size, either through consolidation of existing holdings or the extension of farming on new agricultural land;

- Increased off-farm income to supplement farming activities; and

- Exit from agriculture, involving migration from rural areas.

The relative importance of these poverty reduction strategies differs between system categories. In order to facilitate policy and programme formulation, the three most important poverty reduction strategies for each farming system category are shown in Table 9.1. In aggregate terms, a larger proportion of poverty reduction is expected from improvements on the farm (diversification, intensification and increased farm size) than from off-farm sources (increased off-farm income and exit from agriculture). In the context of farm improvement, diversification is a key strategy for poverty reduction in all eight system categories, whilst intensification is important in those systems with higher potential, notably

Table 9.1 Key Strategies for Poverty Reduction by Farming System Category

Poverty Reduction Strategies	Irrigated schemes (small holder)	Wetland rice based	Rainfed humid	Rainfed highland	Rainfed dry/cold	Dualistic (large/small)	Coastal artisanal fishing	Urban based
Intensification	■	■	■			■		
Diversification	■	■	■	■	■	■	■	■
Increased Farm Size						■		■
Increased off-farm Income	■	■	■	■	■		■	■
Exit from Agriculture				■	■		■	

Note: See Table 8.2 for details. Key strategies are those which rank first, second or third for each system category.

irrigation and dualistic systems. Increased farm, herd or business size is of significance only in dualistic and urban based systems.

Millions of farmers are also expected to escape poverty by increasing off-farm income, which is second only to diversification as a key strategy for poverty reduction, in seven of the eight system categories. The exit of farmers from agriculture within a particular farming system is expected to be an increasingly common phenomenon, and of particular importance among smallholders in low potential rainfed highland and dry/cold systems.

As indicated above, there are important complementarities between the poverty reduction strategies. In fact, many farmers simultaneously intensify and diversify their production. The intensification and diversification of farming creates the conditions for the development of the non-farm economy and the increase of off-farm income, which in turn stimulate further agricultural growth. Over time, poorer agricultural households may progressively increase the emphasis on off-farm income until they finally abandon agriculture altogether.

A GLOBAL STRATEGY FOR THE REDUCTION OF HUNGER AND POVERTY

The common elements of a global strategy for reduction of hunger and poverty were outlined in Chapter 8, and are summarised in the following paragraphs and in Box 9.2 below.

Refocusing institutions, policies and public goods
A key challenge in relation to the reduction of hunger and poverty among farm households is the creation and effective delivery of reliable and pro-poor international, national and local public goods, within an environment of established

---

Box 9.2 Elements of a Global Strategy for Reduction of Hunger and Poverty

REFOCUSING INSTITUTIONS, POLICIES AND PUBLIC GOODS
- Establish equitable, secure, transferable and flexible resource user rights;
- Provide sustainable infrastructure to poorly serviced areas;
- Support small-scale farmer managed irrigation schemes;
- Continue agricultural policy reform and strengthen meso-level institutions; and
- Strengthen targeted safety nets.

BENEFITING FROM TRADE LIBERALISATION AND MARKET DEVELOPMENT
- Ensure trade liberalisation is a two-way street;
- Focus smallholders on labour-intensive or niche products;
- Satisfy household food security needs during the transition;
- Foster competitive business, especially small rural enterprises; and
- Support agricultural market development.

ENHANCING AGRICULTURAL INFORMATION AND HUMAN CAPITAL
- Ensure wide availability of agricultural information;
- Provide broad, systems-oriented agricultural training, especially for women; and
- Strengthen off-farm vocational skills training, especially for youths.

DEPLOYING SCIENCE AND TECHNOLOGY FOR POVERTY REDUCTION
- Focus technology through participatory research and development;
- Increase labour productivity in low potential areas;
- Increase land and labour productivity in high potential areas; and
- Promote the adoption of biotechnology with safeguards.

ACHIEVING MORE SUSTAINABLE AND PRODUCTIVE USE OF NATURAL RESOURCES
- Focus on the sustainability of natural resource use;
- Recapitalise soil fertility;
- Improve water resources management; and
- Increase capacity to respond to climatic changes.

---

law and order, and enabling policies and institutions. Small farmers require equitable, secure, transferable and flexible resource user rights and sustainable infrastructure – including roads and the structures to support small-scale farmer managed irrigation. In order for farmers to manage their resources sustainably whilst also benefiting from economic liberalisation, stronger local and meso-level institutions and effective alliances among stakeholders are necessary. Targeted safety nets for the poor will continue to be needed in order to overcome natural disasters, and to support small farmers unable to adjust quickly enough to changes in world market conditions.

Benefiting from trade liberalisation and market development

The reduction of rural poverty depends to a large extent on the ability of small farmers to respond effectively to the changes brought about by trade liberalisation and local market development. By focusing on labour intensive activities where they possess a comparative advantage, many poor farmers can benefit from these changes and escape poverty. Even farmers unable to adapt may benefit through employment created as others make the transition. In either case, a focus on safeguarding household food security during the adjustment process will be crucial. An enabling environment for market development is also vital, and must include measures to foster small-scale rural enterprises, as these are often key market and employment sources for smallholder households. Mechanisms are required to overcome market failure, especially in respect of monopolies and externalities.

At the international level, there is a widespread belief within developing countries that trade liberalisation has not been a symmetrical process, as many key agricultural and non-agricultural markets in industrialised countries remain heavily protected. At the same time, commercial farmers in the industrialised world – often generously subsidised – are using trade liberalisation to supply urban markets in developing countries. A failure by the international community to address this imbalance could have adverse consequences for poverty reduction and threaten the entire liberalisation process.

Enhancing agricultural information and human capital

Escape from hunger and poverty will necessitate wider availability of information of all types to small-scale producers and enterprises. Poor and vulnerable groups – including female-headed farm households – need to be assisted to benefit from the information revolution. To be sustainable, this process will require the participation of the private sector. To take advantage of available information, the boosting of the social and human capital of poor farm families through extensive rural education and farmer training is essential. Many rural children will never enter agriculture and their training must reflect their future employment in manufacturing and services. The full potential of available benefits will only accrue to countries which simultaneously overhaul, and invest in, appropriate training of agricultural technicians and professionals.

Improving technology and management of natural resources

The contrasting technological needs of different farming systems deserve fuller recognition. To promote growth in high population density areas, land productivity and enterprise diversification will be important; whereas in low potential and low population density areas, technologies that boost labour productivity are required. It is expected that biotechnology will have substantial effects on plant and animal breeding and disease control technologies; but safeguards are required to ensure that the poor also gain from these changes. There is substantial scope for reducing yield gaps in both high and low potential areas, and this can also assist the poor, whose yields are generally below average.

The revolution in agricultural technology which has occurred in the last few decades, has opened new opportunities for livelihood improvement for some small farmers, but has by-passed many others. Some new technologies – particularly new crop varieties – are scale neutral, but others, such as many types of farm machinery, are irrelevant to small farmers in developing countries. As technologies come to reflect more closely the complexity of the farming systems to which they will be applied, there is an increasing tendency towards integrated production practices and the fuller involvement of farmers in participatory development and adoption processes. Rural communities must be supported in taking the lead in planning, implementing and evaluating agricultural development activities. However, governments must ensure an appropriate balance between the site-specific and often short-term goals of farmers and the long-term investment in public goods required for the well-being of future generations (e.g. preservation of biodiversity, carbon sequestration).

Sustainable resource management will provide the foundation for long-term poverty reduction over coming decades. Both soil fertility and improved water resources management are becoming crucial areas. Finally, any strategy for poverty reduction would be incomplete without mechanisms for increasing international and local capacity to manage and respond to climate change, as this is projected to have significant impacts on many poor agricultural areas during the coming decades.

REFOCUSING STAKEHOLDER CONTRIBUTIONS

The reduction of agricultural hunger and poverty depends ultimately on the decisions and actions of the 500 million farm households that constitute the farming community in developing regions. It is evident, however, that their potential contribution will not be fully realised in the absence of a socio-economic environment that solicits, encourages, supports and protects their aspirations, ideas and initiatives. A vital component of this environment must be supplied by a vigorous private sector – the creation of which has formed the centrepiece of many recent efforts to promote agricultural growth. Nonetheless, despite all that has been written about the benefits of reducing the influence of government on the process of rural development, a central tenet of this book is that the adequate provision of public goods is still a crucial element of the development process. Effective farmer-based development will, therefore, require the participation of a wide range of players; from the poor farmers and their communities, through the private sector and civil society, to local and national governments and international agencies. The refocusing of the roles of each of these stakeholder groups is discussed in the following sections and summarised in Box 9.3.

Box 9.3 Refocusing Stakeholder Contributions for Poverty Reduction

POOR FARMERS AND THEIR COMMUNITIES
- Identifying constraints and planning local level rural development;
- Managing natural resources;
- Developing sustainable technology;
- Financing development based on savings;
- Processing and trading farm produce; and
- Reducing vulnerability to natural disasters and economic shocks.

CIVIL SOCIETY ORGANISATIONS
- Articulating the needs of poor farmers;
- Building social capital with a focus on women and youth;
- Generating development innovations and catalysing entrepreneurship; and
- Disseminating technology and market information.

BUSINESS AND COMMERCE
- Developing markets and introducing production and processing technologies;
- Creating employment and adding value to agricultural produce;
- Financing and providing market information and extension; and
- Providing a wider range of services previously the prerogative of the public sector.

LOCAL AND NATIONAL GOVERNMENTS
- Maintaining the legislative, political and fiscal enabling environment;
- Providing incentives for sustainable resource management;
- Supporting farmer-led learning and technology development;
- Decentralising rural public services, responsive to local needs;
- Creating development alliances and partnerships; and
- Delivering relevant education and training in rural areas.

INTERNATIONAL AGENCIES
- Focusing key stakeholders on issues related to sustainable poverty reduction;
- Mediating transnational and global sustainable resource, pest and disease management mechanisms;
- Mobilising resources for poverty-oriented environmental programmes;
- Monitoring environmental and climate trends and their impact on poverty;
- Forging public-private partnerships for technology development;
- Sponsoring international codes of conduct, standards and regulatory frameworks; and
- Encouraging foreign capital flows into investments that will benefit poor farmers.

Unlock the potential of poor farmers and their communities

The decision making skills, technical know-how, physical labour, capital accumulation, initiative and creativity of farming communities must underpin any successful global poverty reduction programme. However, the specific socio-economic circumstances of different communities greatly affects their relationships with other actors, including the private sector, government and civil society.

At one end of the spectrum, farming communities with systems based on commercial operations, are mainly dependent on the private sector. Nonetheless, they continue to rely on government for a conducive policy environment – including regulatory frameworks – and for much technology development, plus agricultural information to improve the efficiency of operations. At the other end of the spectrum, there are communities with limited land and financial resources, and very weak market linkages. Provision of public goods to these areas could greatly accelerate development and make private sector participation more attractive. For these farmers the pace of future development is largely dependent on government support for infrastructure, agricultural research, information dissemination and market development, and on the provision of safety nets whenever natural or economic disaster strikes.

Community involvement and actions also vary greatly with socio-economic circumstances. In the most advantaged communities the focus tends to be on environmental and natural resource management. In contrast, disadvantaged communities are likely to focus more on the development of basic social infrastructure. There is great potential for communities to identify local constraints and subsequently plan local rural development. In general, however, farming communities in developing regions have had limited involvement in rural development planning. The challenge exists to foster community-based management committees, on which local stakeholders – including government and private sectors – are represented, as well as to provide communities with the tools they need to identify, formulate and implement actions that will accelerate development. Local resource management is a related area in which communities can also take the lead. The advantage of farmers' decisions on resource management – notwithstanding the shorter decision horizons of individual farmers compared to governments – is that they better reflect local circumstances. Where the national interest might diverge significantly from local interests, joint management mechanisms are appropriate.

A further role of poor communities is to develop measures that ensure a systematic reduction of risks, notably the reduction of the vulnerability of poor farm households to natural and economic shocks. Perhaps the farming community's most under-utilised role lies in the area of innovation, technology development and dissemination. The potential for investment in this area is enormous and has been demonstrated in numerous Farming Systems Research or Participatory Technology Development field experiences. This type of initiative should be at the very centre of effective public and private sector technology development.

The capacity of farmers to accumulate savings and to finance development – even in areas of severe poverty – is frequently under-rated. In general, savings-based microfinance has a good track record and should be promoted wherever feasible. In this way, local initiatives can become the self-sustaining core of rural financial systems, linked to external financial institutions. Such mechanisms underpin the wider involvement of poor farmers in the processing and trading of farm produce.

SUPPORT THE ENGAGEMENT OF CIVIL SOCIETY PARTNERS

When their views are actively solicited, poor farmers often say that an important characteristic of poverty is *lack of voice*. In many developing countries, NGOs have traditionally played an important role in articulating the needs of poor farmers and other vulnerable groups. Farmers' organisations often claim to represent small farmers too, but in many countries commercial farmers have traditionally dominated the debate and activities of such groups. Building the capacity of NGOs and small farmers' organisations for advocacy and service provision, such as in the work of IFAD and FAO in Southern Africa, is a high priority.

Whilst NGOs and farmers' organisations have a well-established track record in a wide variety of development fields, their core role in relation to poverty reduction should focus on building social capital (e.g. farmers' groups, farmers' networks, small enterprise associations), catalysing entrepreneurship and disseminating public information. Greater social capital, including strengthened farmers' groups and community organisations, will underpin many aspects of agricultural development in the future. Some civil society organisations can also contribute further through their development innovations. Many of the current best practices in agricultural development have been piloted by NGOs, and such efforts should be systematically expanded.

FOSTER COMPETITIVE AGRIBUSINESS AND COMMERCE AS TOOLS FOR POVERTY REDUCTION

The future role of the private sector covers marketing, processing and other forms of value added, as well as job creation, financing, technology transfer and information dissemination. Experience has shown that, particularly when acting through trade and sector associations, it is capable of undertaking roles – such as phytosanitary inspection, market information and extension – that were at one time considered only possible through the public sector. Nevertheless, despite their versatility, private initiatives must depend on the public sector for the establishment and maintenance of the basic legislative, political and fiscal environment in which they operate. Where no norms and standards exist, where they are unenforced, or where established players are permitted to erect barriers to the entry of newcomers, the role assumed by the private sector can act to increase poverty among small farmers. The ideal situation is to facilitate the making of profits through the acceleration of agricultural poverty reduction.

Where farms are very small and mainly subsistence oriented there are few incentives for larger private companies to be involved in marketing, as the availability of farm products is limited in terms of range of products and volume. In these areas, local traders and small enterprises – sometimes initiated by farmers themselves – are likely to operate more successfully; dealing with low product volumes and often advancing production inputs on credit. Even in these cases, however, local enterprises will often act as agents of larger regional or nationally-based firms that possess the capital and technological capability to provide required inputs or supply agricultural products to large urban and international markets. All too often, small-scale enterprises must operate on the fringes of the formal sector, due to restrictive and complex procedures imposed by legislation and government policy. Removing such obstacles to small-enterprise operation would greatly assist smallholders in developing marketing linkages.

In some farming systems, larger companies have invested directly in agricultural production (e.g. industrial crops). However, political and legal restrictions on land ownership, perceived risk, and relatively low returns to capital, have increasingly led large corporations to reduce their production activities and to adopt a primarily intermediate role. This 'withdrawal' process has often been used to justify public sector investment in large-scale processing facilities previously operated by international enterprises. In a number of countries, governments still maintain such state managed enterprises, whether in processing, marketing, input supply or other areas. These enterprises have, however, been notoriously inefficient and monopolistic, and their losses have led to a serious drain on government revenues. Although many have been privatised in recent years, there is a need for governments to complete the transfer process of these inefficient enterprises to the private sector.

INCREASE EFFECTIVENESS OF LOCAL AND NATIONAL GOVERNMENT ACTIONS FOR POVERTY REDUCTION

Notwithstanding the greater roles that farmers, civil society and the private sector will play in poverty reduction, the contributions of local and national government are critical. These include the improvement of the enabling environment for other stakeholders, as well as the provision of specific knowledge-related public goods – including technology and education for poor farmers – which are examined in the following section. Because of the prevalence of implementation failures, the delivery of public goods and services is also discussed below.

Priority public goods related to agricultural poverty reduction
The term public goods is often associated with physical structures such as roads, hospitals and ports. However, there is a very important set of 'soft' public goods related to the creation of a conducive development environment and the establishment of adequate capacity for the provision of effective public services. These include: (i) ensuring public security; (ii) regulations such as quarantine and food safety; (iii) effective mechanisms for fostering competition, as well as enforcing and resolving conflicts; (iv) education and training; (v) research and information dissemination; and (vi) safety nets.

Government intervention for rural poverty reduction should be facilitative and complementary, not controlling and directive. Decentralisation of government services to local regions and areas will make their development agenda more relevant to local needs. At the same time, government has an important function to create local stakeholder alliances and to support local capacity building, for planning and implementation – either directly or indirectly through contracting NGOs. It is worth emphasising that the required public goods will not be adequately provided where organisations are crippled by funding shortfalls or bureaucratic procedures that limit their ability to sustain the effective delivery of public services to rural areas.

In addition to the need to regulate private enterprise through a suitable normative framework, an efficient public sector land administration system is critical to secure usufruct for poor farmers, ensure functioning land markets, and to facilitate land consolidation. Similarly, although the private sector and civil society will play the key role in information dissemination, governments need to create an enabling environment and ensure that relevant information reaches vulnerable groups.

Perhaps the single most important public good that can be provided by governments, however, is effective primary and secondary education in rural areas. In combination with participatory processes and farmer-led learning, education empowers farmers to become dynamic partners in development, rather than passive beneficiaries. Most studies show that level of schooling is strongly correlated with the adoption of technology, the local development of alternative livelihoods and out-migration to more remunerative employment. There is a need for rural education to recognise explicitly the reality that many rural children and youths will earn their livelihoods beyond the agricultural sector; and thus to strengthen the provision of vocational training for off-farm employment.

Effective delivery of public goods

Poverty reduction depends not only on the adequate funding of public goods, but also on an appropriate mode of delivery; some effective modalities are listed in Box 9.4. Successful outcomes, both for intensive, complex farming systems in high potential areas, as well as for risk-prone systems in lower potential environments, are often the result of integrated approaches. Whilst integrated rural development projects implemented during the 1970s and 1980s proved institutionally unwieldy and yielded poor long-term results, recent successful experiences with high quality participatory and multi-stakeholder approaches suggest that experimentation with a new generation of integrated service delivery models would be worthwhile. The successes that have been observed demonstrate that improvements in household livelihoods and resource management require co-ordinated attention.

Box 9.4 Some Characteristics of Effective Delivery Modalities for Public Goods

- Facilitative and complementary;
- Integrating service delivery;
- Decentralised, responsive to local needs;
- Applying participatory methods;
- Involving multiple stakeholders and partnership models;
- Building on farmers groups and associations;
- Using matching grants;
- Encouraging farmer-led learning; and
- Recognising vulnerable groups especially women and youth.

When decentralisation occurs in the context of greater local control over resources and appropriate local capacity building, it can bring decision-making closer to the level of the farm household and so ensure relevance in the planning and delivery of public goods. A decentralised system can be better tailored to the diverse needs of local farming systems. However, successful decentralisation requires adequate resources and expertise at the local level, and responsibilities must be passed to regional, local and community governments with corresponding budgetary adjustments. The capture of resources and services by local elites must also be avoided.

Matching grant schemes are another promising mechanism for ensuring that public goods respond to local needs. Recipients will not contribute their own resources unless they value the intervention. At the same time, matching grants provide a way of channelling resources towards specific public priorities through the establishment of specific funding categories. The recipients' contributions also represent additional resources, which may not have been available in the absence of the scheme. Given both transparent criteria and selection processes, an open invitation for proposals generally results in an improved portfolio of activities. Adding a competitive element can further enhance the effectiveness of these schemes.

Farm households have a great potential for experimentation, learning and exchange of experience; and it is this type of innovation and learning that lies at the heart of the evolution of farming systems. There is considerable scope for investing in systematic support for all types of farmer-led learning; for example in testing and adaptation of technologies and farmer-to-farmer extension. Although the development of specific innovations cannot be planned, a number of measures can accelerate the innovation process. These include fostering adult learning, innovation circles, prizes and other forms of recognition, plus the systematic assessment and documentation of innovations.

The formation of associations or groups of poor farmers or small traders can greatly increase their economic power – especially when confronted with powerful players such as large traders or agribusiness firms. Associations may reduce barriers to entry and operating costs, and can facilitate the development of endogenous capacity, whether it be in identifying and adopting technologies, accessing financing, or simply improving knowledge of market conditions and requirements. Such groups also provide a point of entry for the planning and design of a wide range of public goods.

Much of the variation within farming systems arises from differences in family composition. Female-headed households tend to control fewer assets and have less available labour, yet they often represent a disproportionate number of the chronically poor. During the implementation of programmes, it should be recognised that women are often confronted with more severe constraints than men in otherwise similar situations, and may well have less access to traditional rural institutions. It is now also apparent that the role of youth and children often needs to be carefully considered.

EXPAND THE ROLE OF INTERNATIONAL PUBLIC GOODS

Regional and global public institutions have a crucial role to play in sustainable agricultural development and poverty reduction. In the context of the rapid pace of change in policies and development problems, international agencies can act as clearing houses for information and experience in order to create global public awareness and to keep key stakeholders updated on critical emerging issues. Globalisation has increased the need for internationally agreed modes of behaviour and for standards that contribute to fairness, transparency and safety in international commercial relations. Progress has been made in establishing international codes of conduct in such areas as fisheries, and in obtaining prior informed consent agreements covering trade in genetically modified organisms and in pesticides. The work of the Codex Alimentarius Commission on food standards is also of major importance in safeguarding food safety and providing standards which can be applied to traded goods – thereby reducing transaction costs. Over the coming years, the need for extending the scope and depth of such fora and agreements is expected to rise quite rapidly. The development of a code of good farming practice could be one contribution.

One of the major challenges in the near future will be to develop practical means of mediating transnational and global mechanisms for resource, pest and disease management – including, for example, medfly, onchocerciasis and tsetse. The creation of incentives to farmers to adopt more sustainable land management could include the sequestration of greenhouse gases through adjustments to tillage methods and through afforestation. The Clean Development Mechanism offers a potentially attractive means of increasing transfers between developed and developing countries, but considerable difficulties remain in developing low cost and reliable verification methods.

Measures at an international level to reduce the vulnerability of rural populations to disasters include steps to reduce the risk of conflict – for instance sponsoring of agreements on the sharing of international water resources. They also include: (i) improvements in early warning systems relating to adverse climatic events; (ii) timely interventions to prevent the spread of transboundary livestock and crop pests and diseases; and (iii) brokering of measures to ensure the sustainable productivity of shared agro- and marine ecosystems.

The creation of the Global Environment Facility (GEF) is an acknowledgement of the need to mobilise resources internationally in order to encourage individual countries to undertake actions consistent with the goals of international conventions (on sustainable development, biodiversity, etc.), which would generate environmental benefits beyond their borders and to compensate them for the marginal costs of securing such actions. The reach of the Facility, however, remains very small in relation to the scale of the threats. There is also a need to provide technical assistance and to increase the intensity of global monitoring of natural resources – especially the condition of oceans and forests – and to ensure that findings can be translated into effective damage limitation measures.

International research efforts now involve new partnerships that are being created to share costs and experience in technology development. Biotechnology is likely to spawn a variety of models for public-private partnerships at national and international level. The setting of regional and global research priorities will also require international research partnerships, perhaps focused on common problems across the farming systems outlined in this book.

At present, the flows of foreign direct investment to middle income countries are increasing; some of which are allocated to agricultural production (e.g. intensive poultry production) and to agricultural services (e.g. variety development, input provision and processing). In aggregate, however, foreign direct investment would appear to have had limited impact on food insecurity or poverty reduction. International financial institutions have, potentially, an important future role in encouraging further foreign capital flows to least developed countries and into investments that will benefit poor farmers.

WAYS FORWARD: BUILDING ON THIS BOOK

The analysis contained in this book is based on wide-ranging expert judgement, selected secondary data and the latest available spatial data on population, resource use and climate. The analytical frame is consistent with recent global trends, which are generally widely recognised. However, present trends could be radically modified by unanticipated world events. The most significant of these factors emerging in recent years have been climate change, HIV/AIDS and globalisation.

While there was remarkable consistency in the qualitative judgements of the wide range of experts who participated in the assessments, quantitative data proved far more difficult to assemble. FAO agro-ecological zone and statistical databases provided an excellent point of departure for the analysis. In recent years satellite-based imagery and associated databases have become available, and data on natural resources, population, climate and irrigation have largely been derived from these sources. For the farming systems that were analysed in detail, information was extracted from local studies and typical administrative areas, and then extrapolated across the system. However, the quality of local data available varied widely from one region to another, and proved almost impossible to access for countries of the former Soviet Union.

Remarkably, it proved impossible to consistently identify either local statistical data or GIS databases that map the sub-national extent of poverty or hunger[1] across the developing world, and this probably constituted the largest data gap faced by the authors. In the face of this shortcoming, expert judgement, framed within available national and regional data, was relied upon for specific poverty estimates. Spatial data for livestock populations were also only available for some regions.

It is expected that, within two to three years, spatially accurate databases, of hunger, poverty, human and animal populations, and crop areas, will become available. At this point, the updating of this analysis on a global scale would generate a more detailed picture of emerging trends and issues and of strategic priorities. These analyses could be further enriched by the dynamic modelling of selected farming systems, permitting planners to understand the likely impact on hunger, poverty and rates of economic growth of changes in key parameters (e.g. household incomes, or yields and prices for key agricultural products). Even with existing data, a number of useful supplementary analyses could be conducted. These concern the impact on food security and poverty of global climatic changes, of different levels of carbon sequestration, of research prioritisation, or of the strengthening of local institutions.

The focus of the analysis within this book has been at regional and global level. Applications of the farming systems framework and analytical approach at the national and sub-national levels would represent a powerful extension of this work. Not only can the framework of objectives be articulated more precisely at the national level, but much more biophysical and socio-economic data are available. The relatively small number of regional farming systems can be enriched by the definition of further sub-systems within national boundaries (preferably in consultation with neighbouring countries, so as to avoid duplication and conflicting definitions), which can then be used to refine national and local priorities.

---

[1] Innovative work being undertaken at the World Bank and FAO is leading to the development of statistical techniques to overcome this data gap, but has so far only been completed for a relatively small number of countries. A recent World Bank sponsored Poverty Atlas of South Africa, providing fully spatially referenced poverty data, is the first of its kind developed.

Other, non-national, refinements of the farming systems defined here might also prove valuable. In recent decades an increasing number of rural development investments have crossed national boundaries; an implicit recognition of the importance of farming systems in determining patterns of resource use and economic growth. Nowhere is this more important than in relation to water use among countries heavily dependent upon seasonal river flooding or aquifer recharging. Some of the most contentious issues in the Middle East and South Asia concern these transnational resources. Pastoralism also has a transnational character in a number of areas – especially in Africa. Finally, some of the key areas where agricultural growth is anticipated in the coming decades are transnational in scope; including the moist savannahs of West Africa, the Llanos of Northwest South America, and the fertile *chernozem* plains of the former Soviet Union.

CLOSING NOTE

Probably the most important message that can be drawn from this book is the great potential for reducing both hunger and poverty that resides in the improvement of smallholder farming systems. Not only is there a higher incidence of poverty and hunger in rural as opposed to urban areas, but there are many more poor people in high potential areas than in those farming systems with poor resource levels and weak market links. In view of this widespread potential, the international goals of halving hunger and poverty are achievable given the necessary political will and adequate resources to finance key strategies and investments.

The analysis of individual farming systems has revealed the great diversity of development challenges. Furthermore, household livelihood patterns vary, not only between farming systems, but also between areas within the same system and even between different households. However, this diversity can be viewed as a great potential strength which governments can exploit during the implementation of rural development programmes. If governments can create appropriate policy and institutional environments backed up by the effective provision of key public goods, farm women and men will take the necessary decisions to foster agricultural growth, the sustainable use of natural resources and a rapid reduction in hunger and poverty. This implies handing over the leadership of rural development to poor farmers and their communities, and ensuring the highest quality of local participatory and systems based support from public-private stakeholder partnerships. This, in turn, will require adequate funding of national and international public goods.

The rapid reduction of hunger and poverty is an essential first step towards ensuring the sustainable development of agriculture and of rural societies in general. Not only must rural hunger and poverty be eradicated, but farming communities also need secure access to food, water, income and information. In such an ideal future, farmers would be well educated, and be able to enjoy the same basic services as urban populations. As a result of diversification of livelihoods and the existence of effective social safety nets, their vulnerability to climatic and economic shocks would be minimized. Although within most developing countries holdings will continue to be mostly of small to medium size, farmers would have access to a far greater range of technologies for sustainable resource management and production, and would be continuously adding to these options through active learning, innovation and farmer-to-farmer exchanges. They would receive compensation for the production of environmental services and other public goods – as is already starting to happen in the industrialised world – while improved infrastructure and mechanisation would minimise the drudgery of women's work. Rural communities would possess effective and equitable mechanisms for sustainable common property management, and households would participate actively in public decision making and democratic processes, as well as negotiating with institutions and businesses on more equal terms. Moreover, farming communities would take the lead in the planning, implementation and evaluation of local development activities.

This vision of sustainable farming systems without poverty, and of farmers with secure household livelihoods, should drive the formulation of rural development strategies at all levels.

ANNEX I

CASE STUDIES

...

FULL LIST OF CASE STUDIES

All of the following case studies are fully referenced in the bibliography.

GLOBAL CASE STUDIES
Tran, D. & Nguyen, N. *Declining Productivity Gains and the Yield Gap in Rice.*
Le, H. *The Potential of Agricultural Biotechnology.*

SUB-SAHARAN AFRICA
Brinkman, R. *Development in the Moist Savanna Zone of West Africa.*

Mitti, G. *Community-based Seed Supply Systems, Zambia.*

Mascaretti, A. *Tassas - Improved Traditional Planting Pits in Niger.*

Tanner, C. *Community Based Land Tenure Reform in Mozambique.*

MIDDLE EAST AND NORTH AFRICA
Batello, C. *Farming Systems in Arid Rangelands of Syria and Jordan.*

Bazza, M. *Improved On-farm Participatory Water Management to Reduce Mining of Groundwater in Yemen.*

Fe'D'Ostiani, L. *Participatory and Integrated Watershed Management in Upland Areas of Tunisia.*

EASTERN EUROPE AND CENTRAL ASIA
Meng, E. *Advisory Services for Restructured and Co-operative Farms in Extensive Crop/Livestock Regions.*

Kopeva, D. *Transfer of Ownership and Land Fragmentation in the Transition to Family Farms in Bulgaria.*

Martinenko, A. *Natural Resource Use and Economic Viability as Affected by the Transformation of Farming Systems in Southern Ukraine.*

SOUTH ASIA

Agarwal, A. *Water Harvesting and Soil Rehabilitation in India: Potential and Practice.*

Hoque, F. *Integrated Intensified Rice Farming Systems in Bangladesh.*

Kiff, E. & Pound, B. *Integrating Crop Livestock Interactions into Hill Mixed Farming Systems, Nepal.*

Dugdill, B.T & Bennet, A. *Income Diversification in an Intensive Rice-Based System – Milk Vita in Bangladesh.*

EAST ASIA AND PACIFIC

Ishihara, Y. & Bachmann, T. *Stablizing High Altitude Swidden Cultivation in Laos.*

Wang, Z., *Innovative Rice-Based Farming Systems Development: Zhejiang Province, China.*

LATIN AMERICA AND CARIBBEAN

De Grandi, J. *Improved Income Generation among Small Farmers in the Peruvian Sierra.*

Gulliver, A. *Private Sector-Led Diversification Among Indigenous Producers in Guatemala.*

Spehar, C. *Improvement of Farming Systems in the Savannah Lands of Brazil.*

SELECTED CASE STUDIES

Those case studies shown above in bold have been selected for inclusion in a condensed form in this volume, on the basis that they deal with key issues of more than regional importance to farming systems development and poverty reduction. The two global studies examine issues related to intensification of production (declining productivity and rice yield gaps), and the possible contribution of science and technology (biotechnology). The selected regional studies consider expansion of farmed area (opening up of moist savannah areas in West Africa), improved natural resource management (water harvesting in India and tassas in West Africa in a combined presentation) and the process of market development and diversification (private sector-led diversification in Central America).

All 22 case studies can be found in full, in electronic form, on the FAO web-site devoted to Farming Systems at: **www.fao.org/FarmingSystems/**

DECLINING PRODUCTIVITY GAINS AND THE YIELD GAP IN RICE [1]

INTRODUCTION

The Green Revolution enabled rice production to satisfy the rising demands of many growing populations. Since 1990, however, the growth in rice production has slowed down causing concern in terms of food security, particularly among the rural poor. Studies have been conducted to identify the causes of this slowdown and the potential interventions that might support a sustainable increased rice production and may contribute to the alleviation of poverty in rural areas.

Land and water resources for rice production, especially in Asia, have been under increasing pressure from urban and industrial expansion. Improvements in productivity and efficiency would thus appear to be essential for increasing rice production in the future. Low national rice yields and large yield gaps are found in many countries but some countries have succeeded in closing most of the gap between their national yields and the potential yields. This suggests that closing the yield gap might be one possible means of increasing rice productivity. However, it is accepted that the reasons for low rice yields are due to a complex set of biophysical, technical, socio-economic and policy issues which operate in different ways in each major rice-producing country. The relative success of support measures for rice production in many countries over the past 30 years has led to surpluses of rice traded internationally followed by unfavourable terms of trade and consequent reductions in the prices received by farmers. This factor alone could be having a major impact on farmers' willingness to invest in yield-enhancing technologies.

At present, there are about 50 million hectares or more under intensive, irrigated rice-rice, rice-wheat or rice-other crop production systems. Yield and productivity declines which have been observed in these intensive rice production systems threaten, not only sustainable rice production, but also, indirectly, the incomes of small farmers.

RICE PRODUCTION SYSTEMS

The average annual growth rate (AGR) of the world's rice yield was about 2.2 percent during the 1962-1970 period, but decreased to about 1.6 percent between 1971 and 1980 and then increased to about 2.3 percent during 1981-1990. The AGR of the world's rice yield during 1991-1998, however, was only one percent. Rice is grown under a wide range of agro-ecological conditions from irrigated lowland to freely drained upland; from temperate to tropical climates; and from land influenced by tides (mangrove rice) to land flooded with a water depth of several meters for a considerable period (deepwater rice). Yields vary with the agro-ecological conditions during growing seasons. In 1999, the national rice yields in 80 countries were lower than the world average of about 3.8t/ha. In the same year, the gap between the world's highest and lowest national rice yields was about 9 t/ha (Table 1).

More than four-fifths of the world's rice is produced and consumed by small farmers in low-income and developing countries. In 1996, nearly three billion people depended on rice as the major source for daily calories and protein.

Rice and rice-based production systems provide not only food, but also the main source of income and employment opportunities for about a billion poor people in rural areas of Asia, and for smaller members in Africa and Latin America. Small-scale and resource-poor are in the majority in developing countries. They often do not have access to adequate amounts of inputs, especially fertilisers, at the right time for obtaining high yields, as input supply has not been adequately decentralised to village markets. Also, small farmers are generally unable to buy sufficient quantities of fertilisers and to cover other expenses for field operations due to lack of credit. Research and extension support, which is essential to ensure the effective reduction of the gap and improvement rice yield and productivity, is also not always available either.

The intensive important rice-rice systems are common in tropical climate areas, whereas intensive rice-wheat systems are dominant in the sub-tropical zone. Most of the irrigated rice farms in Asia and Africa are small, and farm households are generally poor.

---

[1] This paper is condensed from Tran and Nguyen (2001).

Table 1. World Rice Yield, Highest National Rice Yield and Lowest National Rice Yield

Items	Values
World rice yield	3.84 t/ha
World's highest national rice yield	10.07 t/ha
World's lowest national rice yield	0.57 t/ha
Number of countries with national rice yield below the world average rice yield	80

Source: FAOSTAT.

In non-irrigated areas, rice is planted under rainfed conditions during the wet season and other subsidiary crops are planted during the dry season. Rainfed wetland production systems are dominant in Asia, while in Sub-Saharan Africa and Brazil, rainfed upland rice production systems are dominant. These upland rice production systems, however, are not stable and farmers in Sub-Saharan Africa and in Brazil are increasingly developing wetland rice production systems.

Rainfed rice farmers, both wetland and upland, are generally poorer than the farmers in irrigated areas due to the lower and less stable yields under these production systems. Improvement in the productivity of the rainfed rice production systems will require new varieties and technologies. Recently the West African Rice Development Association (WARDA) developed new upland rice varieties, called NERICA, for use in West Africa and elsewhere.

Yield and productivity levels in rice production systems, especially irrigated ones, could be substantially improved using current technologies, but with appropriate crop management. A UNDP/FAO project in Bangladesh (BGD/89/045 Thana Cereal Technology Transfer and Identification), for example, found that a specific combination of research and extension support to farmers has increased rice yield and reduced production costs. Recommended technological packages, with emphasis on Integrated Crop Management using currently available technologies, were systematically transferred through effective training and demonstrations with the participation of farmers.

YIELD DECLINE IN INTENSIVE RICE PRODUCTION SYSTEMS

There are about 50 million hectares or more under intensive rice-based cropping patterns (rice-rice, rice-wheat and/or rice-other crop), producing two to three crops per year. Average yields are about 4-6 t/ha per crop or about 10-15 t/ha per annum. In several Asian countries such as Indonesia, China, Viet Nam and Bangladesh, farmers grow two to three rice crops, using early-maturing varieties of 90-100 days. In China, farmers grew three rice crops in the early years, but now they are changing to two rice crops and a short-cycle winter crop such as maize or beans. This is due to the fact that the three-rice cropping systems are time-consuming and labour-intensive, but their returns are insufficient to justify the inputs and efforts.

Declining yields and productivity have been observed in several intensive rice production systems. In intensive cultivated areas in the Chiang Mai valley, Thailand, yields declined from 7 to 4 t/ha under normal crop management for unknown reasons (Gypmantasiri et al., 1980). In India, yield declined over 10 years from nearly 6 t/ha to 2-3 t/ha in the Rabi dry season crop (Nambiar and Ghosh 1984).

At the International Rice Research Institute (IRRI) farm at Los Baños Luzan, in the Phillipines, rice yields declined from 8 t/ha in 1968 to 6 t/ha in 1990, while the fertiliser rate remained constant (Greenland 1997). In three other locations in the Philippines, rice yields have been declining by 0.1 to 0.3 t/ha per year over a 20 year period (Cassman et al., 1997). Ladha et al., (2000) reported a declining rice yield in four out of eight experimental sites on long-term rice-wheat systems in the Indo-Gangetic region. Wheat yields remained more or less unchanged or increased slightly in the same experimental sites. In Africa, sharp declines in rice yields in irrigated schemes after a few years of intensive cultivation have been reported in Tanzania (Duwayri et al., 1999), and Burkina Faso, Cameroon and Nigeria (Fagade and Nguyen 2000). Dawe and Dobermann (2000) also observed yield and productivity declines in intensive rice-rice systems, but indicated that these occurred only in limited locations.

In the long-term experiments where yield decline was observed, yield was restored with increased N fertiliser. This suggests that the indigenous N supply of the flooded soil-water system had declined over time (Cassman *et al.*, 1997). However, the number of long-term monitoring sites is limited. Hence, the soils and soil types on which they are located may not fully represent all rice soils. Futhermore, the causes of the yield declines that have been documented vary from one location and ecosystem to another. Often, the causes are not completely understood due to the lack of appropriate measurements. Besides a declining soil nitrogen supply, several other factors - such as zinc deficiency, phosphorus and potassium deficiency, increased pressures of insects and diseases, erosion in yield potential of new genetic materials and changes in the chemistry of rice soils under prolonged submergence - were cited as responsible for yield declines in intensive rice-rice cultivation (Pulver and Nguyen 1999). Similarly, FAO/IAEA (2001) lists decline in organic matter, decreased nutrient supply capacity, declining soil quality or health, micro-nutrient deficiencies and nutrient imbalances as important soil-related problems in rice-wheat systems.

There is little doubt that intensified cropping has profound effects on the biological and chemical processes in rice soils. The availability of modern early-maturing varieties and low cost of nitrogen fertilizer have stimulated crop intensification, especially under irrigation. Insect and disease pressures build up under such cropping systems. Intensification and imbalanced fertilizer application may also lead to depletion of meso- and micro-elements in soils. In Indonesia, Bangladesh, and the Philippines, the drastic reduction in sulphur supply by the increased use of concentrated fertilizers (replacement of ammonium sulphate by urea) and intensive rice cropping has caused increasing S deficiency (Ponnamperuma and Deturck 1993). Also, intensive paddy cropping usually tends to prolong anaerobic conditions in the soils. At the moment, our understanding of organic matter management has not yet kept pace with the intensification of rice cropping systems.

There are also important economic and social factors which have affected smaller and poorer farmers' willingness to continue maximising yields of individual and sequences of crops. These may relate to the availability of ,and returns to, labour, land, water and draught power or mechanisation, access to irrigation and the management of irrigation structures and water, declining farm-gate prices and threats to social capital from modernising interventions.

The Expert Consultation on Yield Gap and Productivity Decline in Rice Production in Rome, September 2000, discussed yield declines[2] in three distinct systems, each with distinct causes. In irrigated African systems, yield and productivity declines appear to be due primarily to deterioration of infrastructure and management problems; in Asia due degradation of the natural resource base. In upland production systems, falling yields over time are due to missing nutrient and shorter fallow periods because of population growth.

In tropical Asia and Africa, the intensive rice production systems provide income and employment opportunities not only to rice farmers but also to the landless in rural areas. The yield declines, which were observed in limited cases, may spread to wider areas under intensive cultivation in the next 30 years, substantially increasing the number of poor people in rural areas of Asia and Africa, unless these problems are addressed within an integrated national development programme that gives priority to the agricultural sector by improving access to inputs and new technologies.

PRODUCTIVITY AND YIELD GAPS

Yield gaps of rice are considered to have at least two components:

- The first component (Gap I in Figure 1) is mainly due to factors that generally are not readily transferable, such the environmental conditions and some component technologies only available at research stations. However, farmers' accumulated knowledge and the availability of innovative technologies have helped to narrow this gap in several countries.

- The second component (Gap II in Figure 1) is mainly due to differences in management. This exists where farmers use what are considered by researchers to be sub-optimal doses of inputs or cultural practices. This is the difference between the mean yield of large plot demonstrations or top 10 percent of farmers in a given location – using the presently available improved technologies and management practices in the best combination – and the average yield of all farmers for that location.

---

[2] Addressed within an integrated national development programme that gives priority to the agricultural sector by improving access to inputs and new technologies.

Figure 1. Components of Yield Gaps (Adapted from de Datta, 1981)

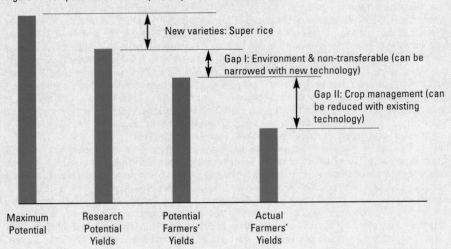

It is widely recognised that, of the various strategies to achieve the production growth needed to raise and sustain yield levels in rice, the most practical short-term strategy is the realisation in farmers' fields of a large proportion of the presently available genetic yield potential. This requires assessment of the yield gap, identification of key technological, institutional, socio-economic and policy constraints, and determination of appropriate remedies.

Attempts to achieve a reduction of the rice yield gap have been advocated by many scientists and developers as a means of increasing rice production with existing technologies. However, despite this approach, such an analysis has not led to a significant 'closing of the gaps'. Social scientists have consistently required technical scientists to examine the wider picture, bring in other social and economic factors and develop a more systemic approach to the analysis. For example, it well documented that in any given rice growing area, yields vary greatly among farmers, suggesting considerable variation in farmers' knowledge, priorities, economic and social conditions which affect their decisions about allocation of resources, not only with respect to rice production.

It has been recognised that only a part of the total yield gap can be remedied by currently available technologies. Policy environment and interventions are considered vital components of the strategy to bridge these differences. Technology exchange and learning groups within research-extension-farmer partnerships play an equally important role.

Factors contributing to the yield gap
There are several groups of key constraints contributing to the yield gap, ranging from the biophysical to the institutional.

- Biophysical (weather, soil, water, pest pressure, weeds).
- Technical/management (labour availability, timing of operations, tillage, variety or seed selection, water, nutrients, weeds, pests, limited use of IPM and post-harvest management).
- Socio-economic (social and economic status, farmers' cultural traditions, commitments and obligations, knowledge, family size and farm profitability).
- Institutional and Policy (government policy, rice price, credit, input supply, land tenure, markets, Research, Development and Extension, RD&E).
- Technology learning and linkages (competence and resources of extension staff, RD&E integration, limited use of Farmer Field Schools, knowledge and skills, linkages among public, private and NGO extension staff).

The work of Ramasamy (1996) indicated that yield gaps in Southern India are due to diverse factors: physical (problem soils, nutrient deficiency and toxicity, drought, flash floods, temperature stress); biophysical or management-related (varieties, weeds, lodging, imbalance in fertilizer application), and, particularly, socio-economic (labour shortage, cost-benefit, farmers' knowledge, skills and others).

During the next three decades, farmers' knowledge will also be continually improved and practical innovative technologies will become increasingly available, which should lead to a reduction in one component of the yield gap of rice. However, as the yield potential of rice plants will also increase through the above-mentioned emerging technologies, a yield gap will inevitably continue to exist, but may be smaller than at present, particularly in countries with strong national agricultural research systems which can engage farmers more effectively in the research process. Most importantly, scientists and extensionists need to understand the context of different rice-based systems and accept that rice, even though it may dominate farm production, is but one component in complex livelihood system.

RECOMMENDATIONS FOR ACTION
The food security and income situation of small rice farmers in the world, especially in South Asia and in Sub-Sahara Africa, might be substantially improved by reversing the declining trend in productivity. Appropriate government policies aimed at improving the supply of inputs, credit and prices to farmers as well as infrastructures in irrigated rice systems will be a vital part of the future efforts. These measures also need to be complemented by improvement in farmers' knowledge of, and access to, more sustainable crop management practices.

To reverse the productivity decline
- Many researchers, extensionists and farmers are not adequately aware of the dangers of long-term negative P, K and micro-nutrient balances. Education and training of relevant stakeholders regarding the benefits of balanced plant nutrient applications will help alleviate the problems caused by nutrient mining.

- When cropping systems are so intensive that the soil is kept continuously submerged, remaining in anaerobic conditions for long periods, yield and productivity declines may become serious. This phenomenon has been documented in several places around the world. While an increased intensity of cropping may be necessary to ensure food security, national research should be aware of the potential dangers of excessively intensive cropping and take adequate steps to alert farmers to them.

- The continued use of the same varieties for an extended period, especially ones without substantial resistance to pests and diseases, is likely to lead to yield and productivity declines. Yield stabilisation and increased yield potential can be achieved by incorporation of a more diverse crop variety base, including traditional and culturally important varieties, and the introduction of yield stabilising traits (resistance to biotic and abiotic stresses) through conventional and innovative breeding methods.

- Declining soil organic matter content may be a causal factor of yield decline in the rice-wheat cropping system. A move towards more organically based systems might reverse this trend.

- Salinisation and sodication processes may affect rice yields and soil quality. This may be remedied by changes in land and water use and management combined with the breeding of tolerant varieties.

To reduce the rice yield/productivity gap
- The main groups of factors constraining productivity need to be identified and understood in the widest possible context. These will involve socio-economic, institutional and/or policy areas both inside and outside farmers' direct control, so any solutions need to emerge from collaborations among many stakeholders.

- A critical path analysis may be needed to identify and prioritise the policy, economic, technical and social constraints and to determine how they might be addressed in each situation.

- Objective crop management recommendations and yield targets, developed by all actors, must be developed for specific conditions and areas. This can assist farmers, both men and women, to evaluate their own role and performance, identify strengths and weaknesses, and take action to improve these.

- Institutions and training mechanisms should develop procedures to evaluate, refine and deliver the learning messages in close collaboration with men and women farmers, e.g government extension service, NGOs, voluntary organisations, private sector agencies, Farmer Field Schools, farmer groups or grower associations.

- Researchers and extension officers must be trained in participatory methods and group facilitation skills with farmers as well as having ready access to up to date technical knowledge.

- Within a rational economic framework, inputs, credit, and other incentives should be made available to facilitate the evolution of appropriate practices by farmers. There is an additional opportunity to involve agribusiness in providing inputs, services and technical support to farmers.

- Participatory monitoring and evaluation of crop and farming system performance over time should be undertaken by teams of extensionists, researchers and farmers.

- Successful management options must be disseminated among farmers and others through appropriate communication strategies for wide impact, e.g. farmer-farmer exchanges, market information, guidelines, decision support and recommended timing for various operations, warnings of pest outbreaks, etc. in print media, radio and TV.

- An effective research and extension infrastructure should be available to address problems and provide technical support to farmers. This will strengthen the linkage between research, extension and farmers.

It is recognised that none of these measures will be effective without an enabling policy environment including support services, marketing and equitable terms of trade. In addition, Governments inevitably face the need to balance the demands of growing urban populations for adequate supplies of rice at a reasonable prices, with the need to earn foreign exchange from export markets, as well as responding to the needs of rice growers for adequate rewards and incomes from their efforts.

CONCLUSIONS

This paper suggests that rice production systems are facing two key problems;

The first relates to the differences that have been acknowledged for many years between the high rice yields that are known to be possible on research stations and the generally lower average yields found on many rice-based systems[3]. It is the thesis of this paper that this 'gap' can be reduced through the application of a combination of technical, social, economic and policy measures and partnerships between many stakeholders – researchers, farmers, extensionists and planners.

The second relates to the evidence for the apparent stagnation and sometimes, declining, yields and productivity of rice in many areas where yields have been high for many years. The reasons for this are complex and need further investigation in many situations, but it is also suggested that these declines can be reversed though a better understanding of the social, economic, biophysical and technical context of rice-based systems and their interaction with their wider environments and by the combination of the measures referred to above.

ANNEX 1: CASE STUDY 2

THE POTENTIAL OF AGRICULTURAL BIOTECHNOLOGY[4]

INTRODUCTION

FAO estimates that, over the next 30 years, more than three quarters of the growth in crop production that is needed to satisfy increasing food needs, will have to derive from increases in crop yield. This will only be possible if substantial technological innovation takes place. Modern biotechnology tools of recombinant DNA, including genetic engineering, offer some opportunities for generating such innovation.

Although the use of genetically engineered drugs and vaccines has not stirred much controversy, the deployment of genetically modified (GM) crops has met with fierce resistance, particularly in Europe on

---

[3] However, it is also recognised that rice yields on some farms can sometimes exceed those achieved on research stations.

[4] This case study has been condensed from Le (2001).

ethical grounds and on concerns of perceived negative impacts of GM crops on the environment and food safety. Ethical considerations revolve around topics such as the 'unnatural' nature of gene transfers across species; possible socio-economic impacts of widening the gap between the rich and poor farmers and countries and the fear that agricultural biotechnology will increase the dependency of global food supply on few multinational corporations controlling the seed industry. With all the negative publicity of GM crops, there are concerns that the resistance to GM crops by consumers in Europe may have hindered the transfer of this new innovation to the developing countries where increasing crop productivity is most urgent.

Despite the resistance which has arisen among some groups, biotechnology is already changing the way in which the many necessities of life - food, feed, fibre, fuel and medical drugs, are being produced. In the agricultural arena, biotechnology tools have been used for animal and plant disease diagnostics, for production of recombinant vaccines against animal diseases and for the improvement of livestock and crops. Cultivation of GM crops has grown from two million ha in 1996 to 44 million hectares in 2000 (James 2000) with the bulk of transgenic acreage in three countries, namely, the USA, Canada and Argentina (UNDP 2001). Although land under transgenic crops in developing countries has increased steadily from 15 percent in 1999 to 23 percent in 2000, this increase was mainly in Argentina at 10 million ha. Had Argentina's acreage not been accounted for, this would have left the developing countries' transgenic acreage at less than one percent. Apart from Argentina, significant commercial plantings in the developing world are limited to China, Mexico and South Africa. In addition, in only a few crops are GM varieties yet of commercial significance, principally soybean, maize, cotton and oil seed rape, potato, squash and papaya.

The lack of support for the development of GMOs in the fight for food security has not gone unnoticed. In June 2000, seven National Academies of Sciences released a report calling for a concerted effort by all sectors, public and private, to develop GM crops – especially food staples - that benefit consumers and poor farmers, particularly in developing nations. It called for the sharing of GM technology developed by private corporations for use in hunger alleviation and to enhance food security in developing countries. The report also proposed special exemptions for the world's poor farmers to protect them from inappropriate restrictions in propagating their crops (NAS 2000).

THE ROLE OF BIOTECHNOLOGY
Broadly speaking, biotechnology involves the use of living organisms for human benefit. It consists of two components: 1) Tissue and cell culture and 2) DNA technologies including genetic engineering. Both components are essential for the production of GM plants and animals.

Plant tissue and cell culture are relatively low cost technologies which are simple to learn, easy to apply and widely practiced in many developing countries. Plant tissue culture aids crop improvement through a range of actions, including: (a) mass propagation of elite stock; (b) the provision of virus-free stock through *in vitro* culture of meristem; (c) the selection and generation of somaclonal variants with desirable traits; (d) the overcoming of reproductive barriers and the transfer of desirable traits from wild relatives to crops by widecrosses; (e) the facilitation of gene transfers using plant protoplast fusions; (f) anther culture to obtain homozygous lines in a breeding programme; and (g) *in vitro* conservation of plant germplasm.

The second component of biotechnology, i.e. DNA technologies, including genetic engineering, utilises newly emerging knowledge of the genes and the genetic code to improve crops, trees, livestock and fish.

Important applications of DNA technologies include the use of DNA probes, specific to pathogens and pests, for their identification, monitoring and control. DNA-based markers are particularly useful for gene map construction for gene isolation. This non-controversial technology is being used to enhance efficiency of conventional plant breeding programmes and to characterize genetic resources for their conservation and use.

One of the important features of DNA transformation is the ability to move genes even across kingdoms helping to enlarge the gene pools for all organisms, including crops. Though controversial for the time being, genetic engineering allows useful genes from any living organism to be transferred to crops or animals for improving their productivity. Genetically altered bacteria or trees can be used in soil remediation. Furthermore, biosynthetic pathways can also be manipulated to produce added nutritional compounds in crops, high value pharmaceuticals and other polymers, using plant as bioreactors. The few examples of technologies present today only vaguely present the vast implications for potential importance of biotechnology on agriculture in the next two decades.

Although GM crops currently available target only simple traits and single genes, technological advances now permit the transfer of as many as 12 genes into a single plant genome (Zhang *et al.*, 1998), although not all genes have been expressed. This may permit the manipulation of more complex, but also more valuable, traits such as yield and tolerance to drought, salinity, heat, chill and freezing, as well as tolerance to problem soils such as salinity and aluminum toxicity. In addition, great progress is being made in using GM crops to produce vaccines at low cost and which are suitable for storage conditions in developing countries (Artzen, 1995, 1996; Landridge 2000).

Research into the physiological and biochemical basis for abiotic tolerance has been greatly aided by advances in molecular biology. Japanese (Kobayashi *et al.*, 1999) and American researchers (Jaglo-Ottosen *et al.*, 1998) have independently isolated a transcription factor that when being over-expressed in GM plants resulted in significant tolerance to drought, salt and freezing stresses. Through an entirely different mechanism, tolerance to salinity was achieved in GM *Arabidopsis* and tomato engineered to over-express a vacuolar Na+/H+ antiport gene (Apse *et al.*, 1999; Zhang and Blumwald 2001). Improving stress tolerance to enhance yield stability while remodelling photosynthesis by genetic engineering may increase crop yield potential. The transfer of photosynthesis genes from maize to rice experimentally resulted in an increase of 35 percent of rice yield as compared with lines of similar genetic background (Maurice *et al.*, 1999).

In forestry, progress has been made in tree engineering to produce wood with reduced lignin contents for the pulp and paper industry. In addition, research is being made to manipulate genes involved in floral development to produce non-flowering trees, thus improving wood productivity (Rick Meilan, *pers. comm.*).

The knowledge of genes, of clustering of genes with similar expression patterns and their order in *Arabidopsis*, a dicot, and rice, a monocot, may be used to isolate and characterize the corresponding genes and to understand gene order and expression patterns in other crop plants (Somerville and Somerville, 1999). This knowledge coupled with opportunities to move genes across species barriers, broadens crop gene pools, which has not been possible, or with tremendous difficulties, using conventional approaches. Agricultural biotechnology, particularly that of crops and trees, is benefiting greatly from Arabidopsis and the rice genome sequencing projects.

REGIONAL SCENARIOS IN BIOTECHNOLOGY

There have been attempts to classify countries into categories, based on biotechnological capacity, useful for appropriate developmental assistance (Byerlee and Fischer 2000). The gene revolution, as it has been known, started from developed countries and spread to developing countries such as Argentina, Brazil, China, India, Mexico and South Africa. These countries have not only been able to take advantage of technology "spillovers" but also have become technology developers. They have well-established traditional plant breeding programmes and expertise in plant tissue and cell culture. It is, therefore, feasible to build expertise in recombinant technologies on already strong foundations. This is because tissue and cell culture expertise is necessary for DNA transformation. The transformed cells, with desired genes, need to be regenerated into whole plants and evaluated for stable gene expression at acceptable levels in subsequent generations. Although progress made in pollen transformation may make the tissue culture phase unnecessary (Burke *et al.*, 1999; Saunders *et al.*, 1997), a functional plant breeding programme is a prerequisite for any crop biotechnology programme. The GM plants still need to be tested for adaptability and performance under local conditions prior to large scale commercial release.

Africa

There have been some national and international initiatives in crop biotechnology. Recently Kenya started field testing of GM sweet potato engineered with the coat protein of the feathery mottle virus (Wambugu 2000). In South Africa, sophisticated research in molecular biology has been in progress for more than 20 years. Recently, work has been carried out to isolate and characterize genes from the resurrection plant *Xerophyta viscosa*, that are functionally important in osmotolerance with the objective to engineer crop plants which would exhibit greater tolerance to envronmental stresses such as drought. South Africa already has biosafety legislation that allows commercial cultivation of several GM crops such as Bt-cotton and Bt-maize[5]. In both Kenya and Zimbabwe, recombinant vaccines are being used against animal diseases

---

[5] Bt-crops are those that have been engineered with genes, derived from the bacteria *Bacillus thurigiensis*. These genes encode for endo-toxins which are toxic to specific classes of pests.

with great success. Interestingly, while European's reaction to genetic engineering has not been enthusiastic, government officials in Africa, particularly in Nigeria and Kenya, have expressed their wish to have access to biotechnology (Amadu 2000).

Asia

In Asia, regulations are in place for field-testing and approval of GM crops in China, India, Indonesia, Japan, Philippines, Taiwan, and Thailand. China has the largest area under GM crops (Teng 2000), having released GM virus resistant tobacco and tomato varieties in 1990. Since then, China has carried out 31 GM field trials, mostly for virus resistance, with canola, cotton, potato, rice and tobacco. Contained experiments with GM crops are being conducted in India, Philippines, Thailand, Vietnam, Singapore, Malaysia, Indonesia and China, while field experiments with GM crops are underway in Indonesia, Philippines, Thailand, India and China.

Thailand has been successful in using molecular approaches in diagnostics and control of virus disease of shrimp. The Philippines government has recognized biotechnology as a major strategy to increase agricultural productivity but the field testing and commercial use of GM crops has been constrained due to public concern (De la Cruz 2000). In India, government support for biotechnology has been extensive and the country has an impressive research capacity. Nevertheless, there has not been any commercial release of GM crops in India. Sri Lanka has recently banned the import of all GM crops and food.

Middle East

Within the Middle East, Egypt, with its Agricultural Genetic Engineering Research Institute (AGERI), is probably the most advanced country in applying biotechnology. It has conducted field testing in West Asia and North Africa for a large number of GM crops. Thanks to the collaboration with the private sector under the USAID-ABSP administered by Michigan State University, AGERI isolated and patented its own indigenous Bt-genes - a successful case of private and public sector collaboration between developing and developed countries (Lewis 2000).

Latin America and Caribbean

This region has benefitted greatly from the FAO-sponsored REDBIO network which incorporates 619 laboratories in 32 countries within a single information network. The region also boasts a number of countries with advanced biotechnology capabilities, such as Mexico, Brasil, Argentina, Costa Rica and Cuba. Research conducted in Mexico on the molecular biology of aluminum tolerance in plants has great potential for the development of GM crops productive on such problem soils. Since 1998, Mexico has evaluated GM corn, cotton, potato and tomato in the field. It is an interesting case study for biosafety as the country is the centre of origin of maize. Mexico has also had commercial planting of Bt cotton. Although Brazil has been the front runner in research and development as well as in field testing of GM crops, a recent court case that bans their cultivation or testing may slow Brazil's earlier progress (Amstalden Sampaio 2000). Brazil is the first country in the developing world that completed the genome sequencing of a bacterial strain of *Xylella fastidiosa*, that attacks orange trees. This sequencing project was financed in part by the Brazilian orange industry (Simpson *et al.*, 2000; Yoon 2000). Costa Rica is using biotechnology to characterize and conserve biodiversity. The country is also seeking to reduce toxic chemical use in controlling banana diseases (Sittenfield *et al.*, 2000). Cuba offers an excellent model for the developing countries in the applications of biotechnology for agricultural development and medical biotechnology. A dozen GM crops have reached laboratory and/or field testing. Cuba has refrained from using GM tobacco, however, for fear of endangering its cigar and tobacco export industries (Lehman 2000).

IMPACT

High returns to GM adoption

Although there have been arguments that the first generation of GM crops, concentrated on input and simple traits designed for developed countries' industrial agriculture, may not benefit small farmers in developing countries, there is increasing evidence that this may not be the case. The cultivation of GM crops in some developing countries with high capacity in biotechnology, demonstrates that it is already making an impact in them through reduced pesticide costs and risks of poisoning, environmental benefits and productivity gains.

369

In China, Pray *et al.* (2000) has presented evidence of higher economic returns to small farmers who planted Bt-cotton, and who required less hospitalisation due to pesticide poisoning, than those cultivating non-Bt cotton. The use of Bt cotton has reduced pesticide use by 80 percent in Hebei Province in China. Since pesticide use in cotton accounts for 25 percent of global pesticide consumption in crops, this has great environmental and health benefit. South African's experience has shown that small farmers can also benefit from Bt-cotton. The number of small farmers' participation in the cultivation of Bt- cotton in this country has increased from 4 to 400 in just 4 years, indicating that they are realising the benefit in growing GM crops (Webster 2000). In Kenya, it has been projected that two sweet potato biotechnologies, GM virus and weevil resistance, will generate annual gross benefit of US$5.4 million and US$9.9 million respectively. Due to the semi-subsistence nature of sweetpotato, the producing households will be the main beneficiaries. The high efficiency of the research projects is confirmed by significantly positive returns on their investments (Qaim 1999).

In Argentina, the high adoption rate of GM crops show that they have already had an impact there. The illegal smuggling of GM seeds from Argentina to Brazil for cultivation indicate that Brasilian farmers, largely commercial growers, appreciate the benefits of GM crops over conventional ones. In Mexico, cultivation of Bt cotton for two years has resulted in an estimated of US$5.5 million in economic surplus, if which about 84 percent accrued to farmers in and 16 percent to seed suppliers (Traxler *et al.*, 2001). In Cuba, the strategy to apply knowledge-intensive biotechnology is promising to give high pay off in terms of royalty from proprietary technologies. Cuba is developing tool kits for plant disease diagnosis. Cuban's genetic-engineered vaccines against cattle ticks and against an enterotoxic *E. coli*, have already been sold in international markets and reduced its pesticde imports (Borroto 2000). Its production of a patented bionematicide will allow the reduction of toxic nematicides used in banana plantation (Lehman 2000). The use of recombinant vaccine against cattle tick has reduced Cuba's pesticide imports from US$ 2.5 to only 0.5 million annually (Borroto 2000).

Biotechnology tools are also being used to investigate the mechanism of apomixis in plants for its potential applications in agriculture[6]. This important trait has enormous potential impact if the technology can be made available to resource-poor farmers who could replant hybrid seeds which retain permanent hybrid vigour in apomictic hybrid varieties.

Experimental work resulting in yield increases of 10 to 35 percent for GM rice using photosynthetic enzymes derived from maize (Maurice *et al.*, 1999) and a quadrupling of yields for GM rice in which a gene has been transferred from barley providing a tolerance to low soil iron in alkaline soils (Takahashi *et al.*, 2001), suggest that considerable further gains are possible.

Improved nutritional and medicinal quality

With 800 million malnourished people in developing countries, there is considerable scope for nutritional genomics which use metabolic engineering to manipulate plant micronutrients for human health (DellaPenna, 1999; Li and della Penna 2001). These have been termed nutraceuticals. And although their production may initially be focused on wealthy consumers in the developed world, genes can be engineered into crops cultivated and consumed by poor farmers to improve their dietary requirements. An existing GM derived variety is that of Golden Rice which contains enhanced vitamin A content in the rice endosperm (Ye *et al.*, 2000). Food quality can also be improved by eliminating the production of certain substances. GM cassava offers reduced levels of cyanogen glycosides (Sayre 2000), thus avoiding toxicity problems associated with current varieties. Currently, there is evidence that GM Bt-crops play an important role in providing safer food than that of traditionally-bred crops through the reduction in mycotoxins produced by fungi infection through insect attack. For crops that are used as bioreactors to produce drugs, the genetic use restriction technologies (GURTs), including the so-called terminator technologies, may be very useful in preventing the contamination of the environment with the drugs and/or vaccines through gene leakages by restricting unwanted transgene flow. The availability of inexpensive, edible plant vaccines against diseases endemic in developing countries such as hepatitis B, cholera and malaria, gives poor people a chance to lead a healthy and productive life. Hopefully, edible plant vaccine against AIDS may one day be developed.

---

[6] Apomixis can be defined as the process of reproduction (e.g. seed production) without fertilization, therefore ensuring exact duplication of the genes of the parent stock.

Utilisation and rehablitation of marginal and degraded lands

Considerable areas of land exist in many developing country regions that are unsuitable for agriculture due to to soil and related constraints, other areas are utilised, but yields are sub-optimal. Work by Mexican researchers in elucidating the molecular mechanism of aluminum tolerance and developing GM plants resistant to this toxic ion could have a great impact on the exploitation of acid soils in developing countries (De la Fuente et al., 1997), particularly the opening up to more intensive cultivation of vast areas in the Brazilian Cerrados and West African moist savannah. Since acid soils occur to some extent over some 43 percent of all tropical areas, aluminum tolerant crops would help to extend crop production in many zones. A further 30 percent of cultivated land is alkaline, making iron unavailable for optimum crop production. Japanese workers recently demonstrated that a GM rice, engineered with barley genes, showed an enhanced tolerance to low iron availability and yielded four times more than non-transformed plants in alkaline soil (Takahashi et al., 2001). Encouraging results are also being made in the area of salinity tolerance. In the presence of 200 mM NaCl, GM tomato and canola plants reached maturity with very good fruit set and oil quality, respectively (Apse et al., 1999; Zhang and Blumwald, 2001 and Eduardo Blumwald, pers. comm. 2001). In addition, climatic variability such as sudden drought or frost may have severe consequences for resource-poor farmers, living in a marginal environment. Biotechnology applications of research on environmental stress tolerance may assure poor farmers of a stable harvest

Biotechnology applications could also have positive impacts on the environment degraded through conventional practices, e.g. restoration of degraded soil using phytoremediation with engineered crops and/or microorganisms. As a source of renewable energy, GM crops can be engineered to produce fuel directly or indirectly through the processing of their biomass. Production of biomass for fuels such as alcohol would not necessarily contribute to additional carbon dioxide to the atmosphere and could be especially beneficial if such fuels, instead of petroleum-based fuels, met the growing needs of the Third World (Guy et al., 2000).

Reducing encroachment to marginal environment

As with any other productivity enhancing technology, the increase in crop productivity due to biotechnology can reduce the pressure to open up new lands, thus reducing the need to encroach on fragile environment in the tropical and subtropical regions. It is often asserted that thanks to increases in yield, land has been saved with diminished pressure on the environment such as less deforestation than otherwise would have taken place (FAO 2000). It has also been reasoned that a crop productivity increase of just 1 percent per annum, equivalent to a cumulative 69 percent increase from 1997 to 2050, would reduce the amount of new cropland needed to meet future demand to 325 million ha. compared to a habitat loss of another 1 600 million hectares if crop productivity is kept at the level of 1997 (Goklany 2000). This is not an unattainable goal as biotechnology research is moving very fast.

Input replacement

One of the main criticisms of the Green Revolution has been that it bypassed poor farmers living in marginal environments and those who cannot afford the cost of inputs such as pesticides, fertilisers and infrastructure cost for irrigation. The 'gene' revolution is, to some extent, redressing this imbalance by developing crops that produce their own pesticides. Research in crop nutrient uptakes and biological nitrogen fixation also holds great promise for resource-poor farmers who cannot afford the cost of fertiliser inputs. This would also help to protect the environment through the saving of fossil fuel needed to produce nitrogen fertilizer. Non-leguminous crops, such as maize or rice, may be able to be modified to fix their own nitrogen. Alternatively an expansion of the host range of nitrogen fixing bacteria would permit more crops to maintain symbiotic relationships with these bacteria. For phosphorus, Mexican researchers have demonstrated that genetically engineered tobacco plants showed significant increase in their ability to take up phosphorus as compared with the control plant (Shmaefsky 2000). In addition, a research group at Purdue University has cloned a phosphate transporter gene from Arabidopsis. These genes were also found in other crops such as tomato, potato and alfalfa. GM plants are also being developed for more efficient uptake of phosphate (Prakash 2000).

Animal husbandry

In parallel with crop biotechnology, poor farmers can also benefit from advances in animal biotechnology due to a livestock revolution occurring now in most developing countries. Research has shown that the rural poor and landless get a higher share of their income from livestock than better-off rural people. Hence, an increase in consumption of animal products can actually help increase the food purchasing power of the poor and this livestock revolution could become a key means of alleviating poverty in the next 20 years if proper policies and investments are in place (IFPRI 1999). Animal biotechnology can supply abundant and healthier animal protein at lower cost. In the pipeline, there are pigs engineered to have less fat, chicken designed to resist illness-causing bacteria and beef that can grow twice as fast on less feed. Poor farmers who own few livestock will have their investments more protected due to an improvement in animal health through better and cheaper vaccines produced by recombinant DNA. The detection of such diseases by using molecular-based diagnostics will also benefit village herds in controlling the spread of such diseases and upgrade livestock health, thereby helping the rural communities at large and providing household food security at the individual family level.

Immediate impacts of tissue culture and micropropagation

Although DNA technologies are beginning to benefit small farmers of developing countries, the immediate impact for many countries, particularly those with low technical capital, will be in the production and distribution of disease-free and high quality planting material of the native clones of vegetatively propagated plants. These include banana, plantain, cassava, yams, potato, sweet potato, pineapple, sugarcane, many fruit trees such as apple, pear, plum, date palm, mango, and litchi, and many ornamental shrubs and flowers. The benefits of micropropagation are immediate, and the availability of cheap labour in the developing countries provides a competitive edge in the use of this technology. Micropropagation of banana and sugarcane has created rural jobs in Cuba and promoted exports of propagules of ornamental plants from India to Europe. Within the last five years, nearly one hundred plant- micropropagation companies have been established in India by the private sector. In Cuba, if micropropagation capacity can be scaled up to satisfy domestic demand, the country can save US$15 million annually for expenditure on import potato seed stock. The Cuban cottage industry, based on tissue culture, is providing part-time employment opportunities for rural housewives. In China, micropropagation of virus-free sweet potato seed in Shandong which resulted in an average yield increase of at least 30 percent, gave an internal rate of return at 202 percent and a net value of US$550 million (Fuglie et al., 2001). In Kenya, disease-free banana plantlets have greatly increased yields from 8-10 to 30-40 t/h (Anonymous 2000).

RECOMMENDATIONS FOR ACTION

There is always inherent risk in any technology, old and new. There are concerns of increased pest resistance as a result of Bt crops that may result in the loss of Bt as an important pesticide. Such risks can be addressed through scientific-based risk analysis and risk management, including post-commercial monitoring, coupled with proper management of cropping systems. Recent experience with large scale Bt GM crops in US support this view. Tabashnik et al., (2000) reported that, contrary to expectations, increased insect resistance has not been observed in the Bt cotton growing region in Arizona. In addition, it is also expected that further genes for insect resistance in addition to Bt will be identified, reducing potential risks in the future.

Increasing the focus on crops and livestock constraints of importance to small producers

In order to fully realize the benefits of agricultural biotechnology to contribute to poverty alleviation and equitable growth in developing nations, it is crucial that a concerted effort be made to ensure that the benefits of biotechnology are available to a broad spectrum of small farmers in a range of developing countries. Not withstanding the achievements and progress described above, the vast majority of funded research has been dedicated to crops such as soya, maize and canola, which are primarily of interest to large commercial producers in the industrialized world. This will only change if considerably expanded international and national public resources are devoted to 'poverty' crops such as sorghum, banana, beans and lentils, as well as to increased disease resistance in small ruminants and poultry, and to traits of particular importance to low-income producers (e.g. biological nitrogen fixation). The sharing of the rice genome sequence data with researchers in developing countries by private sector (IFPRI 2000) and the recent announcement of the sequencing of the banana genome (http://www.inibap.org/new/genomics_eng.htm) are steps in the right direction toward using biotechnology for the benefit of developing nations.

Without doubt, the concerns of the public in industrialised countries as to safety and environmental impact of biotechnologies comprises a key constraint to increased international funding. These concerns must be dealt with, both through improved communication of the real evidence concerning risks and benefits of biotechnology use and adoption, and through improved safety measures. As the introduction of GMs may pose differerent risks in different countries, it is important that international organizations, private and public sectors, donors and other stakeholders in developing countries adequately address public concerns and ensure effective monitoring and regulatory environments.

Developing regulatory frameworks
- Assist in capacity building in biosafety in compliance with the recently agreed Cartagena Protocol on biosafety regulations. This is because the owners of proprietary technologies would be very reluctant to license their technologies in countries that have no biosafety legislation and controls in place. Both UNIDO and UNEP are in position to assist countries whereas FAO has mandates to assist Member Countries on matters related to food safety and biosafety in food and agriculture. The development of biosafety in developing countries is also important in cases where these countries may have to import GMOs for use in breeding programme/testing in their environment and/or for use as food and feed.

- Facilitate access to proprietary technologies to developing countries. The issue of Intellectual Property Rights (IPR) needs to be addressed. It is important that capacity building in IPR is stimulated in order to meet the minimum requirements of the WTO-TRIPS. The owners of IPRs can do as they wish with their propriety technology. They can have their technology licensed at low cost or even royalty free to poor nations and there are already some examples of such arrangements between multinational corporations and developing countries (Qaim 2000; ISAAA, http://www.isaaa.org/inbrief.htm). There has been some discussion by international community on a clearing house mechanism for IPRs for the benefit of developing countries (http://www.cnr.berkley.edu/csrd/technology/ipcmech/IPCM-background.html). This area certainly should be explored further by all stakeholders for it to become a reality. Meanwhile capacity building in IPRs is necessary both for developing countries to protect their own intention and to negotiate the uses and exchanges of proprietary technologies.

Assisting in economic planning
- Help countries to develop national agricultural strategies in which biotechnology is an integral component. These strategies should have clear goals and priorities, incorporating business plans that assess the cost/benefit of biotechnology options as well as providing concrete steps for strategy implementation. These plans would not only have economic indicators such as return on investment, profit margins etc. but also social indicators as to how many poor people would benefit from such development strategies in terms of employment and income.

- Assist countries or groups of countries with a common interest in developing biotechnological research that target their priorities - export crops and/or those for domestic consumption. Market research is necessary and the World Bank and its partners should be in strong position to assist countries to do so. For example, in Africa, cassava has good potential to be an industrial crop and efforts should be made to assist Africa in improving productivity of cassava and developing markets for cassava processing.

Promoting technical assistance among national, regional and international institutions
- Develop further regional networks, modelled after the REDBIO network in Latin America (http://www.rlc.fao.org/redes/redbio/html/home.htm), for information exchange and technical collaboration among laboratories and countries to work on common problems and share experience. Raising public awareness related to biotechnology can be facilitated through these networks. Through these networks, policy makers and scientists can access information to allow them to make sound decisions for a cost-effective use of suitable technologies and associated experts. In addition, the biotechnology compendium field of EcoPort (http://www.ecoport.org) offers a vehicle for crop-specific developments in the field.

CONCLUSIONS
The impact of biotechnology in the next 30 years will depend largely on the strategies that countries adopt to improve their technical capacity and thus capture the benefits of biotechnology. Although biotechnology cannot by itself stimulate economic growth and alleviate poverty, this new innovation certainly provides an additional tool in the fight against hunger. Theodore Schultz showed more than 30 years ago, that poor

farmers are effective business people who use resources and technology at their disposal to obtain maximum return to their investments. The problem is that they reach an equilibrium at a very low level. To bring this equilibrium to higher levels, new innovations are needed.

In the green revolution, many small producers were left behind due to lack of access to the inputs required, as well as inappropriate policies. The 'gene revolution' may finally provide the opportunity for them to share in the benefits of technology, provided appropriate enabling policies and investments are in place. It is important to review proposed strategies (Byerlee and Fisher 2000; Spillane 1999), learn from case studies (Paarlberg 2000) and to devise a global strategy to harness the benefits of agricultural biotechnology for the poor. In this strategy, international institutions (donors, the public and private sectors, advanced research institutions and NGOs), within their varying mandates, pool their scarce resources and co-ordinate their activities through regional technical networks, such as the REDBIO, for technology development and transfers. These activities, aiming to maximize the benefits while minimizing the risks through cost effective biosafety measures, rest on several pillars, i.e. ethics, public dialogue and biosecurities. In this respect, FAO would be in position to collaborate with partners to assist Member Countries. Since 1999, the FAO Conference and FAO's Committee on Agriculture (COAG) has recommended that the agency strengthen its capacity to assist Member Countries in harnessing the power of biotechnology (FAO 1999; http://www.fao.org/unfao/bodies/COAG/COAG15/X0074E.htm and http://www.fao.org/biotech /index .asp?lang=en). However, the success of the strategy will depend largely on national governments who, at the end, are responsible for the development of appropriate policies and allocate sufficient resources in agricultural research in their respective countries.

ANNEX 1: CASE STUDY 3

DEVELOPMENT IN THE MOIST SAVANNA ZONE OF WEST AFRICA[7]

INTRODUCTION
The Guinea savanna zone in West Africa, which lies within the Cereal-Root Crop Mixed Farming System, was selected as one of the case studies because of the potential for development of this major under-utilised natural resource, within which current productivity and household incomes are low. Because of the complexity of the land use systems and the range of interventions required, this case is presented in a general format.

Climate, water and land resources
The Northern and Southern Guinea savannas extend in a broad band through most West African countries. They have a warm tropical temperature regime. The length of the growing period (May/June to September/October) ranges from about 150 days - often with short drought periods in the early part of the growing season, near the border with the Sahel - to about 210 days in the southern part. During most of the growing season, probabilities of drought are small, although a minor mid-season dry period may occur near the southern border with the derived savanna and forest zones, where mid-season droughts have an impact on agriculture. The length of the growing period and the total rainfall vary not only from year to year, but also on a scale of several decades (relatively moist in the thirties to sixties, dry in the seventies and early eighties, relatively moist since then). Average annual rainfall in the area varies from 800 mm in the north to 1200 mm in the south. Potential evapotranspiration is between 1500 and 2000 mm, exceeding annual rainfall. The rainfall surplus during the wet season is generally below 300 mm. Groundwater occurs at varying depth in the valley bottoms and the river plains.

Several rivers pass through the Guinea savanna zone. The Gambia River is strongly seasonal; during the dry season salt water intrudes as far as 250 km upstream. Without major dam construction, it is estimated that no more than 2400 ha could be irrigated in the dry season. The sources of the Senegal River are in the Guinea savanna zone. The annual discharge leaving the zone is estimated at about eight km^3 but during the dry

---

[7] This paper is condensed from Brinkman (2001).

season the river often runs dry. The irrigation potential in the area within the Guinea savanna zone is estimated at about 15 000 ha. The annual inflow of the Niger entering the Guinea savanna zone from the south is estimated at 40 km^3. In Mali, several tributaries with a joint discharge of about 16 km^3 join the Niger before it leaves the moist savanna zone northward towards the inner delta, where much water is lost due to evaporation. The discharge is about 30 km^3 where the Niger re-enters the zone of the moist savanna and about 40 km^3 where it leaves the Guinea savanna to the south. It is difficult to estimate the irrigation potential for the moist savanna zone, but the total irrigation potential for the Niger is about 2.8 million ha.

The sources of the Volta River are located in the zone of the moist savanna. Where the Volta leaves the zone southward, the discharge is estimated at about eight cubic km. The irrigation potential is roughly estimated at 0.7 million ha. The extent currently equipped for irrigation in this zone is in the order of 84 000 ha, excluding the areas of cultivated wetland and inland valley bottoms.

The major soils in this zone (Lixisols) contain low activity clays but have a relatively high base saturation. Associated with these are similar but more acid soils with low base saturation (Acrisols) in the more humid parts and acid sandy soils (Arenosols) in the drier, northern part of the zone. Very poor, largely unproductive soils with a lateritic pan at shallow depth occur scattered over the area and are locally dominant, as in parts of Northern Ghana. The sandy soils are relatively easy to work but nutrient deficient and retain little soil moisture. The acid soils in the more humid part generally have a low natural fertility, and many need lime and phosphate applications to increase yields. In the valleys and major river plains, soils are generally fertile but in many parts they are also intensively used. They may become depleted quite quickly therefore, if not regularly replenished with nutrients.

The Guinea savannas form part of an extensive agro-ecological zone also occurring in Eastern and Southern Africa and in the Cerrados region in Northeast Brazil, as well as in parts of several Southeast and South Asian countries. Agricultural technology from other parts of this zone could be usefully explored for possible adaptation and use in the Guinea savannas, given similar general land conditions[8].

General land use and farming systems

The Guinea savannas, less densely populated than areas nearer to the coast, still have land that is very lightly used, particularly at a distance from the roads. The more easily accessible land is largely used for annual crops, generally with low external inputs, and producing low yields. Crops include maize and sorghum; millets in the northern part; cotton, cassava, soybean and cowpea; yam near the southern border, and wetland rice in parts of the river plains and valley areas. Homesteads often have some vegetables and fruits. Cattle, mainly N'Dama, are held on many farms for draught or for milk but are less common near the southern border because of the tsetse threat. Small livestock is often held in the homesteads. Manure is used to maintain the productivity of the homestead garden, and some manure may be applied on the nearest fields as well. Part of the farms have draught power, mainly oxen, some of the largest farms have a tractor, but many farmers cultivate their land with the hoe, and therefore the extent of their cultivated land is severely limited. Generally the household consumes a large part of the farm produce; some is sold at harvest time.

Five main farming systems or variants (FS) have been identified[9] in the Guinea savanna zone, with different population densities, proportions of land under cultivation and cattle densities (Table 1.). The first system (FS1) covers most of the Nigerian part of the zone, a large area in Burkina Faso, parts of Togo and Benin, and a part of Senegal. It is a mixed farming system where population densities, proportion of cultivated land and cattle density are medium high. There still is room for further expansion as well as intensification. This system tends to occupy a greater proportion of land near the gradual boundary with the two intensive crop-livestock mixed systems practised in densely populated areas and around urban centres (e.g. the Jos Plateau and around Kano in Nigeria, Ouagadougou in Burkina Faso and Dakar in Senegal). In one of these (FS2) the high population density still allows for a high proportion of cultivation and a high cattle density; in the other (FS3) the percentage of land under cultivation and the number of cattle kept show the effect of the urban centres and the very high urban and peri-urban population density. In these two systems, agricultural production increases will have to come from further intensification rather than from expansion.

FS4 covers large areas of Benin, Ghana, Ivory Coast, Mali, Guinea, Guinea-Bissau and Senegal, and the remainder of the countries mentioned above. As may be expected from the lower population density the

---

[8] An example is described in Nachtergaele and Brinkman (1996).

[9] FAO 1999.

proportion of cultivated land and the cattle density are also low. The system comprises mixed farming around villages, and agro-pastoralism and pastoralism in surrounding areas. In addition to local, trypanotolerant N'Dama herds (e.g. in Guinea), there are important numbers of Zebu cattle in areas with relatively low tsetse pressure. These migrated south with their pastoralist owners during the droughts of the eighties (e.g. to Ivory Coast), and many have settled in this zone. Settlement of increasing numbers of people in those places in the Sahel zone to the north where water is available has been restricting the possibilities for rainy-season grazing and further induced the pastoralists to settle in this area. Crop agriculture and livestock herding often co-exist with little integration, giving rise to frequent conflicts. Lack of formal land tenure or uncertain tenure arrangements are contributing factors. In the more humid edge of the zone in Guinea, there is an area with a still more extensive, slightly more livestock-oriented mixed system (FS5).

The areas of these two extensive farming systems have an important potential, particularly for expansion of integrated crop-livestock systems, in so far as factors such as the presence of locally widespread poor soil conditions or the prevalence of onchocercosis or animal trypanosomosis do not inhibit the further development of these mixed agriculture systems.

Table 1. Farming systems in the Guinea savanna zone, West Africa

N°	Population density (People/km^2)	Land under cultivation (%)	Cattle density (Head/km^2)	Ha cultivated /100 people	Cattle number /100 people	Exploitation level
FS 1	63	18	11	29	17	Medium
FS 2	142	84	39	59	27	High
FS 3	238*	37*	20*	16*	8*	High
FS 4	23	5	8	22	35	Low
FS 5	13	2	4	15	31	Low

* Values not adjusted for the presence of urban land and population.

Infrastructure, services and institutions
In Guinea savanna zone countries, public investments in rural transport have generally concentrated on improving main highways. An estimated 50 to 70 percent of the existing feeder road network in the Guinea savanna zone are in poor or very poor state. Also, the connecting access tracks are generally ill maintained and often lack minor but basic structures such as culverts, becoming inaccessible to vehicles especially during the rainy season. These conditions make transport of produce to local or more distant markets expensive, slow and sometimes impossible.

A number of deficiencies affect the agricultural marketing system, particularly the smaller rural markets and the secondary markets that form the link between these and the main consumption areas. Besides the transport problems, these include a lack of common facilities resulting in wastage and spoilage, distortions in produce flow, and inadequate price formation and market transparency. As a result, the marketing system is slow to respond to producer and consumer demands, has high transaction costs and entails a high degree of losses, especially of perishable commodities, including cassava.

Only small percentage of the rural population in the Guinea savanna has safe water supply in easy reach. Most of the traditional supplies, usually from streams and ponds, require considerable time and effort to utilise, may dry up during drought periods, and have very poor water quality in the dry season. Water-borne diseases are prevalent. In most of the countries of the Guinea savanna zone, less than 15 percent of the villages are connected to the national electricity grids. The lack of electricity limits the opportunities for education, rural water supply, irrigation and local processing.

In most countries of the zone the T&V system of extension was introduced, including the unification of sub-services such as livestock, forestry and fisheries. The system has brought some advantages but has generally proven to be financially unsustainable and often fails to function properly within a decentralised government structure. In the recently resettled oncho-freed areas the flow of extension information is often poor or even non-existent.

Readily accessible savings and loan services are generally lacking in the zone. There are occasional credit facilities linked with cotton cultivation. Informal credit is generally at high rates of interest.

In the Guinea savanna zone, farmer-based organisations are generally weak or are lacking, because several areas have been opened for settlement only recently, after eradication of onchocercosis, and villages are further apart and communications are poorer than near the coast. However, most villages have some social cohesion based on traditional structures and relationships. On this basis, rural farmers' organizations could be promoted.

LIMITATIONS AND POTENTIAL FOR SETTLEMENT AND LAND USE CHANGE

Historically, development of this area has suffered from two major constraints: onchocercosis and trypanosomosis. The Onchocercosis Control Programme (OCP), a major ongoing effort since 1974 to eradicate river blindness in West Africa, has prevented several hundred thousand cases of blindness and freed up to 25 million hectares of previously infested cultivated land. Much of the Guinea savanna is now onchocercosis-free, and the programme is working on eradication from the remaining endemic areas, for example in parts of Nigeria. The programme thus has been removing a major constraint to socio-economic development and opened important new economic opportunities for the population in the region. Important parts of the additional agricultural land becoming available as a result of Onchocercosis control (so-called 'new land') is likely to be relatively fertile and have access to surface water or groundwater, because Onchocercosis was most prevalent near rivers where the vector (blackfly) laid its eggs.

While onchocercosis has been effectively controlled in more than 60 percent of the area, tsetse-transmitted African animal trypanosomosis (AAT) still is a major constraint to agricultural development. Distribution of tsetse, and therefore of trypanosomosis risk, is not uniform over the entire area. Besides the presence of different species adapted to either savanna or riverine vegetation), tsetse distribution is affected by climate. Therefore in the less humid northern band of the Guinea savanna zone, tsetse will generally be present only along main drainage systems. This enables livestock keepers to minimise exposure of cattle to tsetse by using adapted grazing patterns. However, in the southern, more humid band tsetse colonises not only the drainage systems but also expands seasonally into adjacent savanna and trypanosomosis risk increases towards the south.

The historical response from farmers to this threat has been trypanotolerant livestock, i.e. livestock that tolerates trypanosomes, the parasite causing AAT. While it has been shown that trypanotolerant livestock do make a contribution towards reducing the trypanosomosis problem, trypanotolerance alone does not enable farmers to keep animals as and where they wish. The presence of the tsetse fly remains a major obstacle to cattle raising and inhibits particularly mixed farming development and intensification. AAT often prevents farmers from making the step from subsistence agriculture to more advanced livestock raising systems. A recent FAO study[10] highlighted the areas where tsetse removal would be most beneficial to livestock. Major areas in the Guinea savanna zone include the West African cotton triangle (Burkina Faso – Mali – Ivory Coast) and the Nigerian middle belt. An ongoing study is assessing the economic benefits of large-scale control operations in more detail.

Tsetse also transmits human sleeping sickness. This is not a major concern in this area, however, since sleeping sickness is confined to a series of foci in the more humid parts south of the Guinea Savanna zone.

MAJOR ISSUES, OPPORTUNITIES AND KEY INTERVENTIONS

The opportunities and development interventions with the greatest effect on poverty alleviation and on productivity and sustainability of farming and household systems in the Guinea Savanna zone, are focussed on the intensification of the mixed crop-livestock farming systems, including: localised irrigation; improvement of services to the pastoral/agro-pastoral system; improving crop-livestock integration (draft animals, feed from cover crops and crop by-products, manure from intensive livestock production); diversification through crop introduction and rotations; promoting local post-harvest value-adding enterprises; and improving infrastructure, services and institutions designed to serve the people and the enterprises in the zone.

The specific opportunities and promising interventions discussed individually below should not be seen in isolation; they are designed to assist households and communities to improve their livelihoods, building on the resources and farming systems of the people in the area, and there are important synergies among them. For

---

[10] Swallow 2000.

example, conservation farming reduces the amount of draft power needed for land preparation, so draft animals could handle more cropland. Conservation farming would reduce free dry-season grazing on cropland but will produce cover crops and increased amounts of crop by-products that can be used to improve livestock nutrition in the dry season. While some of the interventions will already have considerable benefits in the current situation, most will have much greater effect if they are accompanied by improvements in infrastructure, services and institutions such as those mentioned in the last section.

ECONOMIC AND SUSTAINABLE INTENSIFIED CROP PRODUCTION

Farm households can achieve significant improvements in economic and nutritional status through modifications in their approach to soil, crop and pest management. These changes in the farming system lower input costs, create a more even distribution of the workload throughout the year, improve the effect of applied fertilisers and organic materials, reduce weed pressure and the need for insect and disease control activities, and lead to higher and more stable yields. There are three main elements or aspects of these changes.

Conservation agriculture is based on minimum- or no-till methods, direct seeding and continuous soil cover[11], improving resilience against drought and gradually reducing weed pressure. *Integrated plant nutrition management*, based on crop rotation including legumes, continuous soil cover and maximum cycling of nutrients - including from manure and post-harvest residues or waste - improves plant nutrient balance and health and raises the efficiency of applied mineral fertilisers. *Integrated pest and plant management* is based on crop management, to increase its resilience to weed and pest pressures, and systematic periodic observation by the farmers of the balance between pest populations and those of their natural predators. IPPM thus reduces and may eliminate the need for pesticide application, lowering production costs, and improves plant health and yields. An example for all three elements is the cultivation of a *mucuna* cover crop for weed control, enhancement of soil fertility and livestock feed. This practice is already widespread in some parts of the Southern Guinea savanna zone, but still unknown in large areas.

Such improvements in the existing farming system, as well as other changes discussed below, cannot be simply packaged and delivered. They need to be explored, tested and adapted through practical experience, participative learning and discussion, to be thoroughly understood and successfully applied. Methods along the lines pursued by Farmers Field Schools, Farmer Research Committees, Participatory Technology Development, Promoting Farmer Innovators, and Campesino a Campesino have proved effective in raising and maintaining farmers' active interest, co-operation, and initiative. Farmers' organisations, NGOs, and small-scale private extension service providers can all be held accountable by local communities for enabling those communities to make better decisions, based on sound scientific understanding rather than on standard recipes.

A suitable entry point for improvements may be the introduction through participative learning and discovery of no-till and continuous soil cover methods with suitable crop rotations, since these can drastically increase yields and drought tolerance within 2 to 3 years, even with low external inputs. Further improvements can then be explored after this initial success.

Investment for Conservation Farming Equipment

Availability of farm power, particularly to carry out tillage and planting operations, is becoming a bottleneck to increasing or even maintaining agricultural production. Lack of human labour due to migration and diseases, lack of animal draft power due to the occurrence of trypanosomosis or lack of fodder and lack of motorised power due to capital and service shortcomings, are all causing delays in planting and hence low yields, or are restricting the area that can be planted. Conservation agriculture provides a chance to carry out timely planting operations with much less farm power, achieving higher yields and releasing human labour for other, more rewarding activities.

Investment assistance may be necessary for the introduction of this technology, although in the form of credit, rather than as free handouts. The main investment on equipment will be for the planter. In addition, there might be a need for a one-time treatment by ripper or subsoiler on highly degraded soils, and for a sprayer mainly for weed control, particularly in the first 2 to 3 years. Cover crops and crop residues after harvest can be managed with equipment such as the knife roller. This can be easily manufactured locally at low cost[12].

---

[11] Examples of practices in smallholder conservation agriculture are described in FAO (1997).

[12] Examples of local development and production of machinery for conservation agriculture in Brazil are described in FAO (2000).

Investment in livestock development
As discussed above, removal of the tsetse constraint is expected to have a major impact on general agricultural development in the area. Therefore the results of the ongoing joint cost-benefit studies on tsetse control and eradication by FAO and DFID may pave the way for investment in the area. Privatisation of veterinary services and extension is the way forward, but should be based on a review of this sector throughout the region, highlighting the failures and successes, to identify present needs and investment opportunities.

The pastoralists in this zone are now increasingly settled, occupying areas distant from villages that are not yet used for arable cultivation. Some countries still need to put in place policies and legislation to establish legal title or tenure for well-defined holdings, occupied both by pastoralists and farmers. Participatory approaches will be essential for resolving land tenure problems. A good starting point will be to provide legal support for actual, existing settlement and occupation patterns rather than to direct pastoralists to newly created pastoral zones.

The pastoral and increasingly agro-pastoral systems will become more profitable and sustainable through strategic investments combined with the promotion of pastoralists' organizations and training. Specifically, the establishment of well distributed, readily accessible cattle markets and strategically located slaughterhouses is essential to ensure that livestock owners themselves profit from the added value of their cattle. Accessible veterinary care, vaccination and quarantine facilities will improve animal health and productivity, but also enable certification of animals or meat for export, opening new markets and increasing widespread acceptance of the products. These services, as well as markets and slaughterhouses, could be under private enterprise if government controls on health and sanitary quality are put in place.

The promotion of draft animal power is a key factor towards improved integrated livestock and crop agriculture. This issue should not be addressed in isolation but as part of a whole package enabling sustainable draft animal power use within a region. Animals should be drawn from local herds rather than from government ranches. There may be scope for the introduction of improved breeds in those herds, but the emphasis should be on proper selection.

Improved livestock husbandry techniques should be introduced in the mixed farming systems, including night stabling for manure collection, or permanent stabling, with proper feeding and maximum use of crop residues and by-products as well as fodder crops. Introduction of better nutrition through the use of fodder crops and crop by-products would be most profitable in the framework of milk production or stall feeding during the dry season. Short-cycle livestock production at the village level, such as poultry and egg production for local markets and small ruminant fattening for annual occasions can be enhanced using minimal inputs. More complex is the introduction of improved husbandry practices in semi-intensive poultry, small ruminant and pig production. These need functioning extension and veterinary services, access to animal feed and feed additives, as well as reproduction services. All these services can be provided in response to well-organised demand from farmers' associations and with complementary investment in improved access to local markets.

Milk co-operatives in peri-urban areas have not always obtained positive results. Two reasons are often cited for lack of success: competition with cheap, easily stored, imported milk powder, and the fact that stakeholders often are not involved in the processing, retail and delivery systems. While the price of milk powder will remain a major constraint, fully involving cattle owners' associations from the start of such projects might be part of the answer. If successful, a next step can be the genetic improvement of local breeds. Intensive peri-urban poultry, pork and milk production systems are already the focus of private sector investment in several places. Nearby farming areas can profit from the organisation of commercial links with these systems, through sale of feed crops and crop by-products, as well as through the use of manure from these intensive systems.

Affordable, small-scale irrigation facilities
In recent years, simple, affordable equipment for precision drip irrigation has been developed and widely applied in several countries. Systems have proved successful at scales ranging from about 20 square metres, used in homesteads or backyards, to a few hectares, serving several horticulturists. Such systems, already tested in some African countries, will allow dry-season cultivation of vegetables and fruits – for local consumption, as well as for the market – near surface water or where groundwater is available at shallow depth. A few buckets of water per day are sufficient for 20 square metres of vegetables; a hand pump or the

Swiss model treadle pump can supply the requirements for several hundred square metres. Motor pump sets will be needed in larger systems. The treadle pump, already used in Senegal and Tanzania, for example, can be manufactured locally using low-cost standard materials.

Introduction of oil palm cultivation and processing

The recent development of high-yielding, precocious oil palm clones adapted to certain environments outside their traditional range provides an opportunity for their introduction in parts of the Guinea savanna zone, specifically in valleys and river plains with moderately accessible groundwater.

The economic importance of the oil palm derives from its extremely high productivity as oil producers. In the plantation sector, large-scale mills produce crude palm oil for edible oil refining industries, which further process it into cooking oils, margarine and baking fats. Crude oil for household use and local sale is generally produced by traditional artisanal processes. These are relatively simple, but tedious and inefficient with very poor recovery rates. Manual and fully automated processes that are much less tedious and have higher extraction efficiency are widely used for palm oil extraction at the small-scale level. Small-scale extraction equipment is locally produced in a number of countries in the region. There is however a need for improving the efficiency of this equipment.

Local manufacture and marketing of cassava and soybean products

Cassava is generally processed in the household or the village prior to consumption or marketing, not only for the purpose of detoxification, but also to increase its shelf life and facilitate its transport. Primary food processing options for cassava include the production of chips by drying. There is currently a large trade in cassava chips for the feed industry, but it is extremely competitive. Since distribution (transport) costs are an important factor in European cassava chip imports, ports in West Africa may have an advantage with respect to traditional suppliers from Asia. Cassava chips could also become important among the local feed sources for farmers' and pastoralists' livestock.

Secondary processing options include the production of flour (from chips), and a variety of products such as *fufu*, a moistened, highly perishable product prepared from cassava flour, *gari*, a fermented coarse meal, *attieke*, a fermented pre-gelatinised meal similar to gari, *lafun*, a fermented cassava flour, and *chickwangue*, a pre-gelatinised cassava paste usually in the form of balls. All of these products are generally produced at the household to village level, with the use of relatively simple equipment for peeling, grating, de-watering, sieving and heating (frying or steaming). With an investment of a few hundred dollars, a village-level cassava processing industry can be established. A few larger-scale automated lines for the processing of gari, attieke and cassava flour also exist.

Although village and household-level cassava processing is labour-intensive, it offers considerable potential for income generation in rural areas. It would however greatly benefit from improved technologies and training inputs.

Soybeans offer exceptional nutritive value for humans as well as for domestic animals. However, cooking, roasting or extrusion is required in order to render the protein content of the bean digestible for humans. Soybeans can be easily processed at village level. Soymilk and its derivatives such as tofu, yoghurt and ice cream can be relatively easily processed. The production of soymilk is simple, does not require specialised equipment, and can be undertaken in the household. With an investment of a few hundred dollars, a soy milk cottage industry can be established. Fully automated lines for soymilk production are also available from many manufacturers around the world. Small additional investments are required for the production of tofu or yoghurt from soymilk. The solid fraction remaining after filtration of the milk forms the basis for several popular food dishes in Nigeria.

The extruder-expeller process can produce pressed soy oil at small to medium scales. Using this process, about half of the oil contained in the bean is recovered. The resulting high-protein, high quality meal can be milled to flour and used to fortify several other food products for human consumption, increasing their protein content. The meal can also be used as a high-protein component in animal feeds, particularly for intensive peri-urban milk or livestock production systems. Full fat soy meal can be more cheaply produced by direct extrusion, yielding a high-protein high-calorie feed ingredient.

Local maintenance, repair and manufacturing of equipment

From the very beginning of the introduction of conservation agriculture and zero tillage/direct planting, the machinery input supply and service sector must be involved. In different parts of the world equipment for zero tillage and direct planting has been developed and is readily available for a wide range of crops, farming systems and farm sizes. As a result, basic technology is exists for the introduction of zero tillage in West Africa. However, the equipment must be adapted to the local conditions, available materials and handling habits. This requires a close collaboration from the start between rural mechanics or blacksmiths, workshops and small manufacturers as well as with farmers using the new technologies.

Experience has shown that such a technology development process for equipment is best done by the commercial private sector rather than by research stations. From an early point in time the mechanical workshops/manufacturers have to assume ownership for the equipment development. The potential future manufacturers or repair-service providers will need to collaborate closely with the farmers using the technologies, to make sure that the local technologies developed serve the farmers in the practice of conservation agriculture and provide a good long-term business for the commercial sector.

Support for the introduction of conservation agriculture should therefore include mechanisms to facilitate the establishment of a small-scale industry that produces, distributes, services and further develops tools and implements for conservation agriculture. An example of the effective creation of such a small-scale industry can be found in the southern states of Brazil.

Investment in supporting infrastructure, services and institutions

The effective spread of people-driven exploration, innovation and improvements in farming systems and related economic activities will require an effective support structure. Issues to be addressed include markets to absorb the increased supply of produce and derived products, market information, timely availability of the right inputs, seasonal and longer-term credit, technical and scientific support on demand to farmers and their associations, a well maintained transport infrastructure. External assistance will be needed in many cases to finance the needed strengthening of institutions and services and the improvement or rehabilitation of infrastructure, but their operation and maintenance will need to be paid for through service fees or other types of payments by beneficiaries. Management could be by local communities and institutions, private enterprise or provincial or national self-financing entities, accountable to the contributing beneficiaries. Investment in developing financial services should be focussing on training, promoting savings and loan groups in rural areas, facilitating the organisation of local banking institutions and training their staff, rather than on providing external funding for credit.

ANNEX I: CASE STUDY 4

WATER HARVESTING AND SOIL REHABILITATION IN INDIA AND AFRICA: POTENTIAL AND PRACTICE[13]

INTRODUCTION

Most rural people in developing countries are dependent upon a resource-based subsistence economy using products obtained from plants and animals (Agarwal & Narain 1989). However, a large portion of the world's rural poor today live in highly degraded lands and environments. 'Ecological poverty' can be described as the lack of an ecologically healthy natural resource base that is needed for a human society's survival and development. Healthy lands and ecosystems can provide the wealth that is needed for economically viable, healthy and dignified lives.

The challenge today lies in empowering and mobilising people to enable them to escape from their 'ecological poverty', in order to create natural wealth, and to develop a robust local economy. Experience in India and Africa has repeatedly shown that major economic change in rural communities has occurred wherever they have organised themselves to regenerate and manage their natural resource base (Tiffen, *et al.*, 1994). However, externally imposed technocratic resource management systems have invariably failed or been cost-ineffective, making them irrelevant in the financially constrained world of the poor.

---

[13] This paper is a synthesis of case studies prepared by Agarwal (2001) and Mascaretti (2001).

RAINWATER HARVESTING AND ENVIRONMENTAL REGENERATION

Over the last one hundred years, the world has seen major shifts in water management. During much of the last century individuals and communities steadily relinquished their role in water management to the state. The simple technology of storing and using rainwater declined in importance and the exploitation of rivers and particularly underground aquifers became pre-eminent. However, as water from these sources comprises only a small portion of total precipitation, this focus inevitably led to a growing pressure on these sources. In many cases, governments of water-scarce countries have encouraged massive interventions into the hydrological cycle but have done little to sustain the integrity of the hydrological system itself.

In reality, rainwater harvesting and the utilisation of groundwater sources are complements, not substitutes. In drought years, when rain is scarce and rivers dry up, groundwater becomes an important source of water both for drinking and irrigation (Agarwal 2000). However, were effective rainwater harvesting sytems in operation, the need for groundwater extraction in normal years would be reduced to minimal levels in many areas, while even in semiarid areas groundwater sources would be no more than a supplementary role. Water harvesting and groundwater together can drought-proof the country and create local food security.

In the case of India, for example, average annual rainfall is 1170 mm. But more than 50 per cent of this rain falls in about 15 rainy days and in most cases in less than 100 of a total of 8760 hours in a year. It is therefore very important to capture this extremely transitory resource before it is lost for human use (Agarwal & Narain, 1997). Effective rainwater harvesting offers the opportunity to achieve this. Adequate and safe potable water for human consumption could be guaranteed in all areas of the country, and sufficient water would generally be available to grow at least the less water-intensive crops every year.

Rainwater harvesting can also serve another purpose, by reducing the dependence of farmers on weak state institutions. In the African context, attempts to create large-scale capital-intensive agricultural systems have failed in most cases as a result of poor management, policies encouraging inappropriate and inefficient use of water resources, and financial problems that have constrained maintenance and staffing.

This paper presents two case studies. The first is from India and describes the transformation from a state of ecological poverty to a state of sustainable economic wealth. The second case, from Niger in West Africa, describes the use of indigenous technologies to improve water capture and utilization. These case studies are important because they show not only how these simple technologies can radically improve water availability for poor farmers, but also because they illustrate the associated ecological, social and economic impacts. The experiences of Sukhomajri village in India now span over 20 years. The experience of the case in Niger is more recent, but it is still as dramatic and significant.

Over the 1970s and 1980s, India has seen a number of micro-experiences of successful community resource management. What is remarkable is the short time it takes to transform a poverty-stricken, destitute and ecologically devastated village to a rich and green village. This is true for both examples presented in this paper.

EXAMPLE 1: THE SUKHOMAJRI EXPERIENCE - FROM WATER HARVESTING
TO WATERSHED DEVELOPMENT IN INDIA

Introduction

The village of Sukhomajri near the city of Chandigarh has been widely hailed in India for its pioneering efforts in micro-watershed development. In 1976, Sukhomajri - a small hamlet with a population of 455 situated in the sub-Himalayan Sivalik foothills - had a sparsely vegetated environment, with poor agriculture, and high levels of soil erosion and runoff. Though the annual average rainfall was about 1137 mm, groundwater was not available at a reasonable depth. Soil erosion and gully formation was steadily leading to a decrease in farm area. As agriculture was riddled with uncertainty, villagers traditionally kept herds of livestock to minimise risk. They cultivated about 50 ha of unirrigated land and kept about 411 heads of animals. Open grazing by livestock suppressed regeneration and kept the surrounding hills bare.

In 1979, facing a severe drought, the villagers built a small tank to capture the monsoon runoff and also agreed to protect their watershed to ensure that their tank did not get silted up. Since then the villagers have built a few more tanks and have protected the degraded forest that lies in their catchment area (Mishra *et al*, 1980). The tanks have helped to nearly triple crop production and the protection of the forest area has greatly increased grass and tree fodder availability. This, in turn, has increased milk production. With growing prosperity, Sukhomajri's economy has undergone a change.

Economic Impact
The following economic and ecological changes have taken place in the village over the years:

- From 1977 and 1986, wheat and maize production increased. By the mid-1980s, Sukhomajri had turned from a food-importing village to a food-exporting village (Sarin 1996).

- Protection of the watershed has led to increased grass production: from 40 kg per hectare in 1976 to 3 tons per hectare in 1992. Increased availability of fodder led to a transformation of livestock production systems. The number of goats went down while the number of buffaloes went up. This led to increased milk production (ibid). The village began to earn about Rs.350 000 from sale of milk.

- Watershed protection has also resulted in increased production of a highly fibrous grass commonly found in the region called *bhabhar* (*Eulialopsis binata*). This grass provides good fodder when it is young but is also very good pulping material for paper mills when it is mature. Villagers of Sukhomajri use *bhabhar* both as fodder and for sale to paper mills. Some Rs.100 000 are earned collectively from sale of *bhabhar* every year (ibid).

- The 400-hectare Sukhomajri forest today has over 300 000 highly valuable khair (Acacia catechu) trees (Dhar 1997). Each tree provides about 100 kg of wood which sells at about Rs.30 (US cents 70) per kg. Thus, each tree is worth Rs.3 000 and the entire forest is worth Rs.90 crore (Rs.900 million or US$21.08 million). If the forest is harvested on a sustainable basis – say, about 10 000 trees a year with a girth of more than 60 cm – the forest will yield Rs. 3 crore (US$0.7 million) annually (Mittal 1998).

In Sukhomajri, a major incentive for the villagers to protect their watershed came from changes in forest department policies. For example, the forest department would traditionally auction the grass in the degraded watershed to an outside businessman who would charge the villagers high rates to harvest the grass. The villagers argued that as they were protecting the watershed, they should get the benefits from the increased biomass production and not the contractor. The state forest department agreed to give the grass rights to the village society as long as the villagers paid the forest department a royalty equivalent to the average income earned by the department before the villagers started protecting the watershed. The villagers pay their village society a nominal amount to cut grass in the watershed. A part of this is used to pay the forest department and a part is used to generate community resources for the village.

A village-level institution for natural resource management
A crucial role in this entire exercise was played by a village-level institution specifically created for the purpose of watershed protection. The Hill Resources Management Society, as this institution is called, consists of one member from each household in the village. It provides a forum for all households to discuss their problems, manage the local environment and maintain discipline amongst their members. The society makes sure that no household grazes its animals in the watershed and in return it has created a framework for a fair distribution amongst all the households of the resource so generated, namely, water, wood and grass.

Future operational strategies in the Indian case
Despite the success of Sukhomajri and other communities with similar experiences in Ralegan Siddhi and Tarun Bharat Sangh, little adoption of these practices has occurred in other areas. Critics have often used these facts to condemn these examples as non-replicable creations of remarkable individuals who have persevered to bring change. But that is not the correct picture. These examples have remained scattered because a governance system that would foster local control over natural resources does not exist in the country. The current examples exist despite the system rather than because of them. It therefore takes enormous perseverance for individuals to bring change at the micro-level. However, if the system of governance enables local communities to improve and care for their resource base, it would be easier to bring about change. The Rajiv Gandhi Watershed Development Mission of the Madhya Pradesh government has shown that the state can replicate these community-based efforts if there is adequate political will and pressure on the technical and administrative bureaucracy to deliver.

In order to develop a sustainable village-level natural resource management programme, it is essential to develop a conceptual framework that addresses both the private and common property resources of the village, its diverse biomass needs, and the interests and requirements of different socioeconomic groups within the village community. Such a programme sets into motion a series of ecological successions, beginning with increased quantity and productivity of croplands as a result of increased water conservation. This in turn leads to an increased availability of water for irrigation, expanded grass production, and slowly increased production of fodder and timber resources from the tree and forestlands. Each of these stages of ecological succession generates its own economic impacts on the village society, which slowly unfold over the years.

Lessons
This case study teaches us that a bundle of policy measures are also needed for good natural resource management. These measures include changes in the current institutional, legal and financial framework in order to engender community-level, participatory democracy. It is only once this policy package is implemented that these 'isolated' micro-experiences will bloom into a 'million' villages.

Structures with a social process
Ecological change in Sukhomajri started with water harvesting. Building water harvesting structures is a comparatively easy task. But starting off a process of self-management in village communities is much more difficult. This is possible only if each water harvesting structure is the result of a co-operative social process. Strong social processes precede each structure to build 'social capital'. This is an area where the track-record of government agencies is literally non-existent and inflexible government rules militate against the very principle of social mobilisation. Social mobilisation means, firstly, creating awareness and confidence in the people that water harvesting works. Once this is achieved, it means creating village institutions that will decide where, when and how the water harvesting structures will be built, who will build them, and how much the villagers will contribute to construction costs. Once the structure is built, a key consideration is how the benefits - that is, the water - will be shared amongst the villagers, especially in the early years when water is scarce, and how will its use be regulated. Every part of the community will have to be involved by making each section - from the landed to the landless and women's groups - appreciate the benefits it will derive from the exercise. And by making efforts to ensure that benefits do indeed flow to each section of the community.

It is for this reason that water harvesting works best when combined with watershed development. It is in the nature of structures to be of value primarily to those who have land leaving the landless without any benefits and therefore alienated from the exercise. The development of watersheds to conserve both water and soil increases both soil and water conservation and leaf and grass production on what are usually common lands, thus greatly benefiting landless households. In addition, the process extends the life and effectiveness of the structures that benefit the landed by reducing siltation.

EXAMPLE 2: TASSAS - IMPROVED TRADITIONAL PLANTING PITS IN NIGER

Introduction
This second example presents the experience of the IFAD-funded Soils and Water Conservation sub-programme in Niger and its success in promoting the tassa technique, a low cost soil and water conservation and water harvesting technique. Tassas are a farming technique that helps to soften up deeper lying soils and enrich their organic-matter content; the technique consists of digging small holes and then planting seeds on the ridges formed by the dirt removed from the holes. Application of simple, low cost techniques such as the tassa makes it possible to recover degraded and abandoned land and transform it into productive cropland through individual and group action. There are many similar examples from Africa (Reij et al., 1996).

The IFAD-funded Soil and Water Conservation (SWC) Project started in 1988 and targeted the Illéla district (400 mm average rainfall), south of Tahoua. Population pressure and catastrophic droughts (1972-1973 and 1982-1985) had led to degradation of croplands (shortening and, in some cases, disappearance of fallow periods), pasture land and wood resources, as well as progressive fragility of production systems. The large majority of the population in Illela district is sedentary farmers (mainly Hausa). The IFAD project concentrated its activities mainly on 77 villages with about 100 000 inhabitants. Rainfed agriculture is the dominant mode of production with millet, sorghum and cowpeas as the major crops. However, most people cannot survive on rainfed crop production alone. Livestock and commercial activities are important sources of income. Seasonal migration of young men is also common.

The programme was designed as a pilot action. But an overall area of 6 350 ha was developed, more than twice the initial expectations. Off-farm measures consisting of collective silvo-pastoral initiatives were carried out on 585 ha, while collective cropland actions were carried out on 5 800 ha. Although large-scale erosion-control activities (i.e., construction of stone bunds) fell short of expectations, the *tassas* – which were not among the initially planned SWC techniques – were a resounding success, and their use continued to spread on individual plots even after the project closed.

The techniques focused mainly on bringing land back into production, reducing inter-annual variability of production and enhancing the resilience of agricultural systems to climatic risk. The *tassa* technique, in particular, is spreading at a surprising rate, encompassing an additional 2 to 3 hectares per annum on some holdings. *Tassas* are best suited to landholdings where ample family labour is available, or where farm hands can be hired. The technique has spawned a network of young day labourers who have mastered this technique and – rather than migrating – go from village to village to satisfy farmers' growing demands. There have even been cases of land being bought back by farmers who recognised early on the profit that can be earned from this land. The SWC sub-programme in Illéla can be considered one of IFAD's most successful actions to develop rainfed agriculture in semiarid zones and improve food security. On average, food availability in participating households rose between 20 percent and 40 percent, depending on local rainfall conditions.

A new approach: Low cost and replicable techniques

A major objective of the project, in contrast to previous efforts, has been to introduce simple, low-cost soil conservation and water harvesting techniques, which could easily be mastered by farmers. The main targets of the project were to construct contour stone bunds on 2 300 ha in four years and to develop 320 ha with half moons (*demi-lunes*). The project changed course in the second year. Ten farmers were sent to the Yatenga region in Burkina Faso where they observed various types of SWC techniques employed, including improved traditional planting pits (*zaï*). These reminded them of a traditional technique (called *tassa* in Hausa) used in their own region, which had been more or less abandoned. The traditional *tassa* consisted of just tiny pits made with a hoe to break the surface soil crust before the onset of the rains. The improvements in the *zaï* technique consisted in increasing their dimensions (from a diameter of 10 cm to 20-30 cm and from a depth of 5 cm to 10-25 cm) to collect more rainfall and putting organic matter in the pits to improve soil fertility. The organic matter attracts termites, which digest it and make the nutrients more easily available to the plant. Termites also dig channels thus increasing the infiltration of water into the soil.

On return, the improved *tassas* were tried out on four ha of land in the village of Nadara. The impact was spectacular. Some 70 ha of degraded land were rehabilitated in 1990. Only in the tassa pits was a reasonably good yield obtained during the drought of 1990. This convinced farmers of the great advantage of this technique so that in 1991 they applied the technique to 450-500 ha and in 1992 a further 1 000 ha. By the end of 1995, about 3 800 ha had been treated in Illéla district alone. These figures underestimate the achievements of the farmers because they are based exclusively on what the extension agents have been able to measure. No figures are available for other districts, however, field observations indicate that they are increasingly being adopted elsewhere.

The Extension System

The project organised exchange visits between villages, to share experiences and train villagers in the various aspects of SWC works. These exchange visits became one of the key activities, very appreciated by farmers, and which had an important impact in accelerating the diffusion of the SWC technologies.

Impact

The IFAD-funded project has measured the impact of the *tassa*, half-moons (*demi-lunes*) and contour stone bunds on a large number of farmers-managed demonstration plots. A comparison of the different SWC/WH techniques on millet yields show that in years of drought, *demi-lunes* perform on average slightly better than *tassa* because *demi-lunes* have a larger catchment area, so more runoff is available to plants. In contrast, in a year of good rainfall, *tassas* do slightly better than *demi-lunes* when only manure is used. These results show that water harvesting on its own has an important impact on yields and adding manure increases yields further. The rehabilitation of degraded barren land using *tassa* is clearly an economic proposition as farmers and traders are now increasingly getting interested in buying degraded land.

Impact on food security: While in a year of good rainfall, most families in the Illéla area produce more or less sufficient food crops, in all other years, and in particular in low rainfall years, these families get into serious trouble. To procure their cereals requirements, they are obliged to sell livestock or earn cash through migration. Families who have invested in SWC still have a cereal shortage in a drought year, but much lower than before. If they store some of their surplus gained during a good rainfall year, they will be able to meet their cereal needs even in years of low rainfall.

Management of rehabilitated soils: Maintenance of conservation works and soil fertility is necessary to ensure the sustainability of yield levels. A survey conducted in December 1998 showed that farmers rarely re-dig *tassas* every year. They usually continue to use the same pits. The *demi-lunes* need to be cleaned and the ridge repaired every two to three years. In general, maintenance is irregular, but more so for the *demi-lunes* since their total maintenance requirements are more demanding.

Because livestock raising is an important component of livelihood systems in the semiarid region, most farmers have access to adequate quantities of manure. The major bottleneck is the transport of manure to the fields. Only a minority of farmers applies manure to their tassa every year. The majority does so every second year. In current economic circumstances, mineral fertilisers are neither available to the majority of farmers in Niger nor would their use on millet be economic.

Role of paid labour: To rehabilitate degraded land with tassa requires a considerable investment in labour. Family labour is usually not sufficient and farmers have to either hire labour or organise traditional work parties. In several cases, young men have organised themselves in small groups of 5 to 10 persons, which can be contracted out by individual farmers to undertake specific SWC activities. Many families increasingly rely on hired labour. Many analysts assume that resource poor farmers in particular benefit from this emerging labour market. This new source of cash income means that they don't have to sell all or most of their small livestock in case of a bad harvest and they can avoid migration.

An emerging land market: In the Illela project, the use of simple and effective SWC techniques that could be applied by individual farmers meant that they could treat lands over which they had land use rights. This situation is very different from other SWC operations in which large blocks of land were treated, which almost always created land tenure conflicts.

Badly degraded land on the plateau in Illela has become productive again and a land market has now emerged. Farmers buy and sell degraded land for prices that increased considerably between 1992 and 1994. The emergence of a market for degraded land shows that farmers believe that tassa are an efficient and cost-effective means for bringing degraded land back into production.

Recommendations for Future Operational Strategies and Actions

The identification and adaptation of local technologies is what characterised the successes observed by the *tassas* in Niger. Farmers decide whether or not to adopt and replicate a particular SWC technique based on how easy it is to implement, how it fits into the crop year and, especially, whether it has an immediate impact on production. Other than the *tassas*, measures such as stone bunds and *demi-lunes* have also been widely replicated in West Africa. These measures were largely appreciated by those interested in bringing degraded land back into production. They triggered a significant shift in the rural exodus as they offered appealing options for immediate returns and paid work.

An appropriate conservation programme strategy normally requires a slow and modest start to implement. Governments and funding agencies must be prepared to re-examine programme content and budgets after some time. It is essential to combine the short-term perspective with the longer-term view of how productivity increases and conservation will continue to be supported. In this context, it seems more relevant to develop 'programmes' rather than 'projects' to integrate SWC activities properly with long-term efforts to develop agricultural production.

The Niger project shows that the first step must be to reinforce mechanisms for the identification and analysis of local technologies and know-how. The project teams must be encouraged to undertake this kind of 'inventory'. It also means that extension agents need to be trained in diagnostic methods for their individual areas of technical expertise. The adaptation of appropriate technologies entails close co-operation between farmers and researchers and means steering them toward the adjustment and local adaptation of principles tested elsewhere.

In most cases, the research and innovation potential (and not only "traditional practices") of the farmers themselves has not been adequately recognised and exploited. In view of the very limited facilities available for institutional research, and hence its inability to respond to diversity (and often to even perceive that diversity), only by mobilising the research/experimentation capacities of smallholders can innovation needs be met.

Once a promising technology has been identified and adapted by farmers, it is very important to support the local systems of farmer-to-farmer diffusion. This method of diffusion is low cost and usually produces very good results as well as creating an informal network between farmers, which can lead to other initiatives.

CONCLUSIONS

Local soil and water management provides the key to the transformation of the ecological and economic base of communities dependent on natural resources. Both these examples illustrate the need for fundamental changes in current water management policies and strategies.

Both examples illustrate the power and value, to individuals, communities and wider regions, of combining individual and collective knowledge and energy in soil and water harvesting and conservation.

ANNEX I: CASE STUDY 5

PRIVATE SECTOR-LED DIVERSIFICATION AMONG INDIGENOUS PRODUCERS IN GUATEMALA [14]

INTRODUCTION [15]

One of the key issues facing farming systems with many small-scale producers largely dependent upon low yielding staple crops is that of income generation. Few farming households are completely susbsistence based, and cash earnings are vital not only for adequate nutrition and access to services, but also as a source of demand for local goods and services that provide livelihoods for many more households. Even where yields or cultivated areas are increasing, declining terms of trade and domestic prices for staple crops in many farming systems are leading to reductions in smallholder incomes, pushing producers ever deeper into poverty and strangling rural economic growth. Yet creating the initial conditions for rural income growth has generally proven difficult. Development projects tend to focus on strengthening technologies, human capital and infrastructure rather than on increasing farm incomes directly, and in any case their impact tends to diminish once the implementation period is concluded.

The following case study documents an example of substantial and sustained growth in smallholder family incomes that has occurred within a part of the Mesoamerican hillside maize-beans system as a result of diversification of small-scale producers into export horticulture. The case is particularly interesting because the beneficiary population is largely indigenous, many not even speaking Spanish, and because their domination of the U.S. market for snow peas has been achieved entirely on the basis of micro-level production by over 20 000 family production units.

This impressive position has been reached without any external support from Government or development agencies. Rather it arose from the activities of a private sector that was, in turn, responding to emerging international market opportunities. However, the study argues that the effectiveness of the private sector actions, and hence the success of the small-scale producers, was greatly enhanced by the concurrent emergence of a private sector association dedicated to non-traditional products, and a series of national governments generally supportive of the needs of an emerging export sector. Thus major gains for poor, indigenous farming families resulted, in part at least, from a favourable environment for business development.

[14] This case study is condensed from Gulliver (2001).
[15] This case study draws heavily from Contreras, 1996 and Gulliver et al., 1996.

DESCRIPTION OF THE SYSTEM

The Mesoamerican hillside maize and beans farming system occupies 650 000 km^2, and encompasses the long mountainous chain connecting North America to South America through Mexico and Central America[16]. It is bounded for most of its length on both the Pacific and Caribbean sides by the Coastal Plantation and Mixed Farming System. As is common in the region, the Mesoamerican system is highly dualistic, with large numbers of poor and extremely poor small-scale producers occupying marginal and sub-marginal hillside and slope lands, while the better soils of the valleys and intermittent lowlands within the system are incorporated into large estates or commercial family farms with coffee, sugar cane, rubber, cattle or other agricultural activities. The proportion of population in rural areas is high by Latin American standards, reaching over 60 percent in Guatemala[17], and agriculture plays an important role in GDP, contributing as much as 28 percent in Nicaragua.

Poverty levels are high within the system – exceeding 80 percent of population in extreme poverty in the highlands of Guatemala, where this case is drawn from – and are often directly correlated with the percentage of indigenous people in the system (65 percent of the population in Guatemala, possibly exceeding 90 percent within the area of the farming system). Rising population levels have led to an increasing fragmentation of holdings and a concomitant reduction in farm sizes[18], which in turn has increased pressure on land and water resources and led both to the expansion of the agricultural frontier (often onto steep or otherwise constrained soils incapable of sustained arable production) and to further poverty. In the 1980s, FAO studies estimated erosion and serious soil degradation to be affecting as much as 35 percent of lands in Guatemala, suggesting that the problem on slope lands within the Mesoamerican system was likely to be even more serious. The crucial importance of land is clearly illustrated by the numerous rurally-based armed conflicts which have erupted over the last 30 years within system boundaries.

Smallholder production of maize and beans is a core activity for most households and is largely consumed on-farm. Yields are low[19], reflecting the limited use of external inputs and marginal soils. Coffee is the favoured cash crop where altitude and soils permit, but communities near urban centers may have traditions of fruit and vegetable production. Cattle can play an important role, but are of less importance at higher altitudes, except in the Guatemalan and Mexican altiplanos where sheep are common. More isolated communities often resort to seasonal or long-term migration as a means of supplementing cash incomes. Despite these alternatives, maize and beans continue to occupy a key role culturally, nutritionally, and financially for the majority of small-scale producers, and the sale of surpluses of these products provides the basic income for the majority of families. Yet real domestic prices for these commodities have been stagnant or declining in recent decades as a result of expanded external access to domestic markets, and lower levels of domestic market protection.

The presence of public services and infrastructure is weak throughout much of the system, and diminishes rapidly as one moves away from administrative centers. Widespread civil strife has added to the gulf between large urban centers and rural communities. Even in Costa Rica, often seen as a model for economic development in the region, recent data shows the human development index is nine times higher in key urban areas than in rural indigenous communities[20]. Over the next 30 years the future looks bleak for those small-scale producers dependant on maize and beans for their livelihood, and even bleaker for their children, who will inherit ever smaller and more degraded holdings from their parents.

THE CASE AND ITS CONTEXT

Over a period of approximately 20 years, from 1974-1994, a number of key changes occurred in Guatemala that combined to profoundly affect the lives of over 150 000 poor inhabitants of the Guatemalan rural highlands. In broad terms these changes can be grouped into three categories:

---

[16] See Gulliver et al (2001) for further description of the Mesoamerican hillside maize and beans farming system.

[17] Proyecto Estado de la Region 1999.

[18] According to national agricultural census data, the number of holdings growing maize in Guatemala has increased from 321 000 in 1964 to 667 000 in 1996 – an increase of over 100 percent in 32 years. Average holding sizes of maize producers in 1996 was approximately 3.6 ha.

[19] Average yields are less than 1.5 t/ha. for maize and 0.75 t/ha. for beans.

[20] Proyecto Estado de la Region 1999.

(a) The emergence of small-scale producers and small to medium-scale enterprises as key players in the creation of a major export trade for snow peas, broccoli and more recently other products;

(b) The formation and growth of the exporters' trade association GEXPRONT, and its role in facilitating the growth of the non-traditional agricultural sector; and

(c) The recognition by the Government of Guatemala of the importance of exports in driving economic growth, and its adoption of export-friendly policie.

Although described separately below, in order to clarify the actions taken and illustrate clearly the role of each group, the development and impact of the three sets of factors were clearly inter-related, and should be understood as such.

The Emergence of Snow Peas and Broccoli in Guatemala

In the early 1970s, growing demand for snow peas (*Pisum sativum*) in the U.S. faced a major constraint; fresh supplies from California were only available from June to October, yet the frozen imports from Taiwan were viewed as poor replacements. An alternate source of fresh snow peas might be very profitable. Initial interest had focused on Chile, but in 1974 an American entrepreneur started to experiment with snow pea production in Guatemala. Snow peas were agronomically well suited to the altiplano of Central and Western Guatemala where the temperate climatic conditions permitted harvesting from October to May. Results from pilot plots were encouraging and a number of agribusinesses commenced production.

Demand for snow peas continued to grow rapidly through the 1970s and 1980s, but expansion in Guatemala proved difficult; obtaining land within the densely populated highlands, where few owners have legal title, was expensive and time consuming. Supply could not keep up with demand and the agribusiness corporations had to turn increasingly to independent producers to supply their buyers. By the beginning of the 1980s, a number of smaller producers started to bypass the agribusinesses and deal directly with small exporters and processors.

Despite their lack of formal education or capital, local indigenous producers enjoyed a number of advantages. Many of the early producers, at least, were familiar with horticultural production, having grown onions, tomatoes and similar crops for local markets. Their land was available at no cash cost, and their desire to maximise the use of family labour was ideally suited to a crop which required an input of 516 person/days/ha over a four month period.

With labour comprising 35 percent of total costs, even at the low wage rates paid in rural Guatemala, smallholders using unpaid family labour could earn extremely high returns from snow peas compared with traditional alternatives. A quarter hectare of snow peas (a typical holding) could generate US$500 before returns to land and labour were taken into account. By contrast, the same area of maize would earn only US$50. Agribusiness operations were unable to compete[21]. Furthermore, with supplemental irrigation, it was possible to produce two consecutive vegetable crops - snowpeas and broccoli - in one year and maize in the next. As a result, broccoli production, already known in Guatemala but previously not considered attractive by small growers, increased greatly in importance. The very small areas of land required to generate significant increases in household income also permitted producers to continue with maize and beans on the remaining cultivated areas. By the mid-1990s, an estimated 21 500 families were involved in snow pea and/or broccoli cultivation, producing 23 000 MT of snow peas and 43 000 MT of broccoli annually on approximately 4 350 has.

The growth of independent producers was only possible because of a parallel growth in intermediaries and exporters. Managing the daily output of so many producers scattered over perhaps 3000 km[2] of poorly serviced rural highlands, and ensuring that it is selected, packed and shipped within no more than 24 hours of harvest, requires a sophisticated distribution system. No estimates exist of the number of intermediaries involved, but at the time of the studies in the mid-1990s, at least 50 companies were making regular export shipments of fresh snow pea during the harvest season; some using air freight, others reefers (the latter primarily to Europe)[22].

By the 1990s many producers – estimated at more than 60 percent - had regular contractual arrangements with local intermediaries, who in turn generally represented specific exporters. For growers, the benefits of

[21] Cost of production data for commercial operators in the early 1990s show that, with labour at Q.4/personday (equivalent to approximately US$1 at that time), they faced an additional US$2 064/ha. in labour costs.

[22] Frozen snow pea has never accounted for more than 10 percent of overall snow pea production, in contrast to broccoli which is exported almost entirely in frozen form.

contractual production lay in access to working capital, generally in the form of seed and agrochemicals. For exporters, on the other hand, the opportunity to plan and co-ordinate harvesting dates and volumes so as to maximise volumes at key points in the price cycle was the key incentive. Some growers stayed independent, selling their output, often in lots of less than 100kg, at specialist auctions in communities around the altiplano. Starting at 5 p.m. and ending at around midnight, intermediaries with pickup trucks would receive contracted deliveries and bid for non-contracted supplies to fill their nightly quotas, either for direct delivery to an exporter, or for onward sale before dawn at one of five major wholesaling centers that evolved to serve the market. As much as 1.5 million lbs. (650 MT) per week might flow through these channels during the peak of the harvesting season. Through the 1980s and 1990s other smallholder non-traditional products emerged, increasing diversification. These included mini-vegetables, baby corn, sugar-snaps, blackberries and especially raspberries.

The Role of GEXPRONT
In 1978 the Government of Guatemala created a public-sector agency, GUATEXPRO, to promote national exports, but the institution lasted only two years. Nevertheless, it convinced a number of exporters of non-traditional products that, lacking the power of the traditional sugar, coffee or livestock sectors, they needed a forum that would provide influence and co-ordination to the mostly small and medium-scale enterprises active in the sector. Thus in 1982 the Guatemalan Non-Traditional Exporters' Association (GEXPRONT) was founded. GEXPRONT received a major boost in 1986 when USAID commenced financial support. Although GEXPRONT comprises five commissions, this case study deals only with that active in the area of agricultural products. By 1995, the agricultural commission of GEXPRONT (now referred to as AGEXPRONT) had over 250 registered members. In co-operation with its sister commissions, and often in collaboration with other private sector entities such as the Chamber of Industry and Commerce, AGEXPRONT lobbied for, and contributed to, a number of key changes within the export sector. It placed little emphasis on direct market development, although some activities were designed to support individual enterprises in their commercial relations with overseas buyers. Instead, AGEXPRONT focused on resolving systemic problems impeding its members in conducting and expanding their operations. These were primarily issues of importance to small businesses, and often involved the management of functions hitherto considered the sole mandate of the public sector. Apart from contributing to changes in Government policy (see below), the key changes instituted by AGEXPRONT in their first decade included:

- The founding of an annual export fair 'Agritrade' to promote contacts between foreign wholesalers and brokers and local exporters;
- Co-founder of COMBEX-IM, a not-for profit private company, to manage all air cargo passing though Guatemala International Airport, which streamlined cargo handling procedures, and expanded ambient and cold storage space for perishable cargoes;
- Pre-certification programmes for agricultural exports, including paying the costs of USDA inspectors stationed in Guatemala, and certification of Guatemalan staff in the U.S, allowing most containers to pass though designated U.S. ports of arrival without stopping;
- The organization of visits by international experts who would, on payment of a fee by a member to AGEXPRONT, visit the exporter's facilities and provide advice. Thus small companies were able to access experts at a fraction of the cost they otherwise would have had to pay; and
- An agreement with the Ministry of Foreign Affairs to cover part of the cost of commercial attachés based in five key trading cities, permitting AGEXPRONT to participate in defining their duties and evaluating their performance, ensuring greater responsiveness to exporters' needs.

By the beginning of the 1990s, yields had begun to stagnate for both broccoli and snow peas and supply was once again a problem despite the much wider range of non-traditional crops now being grown. Poor rural infrastructure rendered opening up new production areas difficult and the best lands for broccoli and snow peas had already been brought into production. Increasing concerns over chemical contamination were emerging in foreign markets. As a result, the support programmes offered by AGEXPRONT also started to change focus:

- Regional sub-commissions were created, bringing together exporters in specific geographical areas, dedicated to resolving regional problems such as roads and electricity;

- A USAID funded demand-driven research fund contributed half the cost of production-based research, where companies or sector groups were willing to put up the remaining half;

- Working with representatives of the sector, an agreement was brokered to collect cesses from snow pea exporters[23] to finance research and extension activities related to the crop;

- Public and private sector funds were obtained to finance testing and regulatory approval for the use of clorotalonil on snow peas. Although approved for broccoli, the unapproved use of this fungicide on snow peas was a cause of increasing friction with U.S. sanitary authorities; and

- All companies engaged in broccoli freezing agreed to contribute according to their volume of operation towards the cost of two broccoli extension officers, who would provide assistance to any broccoli producer, irrespective of the plant to which they sold their output.

In the second half of the 1990s, GEXPRONT faced a further challenge; USAID financial support, which had been diminishing for some years, ceased. Member dues and income from sponsored activities were on their own insufficient to maintain the demand-driven research programmes and other high cost activities. Instead, AGEXPRONT started to forge ever-closer links with the Ministry of Agriculture, convincing the government that a private sector agency could make more effective use of public funds than could the Ministry itself. As a result, many of these programmes have since been maintained in operation, with public support.

The Role of Government
While there is no doubt that the key players in the success of snow peas and subsequent export crops have been the smallholders and the exporters with whom they trade, the Government has also played an important role over the last 20 years in setting an appropriate legislative and policy framework that has permitted the non-traditional export sector to thrive. Key measures have included:
- In the mid-1980s the Government devalued the Quetzal, reversing a lengthy period of overvaluation of the currency which had favoured imports at the expense of exports;

- CONAPEX was founded to coordinate public and private sector actions with respect to the export sector. As well as the Chamber of Industry and Commerce, it included the Ministries of Finance, Agriculture, Trade and Foreign Relations, and the Central Bank. GEXPRONT was a founding member;

- CONAPEX coordinated the creation of the 'Ventanilla Unica' (single counter system) permitting exporters to clear all export licensing and permit procedures at a single location;

- In 1989, new legislation established the right to import materials and machinery intended for export production free of duty and taxes; and

- For over a decade into the 1990s, the Government subsidised the development of small-scale irrigation systems in the highlands, greatly increasing the capacity of local producers to enter into double cropping of snow peas and broccoli.

In the late 1990s, the Ministry of Agriculture (MAGA) drastically reduced its staffing and internal expenditures, but increasingly funnelled significant amounts of public funds through GEXPRONT for small-producer support activities. It also formed regional development groups, incorporating the private sector, which have tried to co-ordinate private and public sector development in less favoured rural areas. AGEXPRONT has played a major role in the work of these committees.

IMPACT

The Results
There is no doubt of the enormous impact that the development of snow peas and broccoli exports has had on small-scale indigenous farmers of the Guatemalan altiplano. From 1980 to 1993, the Guatemalan share of the OECD market for fresh, frozen and processed vegetables quintupled, from 0.09 percent to 0.45 percent[24], even while the commercial-scale production of these products was declining to almost nothing. By 1995, Guatemalan supplied one third of U.S. imports of snow peas; for a value of US$55 million per annum. And because no single family could command the labour, capital or water supply to cultivate a large area of these

---

[23] Initially these cessees were set at Q.0.01 per lb., generating some US$65 000 annually.

[24] Inversiones y Desarrollo Corp., 1995.

intensive vegetables, the returns were widely spread within the indigenous community, with average holding sizes devoted to the crop of 0.24 has. No producer was recorded with a planted area of more than 0.5 has.

By 1996, it was estimated that 21,500 indigenous families were involved in direct production of these two crops, generating estimated gross farm incomes in the region of US$30 millions. This equates to almost US$1400 per family. On the basis of an estimated 516 person days of labour per hectare for snow peas, and 191 person days for broccoli, it can be calculated that this family income was achieved for an average of 0.5-0.6 person years of labour input per family, or an earning of approximately US$2500/annum/person year employed[25].

A further US$28 million was calculated to accrue annually to the wholesaling, processing, packing and export sector within Guatemala, some of which would benefit rural inhabitants engaged in collection, packing and transport activities. In fact, a study undertaken in 1994 estimated an indirect labour multiplier of 0.26 in relation to non-traditional agricultural activities[26], suggesting that as many as 27000 families may have derived employment from these activities, without counting those occupied in producing mini-vegetables, raspberries and other later crops. With a conservative family size estimate of six persons, these two non-traditional crops may have contributed to poverty alleviation for over 160000 rural poor in Guatemala. Further more, these numbers do not take into account providers of good and services in rural areas, who were able to establish business in response to rising rural demand. These certainly exist but no data on their numbers ia available.

Key Contributing Factors

Although the innovation and risk taking of indigenous producers and small-scale trading enterprises was critical to the success of the snow pea/broccoli system in Guatemala, a number of other factors were probably equally important. The low costs of entry into both production and export of snow peas resulted in a system that was fiercely competitive, with no apparent advantages of scale such as were seen in broccoli freezing (perhaps contributing to the much lower returns for this crop). As a result, over 40 percent of the destination market price for snow peas was captured by the growers, a high proportion for a perishable export crop.

As important, however, was the role played by AGEXPRONT in creating (and in relation to Government, promoting) a framework within which such competitive behaviour could flourish, providing new entrants with market support and facilities that would otherwise have been very costly to develop. In general, AGEXPRONT resisted the temptation to pick winners, undertaking only a single exercise of this type in the period to 1996. Perhaps this was best; enthusiasm for asparagus, identified in the 1987 study, led to a number of large investments which were all failures.

Unusually for an exporters' trade association, however, AGEXPRONT took a leading role in promoting enterprise-producer linkages, seeing it as a key to increasing product availability, and hence turnover, for its members. From an early point, AGEXPRONT encouraged exporters in the same product line (melons, mangoes, snowpeas, broccoli, cut flowers, etc.), to form sub-commissions aimed at identifying and alleviating common obstacles to the development of that product. It was this strategy that directly led to the establishment of the USAID financed shared-cost field research programmes, and subsequently the privately funded extension services, as exporters agreed on a common need to deal with low yields, contamination issues or other problems. In 1997 AGEXPRONT created its newest sub-commission; for exporters of environmentally friendly products and services.

The relationship between the private sector and the Government of Guatemala has also been crucial for the rapid development of the non-traditional export sector, and hence ultimately for income generation among small-scale producers. Although Government attitudes have varied over the last 20 years, and not all policies have been to the sector's advantage (following the readjustment of exchange rates in the 1980s, there was a long period of overvaluation of the currency again in the 1990s), the Government has, in general, been supportive of small-scale enterprises. In the longer term, the willingness of MAGA to utilise AGEXPRONT as an executive arm for channelling and managing public sector funds has shown that international funding is not the only way for such private sector bodies to access the financing they need to continue their activities.

---

[25] It should be remembered, however, that this return does not take into account the value of the land utilised.
[26] Samayoa Urrea 1994.

Sustainability

Small-scale non-traditional vegetable and fruit producers in Guatemala face intense competition from many other producers. Nonetheless, it has managed to maintain and even expand its position, utilising its favourable climate, low family labour costs, and efficient marketing system. The most serious threats it faces are a consequence of its greatest strength; its highly dispersed and atomistic production and marketing system. This has raised serious concerns over contamination, firstly from prohibited agrochemicals, and more recently as a result of the suspected biological contamination of raspberries with cyclosporin. With so many producers and exporters, determining the source of any contamination or infection is very difficult, and entire shipments may be contaminated by a single producer. A second possible threat to system sustainability are the difficulties still experienced by exporters in matching peak supply with periods of highest demand (and hence price).

Controlling output is certainly easier where production is concentrated among a small number of producers, but is not impossible for dispersed production systems. The future of the current system may depend on convincing small growers of the critical importance of proper chemical and sanitary management of their products, and the need to match planting times to market demand. Curiously enough, it may be these needs that propels participating indigenous farmers into 21st century production techniques, through the use of internet-based harvesting forecast systems, computerized coding of producer batches, and automated sampling and analysis of products.

On the positive side, it seems inevitable that the U.S. share of its own domestic market will decline significantly in the future, even as demand for exotic and high-value horticultural products and fruits continues to increase. California, the chief production area in the U.S., has many competing demands for its land, and the continued production of high labour-input crops, even behind high levels of tariff and pseudo-tariff protection, can have little long-term future. This may open up major new growth prospects for Guatemala, if Mexican competition can be held at bay[27].

Finally, it is a cause for some concern that the sector has achived so little progress at creating added value through processing. In the mid-1990s, nearly 90 percent of the value of non-traditional agricultural exports was still accounted for by fresh products, and even the 10 percent that was processed was exported primarily to regional markets in Central America, not to cosmopolitan markets.

RECOMMENDATIONS FOR FUTURE ACTIVITIES

Lessons

A number of important lessons can be drawn from the case presented above:

- Diversification into high value export crops, often dismissed as feasible only for a small number of producers, can indeed have a significant impact, in terms of both numbers of beneficiaries and income generated, and can be a driving force for broader rural economic growth.

- Small-scale, poorly educated and indigenous producers are capable of successfully adopting demanding new perishable crops, even without external training or support. That such groups can out-compete agribusinesses demonstrates that they do possess comparative advantages;

- Pioneer efforts by agri-business entrepreneurs may provide opportunities for smaller producers, by demonstrating the agronomic feasibility of the product and opening market channels.

- An open and competitive production and marketing environment can have a major impact in ensuring that benefits arising from the system are shared equitably within the system.;

- The ability of small and medium enterprises to collaborate in lobbying and sectoral support activities can be very important, especially in reducing barriers to entry and in obtaining the policy support of Government;

- Considerable growth in sector performance can be obtained through improvements in transport, financing, market contact, and regulatory compliance. Attempting to pick and support 'winners' is dangerous and has a poor track record, especially when done by Government;

---

[27] Mexico has managed to capture almost all of the production gains associated with declining tomato production in the Southern U.S.

Replicability

Because this case study describes a series of events, rather than a specific intervention, the question of replicability may be less relevant than for other case studies. Nevertheless, some comments can be made. None of the elements that contributed to the development of snow pea and broccoli exports in Guatemala are unique. A number of niche crops, requiring intensive labour and with limited barriers to entry, offer potential for diversification among poor smallholder populations in many farming systems. There are many countries where exporters' associations exist, although they are rarely as active as GEXPRONT and are difficult to sustain once external funding dries up. There are also many countries where Governments have made an effort to promote non-traditional exports. Finally, there are numerous examples of cases where the private sector has provided the driving force for the emergence of new non-traditional crops and products, whether they be cut flowers in Colombia, shrimp in Ecuador, or orange juice in Brazil. What is unusual in the Guatemala case, is the degree to which the private sector has created a successful partnership with poor, small-scale producers to dominate the largest market in the world for a specific commodity[28]. Other crops have also found success, using the same formula.

For Governments and external financing agencies, perhaps the key to replication of this experience must be to focus diversification and income support projects less on the producers themselves, and more on the environment in which they function. This environment clearly includes elements under Government control, such as infrastructure, legislative controls, fiscal policies and exchange rates, but also depends heavily on private sector activity in marketing, financing, input supply, and employment creation, none of which can be sustainably provided by the public sector, nor adequately dominated by producers themselves.

Yet the private sector is likely to face obstacles, sometimes very serious ones, to these activities. If these can be removed, the environment for diversification and income generation will be much more conducive and – as long as the underlying agronomic, socio-cultural and market conditions are appropriate – the probability of success greatly enhanced. However, the private sector must be convinced of the potential of the small-scale producers as partners. Small-scale enterprises are inherently more willing to accept this premise (large enterprises may find, in any case, that transaction costs are too high when dealing with small-scale producers). Furthermore, only the smaller enterprises are able to adequately identify and assess the importance of the constraints faced in developing atomized production and marketing systems. Hence the importance of enabling small and medium-sized enterprises to play a leading role in the process.

[28] Two other examples can be readily identified. The development of banana exports among small-holders in the Eastern Caribbean in the 1960s to 1980s was led by Geest, a private sector enterprise. Nevertheless, in Geest, growers faced a monopsony buyer, and thus were never equal partners, while the British Government played a major support role for many years. The case of horticultural exports from Kenya is also similar, but there the role of the commercial agribusiness sector in direct production has always been much greater.

ANNEX 2

CLASSIFICATION OF FARMING SYSTEMS
BY BROAD CATEGORY

• • •

AFR	MNA	ECA	SAS	EAP	LAC
SMALLHOLDER IRRIGATED					
Irrigated	Irrigated				Irrigated
WETLAND RICE BASED					
			Rice Rice-Wheat	Lowland Rice	
SMALLHOLDER RAINFED HUMID					
Forest Based Rice-Tree Crop Root Crop Cereal-Root Crop Mixed Maize Mixed			Tree Crop	Root-Tuber Temperate Mixed	Forest Based Intensive Mixed Maize-Beans (Mesoamerican)
SMALLHOLDER RAINFED HIGHLAND					
Highland Perennial Highland Temperate Mixed	Highland Mixed		Highland Mixed Sparse (Mountain)	Upland Intensive Mixed Highland Extensive Mixed	Intensive Highland Mixed High Altitude Mixed (Central Andes) Moist Temperate Mixed Forest-Livestock

AFR	MNA	ECA	SAS	EAP	LAC
SMALLHOLDER RAINFED DRY/COLD					
Agropastoral Millet/Sorghum Pastoral Sparse (Arid)	Rainfed Mixed Dryland Mixed Pastoral Sparse (Arid)	Small scale Cereal-Livestock Sparse (Arid)	Rainfed Mixed Dry Rainfed Pastoral Sparse (Arid)	Pastoral Sparse (Arid) Sparse (Forest)	Dryland Mixed Pastoral Sparse (Forest)
DUALISTIC					
Tree Crop Large Commercial & Smallholder		Irrigated Mixed Forest Based Livestock Horticulture Mixed Large scale Cereal-Vegetable Extensive Cereal-Livestock Pastoral Sparse (Cold)		Tree Crop Mixed	Coastal Plantation & Mixed Extensive Mixed (Cerrados & Llanos) Cereal-Livestock (Campos) Temperate Mixed (Pampas) Extensive Dryland Mixed (Gran Chaco)
COASTAL ARTISANAL FISHING					
Coastal Artisanal Fishing	Coastal Artisanal Fishing		Coastal Artisanal Fishing	Coastal Artisanal Fishing	
URBAN BASED					
Urban Based	Urban Based	Urban Based	Urban Based	Urban Based	Urban Based

ANNEX 3

CLASSIFICATION OF COUNTRIES BY DEVELOPING REGION

•••

The following classification is based on the regional groups defined in the World Development Report (WDR), issued annually by the World Bank, but excludes high-income countries and minor dependencies (large dependent territories are, however, included). The WDR identifies six regions, compared with five regions in the FAO AT2015/30 Interim Report (the latter excludes ECA). Note also that as defined in this publication, South Africa is included AFR, Turkey is included in ECA and Afghanistan is included in SAS.

Sub-Saharan Africa (AFR)
Angola, Benin, Botswana, Burkina Faso, Burundi, Cameroon, Cape Verde, Central African Republic, Chad, Comoros, Congo, Congo Democratic Republic, Côte d'Ivoire, Djibouti, Eritrea, Ethiopia, Gabon, Gambia, Ghana, Guinea, Guinea Bissau, Kenya, Lesotho, Liberia, Madagascar, Malawi, Mali, Mauritania, Mauritius, Mozambique, Namibia, Niger, Nigeria, Republic of South Africa, Reunión, Rwanda, Sao Tome and Principe, Senegal, Seychelles, Sierra Leone, Somalia, Sudan, Swaziland, Tanzania, Togo, Uganda, Zambia, Zimbabwe.

Middle East and North Africa (MNA)
Algeria, Egypt, Iran, Iraq, Jordan, Lebanon, Libya, Morocco, Oman, Saudi Arabia, Syria, Tunisia, Yemen, West Bank and Gaza.

Eastern Europe and Central Asia (ECA)
Albania, Armenia, Azerbaijan, Belarus, Bosnia and Herzegovina, Bulgaria, Croatia, Czech Republic, Estonia, Georgia, Hungary, Kazakhstan, Kyrgyz Republic, Latvia, Lithuania, Macedonia (Former Yugoslav Republic of), Moldova, Poland, Romania, Russian Federation, Slovak Republic, Slovenia, Tajikistan, Turkey, Turkmenistan, Ukraine, Uzbekistan, Yugoslavia Federal Republic.

South Asia (SAS)

Afghanistan, Bangladesh, Bhutan, India, Maldives, Nepal, Pakistan, Sri Lanka.

East Asia and Pacific (EAP)

Cambodia, China, Indonesia, Korea DPR, Korea, Laos, Macao, Malaysia, Mongolia, Myanmar, Philippines, Thailand, Vietnam. Plus 22 Pacific Island nations: American Samoa, Cook Islands, Fiji Islands, French Polynesia, Guam, Kiribati, Marshall Islands, Federated States of Micronesia, Nauru, New Caledonia, Niue, North Mariana Islands, Palau, Papua New Guinea, Pitcairn Islands, Samoa, Solomon Islands, Tonga, Tuvalu, Vanuatu, Wallis & Fortuna Islands.

Latin America and Caribbean (LAC)

Antigua, Argentina, Bahamas, Barbados, Belize, Bermuda, Bolivia, Brazil, Cayman Islands, Chile, Colombia, Costa Rica, Cuba, Dominica, Dominican Republic, Ecuador, El Salvador, Grenada, Guatemala, Guyana, Haiti, Honduras, Jamaica, Mexico, Netherlands Antilles, Nicaragua, Panama, Paraguay, Peru, St. Kitts and Nevis, St. Lucia, St. Vincent and Grenadines, Suriname, Trinidad and Tobago, Uruguay, Venezuela.

ANNEX 4

BIBLIOGRAPHY

···

Agarwal, A. (2000). *Drought? Try Water Harvesting*. Centre for Science and Environment, New Delhi, India.

Agarwal, A. (2001). 'Water Harvesting and Soil Rehabilitation in India: Potential and Practice' Case study for: Dixon, J., Gulliver, A. & Gibbon, D. *Global Farming Systems Study: Challenges and Priorities to 2030*. Consultation Documents, World Bank/FAO, Rome, Italy.

Agarwal, A. (2001) *Personal Communication*. Director, Centre for Science and the Environment, New Delhi, India.

Agarwal, A. & Narain, S. (1989). *Towards Green Villages: A Strategy for Environmentally-Sound and Participatory Rural Development*. Centre for Science and Environment, New Delhi, India.

Agarwal, A. & Narain, S. (1997). *Dying Wisdom: Rise, Fall and Potential of Traditional Water Harvesting System*. Centre for Science and Environment, New Delhi, India.

Amadu, H. (2000). 'We'll Feed Our People as We See Fit'. *Washington Post, 11 Sept*. p. A23

Amstalden Sampaio, M.J. (2000). 'Brazil: Biotechnology and Agriculture to Meet the Challenges of Increased Food Production'. In Persley, G.J. & Lantin, M.M. (eds): *Agricultural Biotechnology and the Poor: Proceedings of an International Conference*, October 1999. CGIAR, Washington, D.C., USA. pp. 74-78.

Anderson, J., Hazell, P., & Evans, L. (1987). 'Variability in Cereal Yields: Sources of Change and Implications for Agricultural Research and Policy'. *Food Policy* 12 (3): 199-212.

Anderson, J.R. & Thampapillai, J. (1990). *Soil Conservation in Developing Countries: Project and Policy Intervention*. World Bank, Washington, D.C. USA.

Anderson, J.R. (1994). *Agricultural Technology: Policy Issues for the International Community*. CAB International in Association with the World Bank, Wallingford, UK.

Anonymous. (2000). 'Central Kenya Farmers Embrace Biotech Farming'. *Africa News Service, 01 Nov*.

Apse, M.P., Aharon, G.S., Snedden, W.A., and Blumwald, E. (1999). 'Salt Tolerance Conferred by Over-expression of a Vacuolar Na+/H+ Antiport in Arabidopsis'. *Science* 285: 1256-1258.

Arntzen, C.J. (1995). 'Oral Immunization with a Recombinant Bacterial Antigen Produced in Transgenic Plants'. *Science* 268: 714-716

Arntzen, C. J. (1996). *Crop Biotechnology in the Service of Medical and Veterinary Science*. National Agricultural Biotechnology Council, Cornell University, Ithaca, N.Y., USA.

Batello, C. (2001) 'Farming Systems in Arid Rangelands of Syria and Jordan'. Case study for: Dixon, J., Gulliver, A. & Gibbon, D. *Global Farming Systems Study: Challenges and Priorities to 2030*. Consultation Documents, World Bank/FAO, Rome, Italy.

Bayou, K. (1998). 'Control of sheep and goat skin diseases' in Ian, B.L., & Kassa, B. (eds): *Proceedings of an in-service training exercise on hides and skins improvement*. FAO, Addis Ababa, Ethiopia, p. 13-20.

Bazza, M. (2001) 'Improved On-farm Participatory Water Management to Reduce Mining of Groundwater in Yemen'. Case study for: Dixon, J., Gulliver, A. & Gibbon, D. *Global Farming Systems Study: Challenges and Priorities to 2030*. Consultation Documents, World Bank/FAO, Rome, Italy.

Borroto, C. (2000). *Biotechnology Seminar: Cuban National Program On Agricultural Biotechnology: Achievements, Present and Future*. Seminar presented October 11 at FAO, Rome, Italy.

Boserup, E. (1965). *The Conditions of Agricultural Growth: The Economics of Agrarian Change under Population Pressure*. Aldine, New York, USA.

Boyd, C. & Slaymaker, T. (2000). *Re-examining the "More People Less Erosion" Hypothesis: Special Case or Wider Trend?* Natural Resource Perspectives 63, ODI, London, UK.

Brinkman, R. (2001). 'Development in the Moist Savanna Zone of West Africa'. Case study for: Dixon, J., Gulliver, A. & Gibbon, D. *Global Farming Systems Study: Challenges and Priorities to 2030*. Consultation Documents, World Bank/FAO, Rome, Italy.

Brooks, K., Krylatykh, E., Lerman, Z., Petrikov, A. & Uzun, V. (1996). *Agricultural Reform in Russia: A view from the farm level*. Discussion Paper 327, World Bank, Washington, D.C., USA.

Brush, S.B. (1987). 'Diversity and Change in Andean Agriculture'. In Little, D., Horowitz, M. & Nyerges, A.E. (eds): *Lands at Risk in the Third World: Local Level Perspectives*. Westview Press, Boulder, Colorado, USA

Burke, J.J., Oliver, M.J., & Velten, J.P. (1999). *Pollen-Based Transformation System Using Solid Media*. US Patent 5,929,300. July 27, 1999. U.S. Patent Office (http://www.uspto.gov/patft/index.html)

Byerlee, D. & Fisher, K. (2000). 'Accessing Modern Science: Policy and Institutional Options for Agricultural Biotechnology in Developing Countries'. *IP Strategy Today No.1-2001*.

Carloni, A. (2001). *Global Farming Systems Study: Challenges And Priorities to 2030 – Regional Analysis: Sub-Saharan Africa*. Consultation Document, FAO, Rome, Italy.

Cassman, K.G., Olk, D.C. & Dobermann, A. (1997). 'Scientific Evidence of Yield and Productivity Declines In Irrigated Rice Systems of Tropical Asia'. *International Rice Commission Newsletter* 46: 7-16.

CEPAL, FAO & GTZ. (1998). *Agroindustria y Pequeña Agricultura: Vínculos, Potencialidades y Oportunidades*. Santiago, Chile.

Chopra, K., Kadekodi, G. K. & Murthy, M.N. (1988). *Sukhomajri and Dhamala watersheds in Haryana. A participatory approach to development*. Institute of Economic Growth. Delhi, India.

Cleaver, K.M. & Schreiber, G.A. (1994). *Reversing the Spiral: The Population, Agriculture and Environment Nexus in Sub-Saharan Africa*. World Bank, Washington D.C., USA.

Collinson, M. (Ed.) (2000). *A History of Farming Systems Research*. FAO, Rome, Italy & CABI, Wallingford, UK.

Comité de Acción para el Desarrollo Social y Económico de Centroamerica/European Commisión (1990). *Los Productores de Granos Básicos del Ismas Centroamericano*. San José, Costa Rica

Contreras, B. (1996). *Estudio del Desarrollo de las Exportaciones de la Arveja China y el Brocolí en Guatemala en Base a la Producción de Pequeña Escala*. Regional Unit for Technical Assistance (RUTA)/Inter-American Development Bank, Guatemala.

Conway, G. (1997). *The Doubly Green Revolution: Food for All in the Twenty-First Century*. Penguin Books, London, UK.

Csaki, C. & Lerman, Z. (1997). *Land Reform in Ukraine: The First Five Years*. Discussion Paper 371, World Bank, Washington, D.C., USA.

Datt, G. & Ravallion, M. (1996). *Macroeconomic Crises and Poverty Monitoring: A Case Study for India*. Policy Research Working Paper 1685, World Bank, Washington D.C., USA.

Datt, G. & Ravallion, M. (1998). 'Why Have some Indian States Done Better than others at Reducing Rural Poverty?' *Economica* 65: 17-38.

D'Avis, B. (2001). *Personal Communication*. Chief, Policy Assistance Branch, Regional Office for Europe, FAO.

Dawe, D. & Dobermann, A. (2000). *Yield and Productivity Trends in Intensive Rice-Based Cropping Systems in Asia*. Expert Consultation on Yield Gap and Productivity Decline in Rice Production. 5-7 September 2000. FAO, Rome, Italy.

de Datta, S.K. (1981). *Principles and Practices of Rice Production*. Wiley-Interscience, New York, N.Y., USA.

de Freitas, V.C. (2000). *Soil Management and Conservation for Small Farms: Strategies and Methods of Introduction, Technologies and Equipment*. Soils Bulletin 77, FAO, Rome, Italy.

de Grandi, J. 'Improved Income Generation among Small Farmers in the Peruvian Sierra'. Case study for: Dixon, J., Gulliver, A., & Gibbon, D. *Global Farming Systems Study: Challenges and Priorities to 2030*. Consultation Documents, World Bank/FAO, Rome, Italy.

Deininger, K. & Binswanger, H. (1999). 'The Evolution of the World Bank's Land Policy'. *World Bank Research Observer* 14 (2): 247-76.

de Janvry, A. & Sadoulet, E. (2000). 'Rural Poverty in Latin America – Determinants and Exit Paths'. *Food Policy 25*: 389-409.

de la Cruz, R. E. (2000). 'Philippines: Challenges, Opportunities, and Constraints in Agricultural Biotechnology'. In Persley, G.J. and Lantin, M.M. (eds): *Agricultural Biotechnology and the Poor: Proceedings of an International Conference*, October 1999. CGIAR, Washington D.C., USA, pp. 58-63.

de la Fuente, J.M., Ramirez-Rodriguez, J.J., Cabrera Ponce, L. & Hererra-Estrella. (1997). 'Aluminum Tolerance in GM Plants by Alteration of Citrate Synthesis'. *Science* 276: 1566-8.

della Penna, D. (1999). 'Nutritional Genomics: Manipulating Plant Micronutrients to Improve Human Health'. *Science* 16: 375-79

Desta, L., Kassie, M., Benim, S. & Pender, J. (2001). *Land Degradation and Strategies for Sustainable Development in the Ethiopian Highlands: Amhara Region*. Socioeconomics & Policy Research Working Paper 32, International Livestock Research Institute, Nairobi, Kenya.

Dhar, S.K. (1997). *Personal Communication*. Chief Conservator of Forests, Government of Haryana, India.

Dillon, J., Plucknett, D. & Vallaeys, G. (1978). *TAC Review of Farming Systems Research at the International Agricultural Research Centres*. FAO, Rome, Italy.

Dixon, J. & Anandajayasekeram, P. (2000). *Status of FSA Institutionalisation in East and Southern Africa and its Implications*. International Farming Systems Research Extension Symposium, November 2000, Santiago, Chile.

Dixon, J., Gulliver, A. & Gibbon, D. (2001). *Global Farming Systems Study: Challenges and Priorities to 2030 – Synthesis and Global Overview*. Consultation Document, World Bank/FAO, Rome, Italy.

Dugdill, B.T & Bennett, A. (2001). 'Income Diversification in an Intensive Rice-Based System – Milk Vita in Bangladesh'. Case study for: Dixon, J., Gulliver, A. & Gibbon, D. *Global Farming Systems Study: Challenges and Priorities to 2030*. Consultation Documents, World Bank/FAO, Rome, Italy.

Duwayri, M., Tran, D.V. and Nguyen, V.N. (1999). 'Reflections on Yield Gaps in Rice Production'. *International Rice Commission Newsletter* 49: 13-25.

Echevarria, Rubén. (2000). 'Opciones para Reducir la Pobreza Rural en América Latina y el Caribe'. *Revista de la CEPAL April* 70:147-160, Santiago, Chile.

Ellis, F. (2000). *Rural Livelihoods and Diversity in Developing Countries*. Oxford University Press, Oxford, UK.

Evenson, R.E. (2000). 'Agricultural Productivity and Production in Developing Countries'. In FAO: *The State of Food and Agriculture*. FAO, Rome, Italy.

Fagade, S.O. & Nguyen, V.N. (2000). *Evolution of Irrigated Rice Yields in Sub-Saharan Africa*. Expert Consultation on Yield Gap and Productivity Decline in Rice Production. 5-7 September 2000, FAO, Rome, Italy .

Fan, D., Hazell, P. & Haque, T. (2000). *Targeting Public Investments by Agroecological Zone to Achieve Growth and Poverty Alleviation Goals in Rural India*. International Food Policy Research Institute. Washington, D.C., USA

FAO. (1990). *Women in Agricultural Development: Gender Issues in Rural Food Security in Developing Countries*. FAO, Rome, Italy

FAO. (1994). *Structural Adjustment and the Provision of Agricultural Services in Sub-Saharan Africa*. FAO, Rome, Italy.

FAO. (1995). *Evaluation of Forestry Resources in Tropical Countries, 1990*. Forestry Study 112, FAO, Rome, Italy.

FAO. (1996a). *World Food Security*. World Food Summit, 13-17 November. FAO, Rome, Italy.

FAO. (1996b). *Synthesis of the Technical Documents*. World Food Summit, 13-17 November, FAO, Rome, Italy.

FAO. (1997). *Conservation Farming Handbook for Smallholders in Regions I and II.*, Zambia. Conservation Farming Unit, Integrated Crop Management Food Legume Project (ZAM/92/003), Lusaka, Zambia.

FAO. (1998a). *The State of Food and Agriculture*. FAO, Rome, Italy.

FAO. (1998b). *Trade Yearbook 1998*. FAO, Rome, Italy.

FAO. (1999). *Agro-Ecological Zones, Farming Systems and Land Pressure in Africa and Asia*. Environmental Research Group Oxford Ltd and TALA Research Group, Department of Zoology, University of Oxford, for the Animal Health Service of the Animal Production and Health Division, FAO, Rome, Italy.

FAO. (1999a). *The Strategic Framework for FAO 2000-2015*. FAO, Rome, Italy.

FAO. (1999b). *FAO Statistical Yearbook*. FAO, Rome, Italy.

FAO. (1999c). *Integrated Crop and Land Management in the Hilly Terrains of Central America: Concepts, Strategies and Technical Options*. Integrated Crop Management Series, Vol 2. FAO, Rome, Italy.

FAO. (1999d). *Biotechnology*. Committee on Agriculture (COAG), FAO, Rome, Italy.

FAO. (2000a). *Agriculture Towards 2015/30. Technical Interim Report*. Global Perspectives Unit. FAO, Rome, Italy.

FAO. (2000b). *The State of Food and Agriculture. Lessons from the Past 50 Years*. FAO, Rome, Italy.

FAO. (2000c). *Irrigation in Latin America and the Caribbean in Figures*. Water Report 20. FAO, Rome, Italy.

FAO. (2001). *Proceedings of Workshop on Biological Nitrogen Fixation*. FAO, Rome, Italy.

FAO/IAEA (2001). 'New FE/IAEA Co-ordinated Research Project'. *FAO/IAEA Soils Newsletter*. 23 (2): 27-40

Farrington, J. & Lewis, D.L. (1993). *NGOs and the State in South Asia: Rethinking Roles in Sustainable Agricultural Development*. Overseas Development Institute, London, UK.

Fe'D'Ostiani, L. (2001).'Participatory and Integrated Watershed Management in Upland Areas of Tunisia'. Case study for: Dixon, J., Gulliver, A. & Gibbon, D. *Global Farming Systems Study: Challenges and Priorities to 2030*. Consultation Documents, World Bank/FAO, Rome, Italy.

Fischer, G., Shah, M., van Velthuizen, H. & Nachtergaele, F.O. (2001). *Global Agro-ecological Assessment for Agriculture in the 21st Century*. IIASA, Vienna, Austria & FAO, Rome, Italy.

Fresco, L. (1986). *Cassava in Shifting Cultivation: A Systems Approach to Agricultural Technology Development in Africa*. Royal Tropical Institute, Amsterdam, The Netherlands.

Fuglie, K., Zhang., L., Salazar, L.F. & Walker, T. (2001). *Economic Impact of Virus-Free Sweet Potato Planting Material in Shandong Province, China*. Future Harvest, Washington, D.C., USA.

Goklany, I. M. (2000). *Applying the Precautionary Principle to Genetically Modified Crops*. Policy Study 157, Center for the Study of American Business. Washington University, St. Louis, USA.

Goldman, I., Carnegie, J., Marumo, M., Munyoro, D., Kela, N., Ntonga, S. & Mwale, E. (2000). *Institutional Support for Sustainable Rural Livelihoods in Southern Africa: Results from Zimbabwe, Zambia and South Africa*. Natural Resource Perspectives 50, ODI, London, UK.

Government of India. (2000). *Agricultural Statistics at a Glance*. Directorate of Economics and Statistics, Department of Agriculture and Co-operation, Ministry of Agriculture, New Delhi, India.

Government of India & World Bank. (2001). *Ground Water Component: From Development to Management. India Water Resources Sector Review*. Government of India, New Delhi, India.

Government of Pakistan. (1998). *Agricultural Statistics of Pakistan, 1997-98*. Economic Wing, Ministry of Food, Agriculture and Livestock, Islamabad, Pakistan.

Greenland, D.J. (1997). *The Sustainability of Rice Farming*. IRRI & CAB International, Oxfordshire, UK.

Gulati, A. & Kelley, T. (1999). *Trade Liberalization and Indian Agriculture: Cropping Pattern Changes and Efficiency Gains in Semi-Arid Tropics*. Oxford University Press, New Delhi, India.

Gulliver, A., Villeda de Garcia, B. and Rodriguez, F. (1996). *Estrategia al Año 2020: Productos Agrícolas No Tradicionales*. Gremial de Exportadores de Productos No Tradicionales (GEXPRONT)/Regional Unit for Technical Assistance (RUTA), Guatemala.

Gulliver, A., de Grandi, J.C., Spehar, C, & Lopes, M. G. (2001). Global Farming Systems Study: Challenges and Priorities to 2030 – *Regional Analysis: Latin America and the Caribbean*. Consultation Document, World Bank/FAO, Rome, Italy.

Gulliver, A. (2001). 'Private Sector-Led Diversification among Indigenous Producers in Guatemala'. Case study for: Dixon, J., Gulliver, A. & Gibbon, D. *Global Farming Systems Study: Challenges and Priorities to 2030*. Consultation Documents, World Bank/FAO, Rome, Italy.

Guy, C. L., Irani, T., Gabriel, D. & Fehr, W. (2000). 'Workshop Reports: Workshop C: Food And Environmental Issues Associated With The Bio-Based Economy Of The 21st Century'. *National Agricultural Biotechnology Council* 19: 8-11.

Gypmantasiri, P., Wiboonpongse, A., Rerkasem, B., Criag, I., Rerkasem, K., Ganjapan, L., Titayawan, M., Seetisarn, M., Thani, P., Jaisaard, R., Ongpraser, S., Radanachales, T. and Conway, G.R. (1980). *An Interdisciplinary Perspective of Cropping Systems in the Chiang Mai Valley: Key Questions for Research*. Faculty of Agriculture, Chiang Mai University, Chiang Mai, Thailand.

Heath, J. & Binswanger, H.P. (1998). 'Policy-Induced Effects of Natural Resource Degradation: The Case of Columbia'. In Lutz, E., Binswanger, H., Hazell, P. & McCalla, A. (eds): *Agriculture and the Environment: Perspectives on Sustainable Rural Development*. World Bank, Washington, D.C., USA. pp. 22-34.

Hobbs, P. (2001) *Personal Communication*. Senior Scientist, CIMMYT, New Delhi, India.

Hoque, F. (2001). 'Integrated Intensified Rice Farming Systems in Bangladesh'. Case study for: Dixon, J., Gulliver, A. & Gibbon, D. *Global Farming Systems Study: Challenges and Priorities to 2030*. Consultation Documents, World Bank/FAO, Rome, Italy.

IFAD. (1992). *Soil and Water Conservation in Sub-Saharan Africa: Towards Sustainable Production by the Rural Poor*. IFAD, Rome, Italy.

IFAD. (1999). *Assessment of Rural Poverty in West and Central Africa*. IFAD, Rome, Italy.

IFAD. (2001). *Rural Poverty Report: The Challenge of Ending Poverty*. IFAD, Rome, Italy.

IFPRI. (2001). IFPRI *Applauds Syngenta's Policy to Share Genetic Discoveries with Poor Farmers*. Washington, D.C., USA.

IFPRI. (1999). 'Are We Ready for a Meat Revolution?' *20/20 Vision News & Views*. IFPRI, Washington, D.C., USA.

Instituto Brasileiro de Geografia e Estatistico. (1996). *Censo Agropecuario*. IBGE, Brasilia, Brazil.

Instituto Nacional de Estadistica Geográfica e Informática. (1995). *Conteo de Población y Vivienda*. INEGI, Aguascalientes, Mexico.

Instituto Nacional de Estadistica e Informática. (1996). *Censo Agropecuario 1994*. INEI, Lima, Peru.

Inter-American Development Bank. (1999). *Seminario Latinoamericano sobre Desarrollo del Empleo Rural no Agrícola*. Country Studies, IADB-FAO-ECLAC-RIMISP, Santiago, Chile.

International Panel on Climate Change. (2001). *Third Assessment Report*. Working Group 2, Cambridge University Press, UK.

International Service for the Acquisition of Agri-biotech Applications. (1999). *Global Review of Commercialized GM Crops: International Service for the Acquisition of Agri-Biotech Applications*. Brief 12. ISAAA, Ithaca, N.Y., USA.

Inversiones y Desarrollo Corporación. (1995). *Análisis de la Competividad Internacional del Sector Exportador de Guatemala de 1980-1993*. IDC, Ciudad de Guatemala, Guatemala.

Ishihara, Y. & Bachmann, T. (2001). 'Stabilizing High Altitude Swidden Cultivation in Laos'. Case study for: Dixon, J., Gulliver, A. & Gibbon, D. *Global Farming Systems Study: Challenges and Priorities to 2030*. Consultation Documents, World Bank/FAO, Rome, Italy.

Ivory, D. (2001). *Global Farming Systems Study: Challenges And Priorities To 2030 – Regional Analysis: East Asia and Pacific*. Consultation Document, FAO, Rome, Italy.

Jaglo-Ottosen K.R., Gilmour, S.J., Zarka, D.G., Schabenberger, O. & Thomashow, M.F. (1998). 'Arabidopsis CBF1 over-expression induces COR genes and enhances freezing tolerance'. *Science* 280: 104-106.

James, C. (2000). *Global Status of Commercialized Transgenic Crops: 2000*. Brief 21, International Service for the Acquisition of Agri-biotech Applications, Ithaca, N.Y., USA.

Jazairy, I., Alamgir, M. & Panuccio, T. (1992). *The State of Rural Poverty. An Inquiry into its Causes and Consequences*. New York University Press & IFAD, New York, N.Y., USA.

Kiff, E. & Pound, B. (2001). 'Integrating Crop Livestock Interactions inot Hill Mixed Farming Systems, Nepal'. Case study for: Dixon, J., Gulliver, A. & Gibbon, D. *Global Farming Systems Study: Challenges and Priorities to 2030*. Consultation Documents, World Bank/FAO, Rome, Italy.

Kobayashi, N.T., Yoshiba, M., Sanada Y. , Wada K., Tsukaya H., Kakubari Y., Yamaguchi-Shinozaki K. & Shinozaki K. (1999). 'Improving Plant Drought, Salt and Freezing Tolerance by Gene Transfer of a Single Stress-Inducible Transcription Factor'. *Nature Biotech* 17:287-291.

Kopeva, D. (2001). 'Transfer of Ownership and Land Fragmentation in the Transition to Family Farms in Bulgaria'. Case study for: Dixon, J., Gulliver, A. & Gibbon, D. *Global Farming Systems Study: Challenges and Priorities to 2030*. Consultation Documents, World Bank/FAO, Rome, Italy.

Krueger, A.O., Schiff, M.W. & Valdes, A. (eds) (1991). *The Political Economy of Agricultural Pricing Policy*. John Hopkins University Press, Baltimore, USA.

Ladha, J.K., Fischer, K.S., Hossain, M., Hobbs, P.R., & Hardy, B. (2000). *Improving the Productivity and Sustainability of Rice-Wheat Systems of the Indo-Gangetic Plains: A Synthesis of NARS-IRRI Partnership Research*. Discussion Paper 40, International Rice Research Institute, Los Baños, Philippines.

Langridge, W.H.R. (2000). 'Edible Vaccines'. *Scientific American* 283(3):66-71

Le, H. (2001) 'The Potential of Agricultural Biotechnology'. Case study for: Dixon, J., Gulliver, A. & Gibbon, D. *Global Farming Systems Study: Challenges and Priorities to 2030*. Consultation Documents, World Bank/FAO, Rome, Italy.

Lehman, V. (2000). 'Cuban Agrobiotechnology: Diverse Agenda in Times of Limited Food Production'. *Biotechnology and Development Monitor* 42: 18-21.

Lerman, Z. & C. Csaki, C. (2000). *Ukraine: Overview of Farm Restructuring Experiences*, Technical Paper 459, World Bank, Washington, D.C., USA.

Lewis, J. (2000). 'Leveraging Partnerships between the Public and Private Sector – Experience of USAID's Agricultural Biotechnology Program'. In Persley, G.J. & Lantin, M.M. (eds): *Agricultural Biotechnology and the Poor: Proceedings of an International Conference*, October 1999. CGIAR, Washington, D.C., USA, pp. 196-199.

Li, T. & della Penna, D. (2001). 'The Promise of Agricultural Biotechnology for Human Health'. Keystone Symposium *Plant Foods for Human Health: Manipulating Plant Metabolism to Enhance Nutritional Quality*. 6-11 April, Breckenridge, Colorado, USA.

Lightfoot, C., Feldman, S. & Abedin, M.Z. (1991). *Households, Agroecosystems and Rural Resources Management. A Guidebook for Broadening the Concepts of Gender and Farming Systems*. Educational Series 12, Bangladesh Agricultural Research Institute and International Center for Living Aquatic Resources Management, Manila, Philippines.

Lipton, M. (1977). *Why Poor People Stay Poor: A Study of Urban Bias in World Development*. Australian National University Press, Canberra, Australia.

Lutz, E., Binswanger, H., Hazell, P. & McCalla, A. (eds) (1998). *Agriculture and the Environment: Perspectives on Sustainable Rural Development*. World Bank, Washington, D.C., USA.

MAG/FAO/CIP/IICA (1996). *Memorias del Seminario Regional para la Promoción de Sistemas de Producción Agrícola Sostenible para el sector Campesino en los Andes Centrales*. Ministerio de Agricultura y Ganadería, Quito, Ecuador.

Martinenko, A. (2001). 'Natural Resource Use and Economic Viability as Affected by the Transformation of Farming Systems in Southern Ukraine'. Case study for: Dixon, J., Gulliver, A. & Gibbon, D. *Global Farming Systems Study: Challenges and Priorities to 2030*. Consultation Documents, World Bank/FAO, Rome, Italy.

Mascaretti, A. (2001). 'Tassas – Improved Traditional Planting Pits in Niger'. Case study for: Dixon, J., Gulliver, A. & Gibbon, D. *Global Farming Systems Study: Challenges and Priorities to 2030*. Consultation Documents, World Bank/FAO, Rome, Italy.

Maurice, S.B., Ku, D.C., Ranade, U., Hsu, T., Li, X., Jiao, D., Eherlinger, J., Miyao, M. & Matsuoka, M. (1999). 'Photosynthetic performance of transgenic rice plants over-expressing maize C4 photosynthesis enzymes'. In: Sheehy, J., Mitchell, P., & Hardy, B. (eds): *Redesigning Rice Photosynthesis to Increase Yield. Proceedings of a Workshop*, 30 Nov.-3 Dec. 1999. Los Banos, Philippines.

Meier, G.M. & Stiglitz, E. (2000). *Frontiers of Development Economics*. World Bank, Oxford University Press, New York, N.Y., USA.

Mellor, J. W. & Johnston, B. F. (1984). 'The World Food Equation: Interrelations among Development, Employment and Food Consumption'. *Journal of Economic Literature* 22:531-74.

Mellor, J. (2000). *Agricultural Growth, Rural Employment and Poverty Reduction – Non-Tradables, Public Expenditure And Balanced Growth*. World Bank Rural Week 2000, World Bank, Washington, D.C., USA.

Mellor, J. (2001). *Reducing Poverty, Buffering Economic Shocks – Agriculture and the Non-Tradable Economy*. Working Paper for the First Expert Meeting on the Documentation and Measurement of the Roles of Agriculture in Developing Countries (19-21 March 2001), FAO, Rome, Italy.

Meng, E. (2001). 'Case Study: Advisory Services for Restructured and Cooperative Farms in Extensive Crop/Livestock Regions'. Case study for: Dixon, J., Gulliver, A. & Gibbon, D. *Global Farming Systems Study: Challenges and Priorities to 2030*. Consultation Documents, World Bank/FAO, Rome, Italy.

Milanovich, B. (1998). *Income, Inequality and Poverty during the Transition from Planned to Market Economy*. World Bank, Washington, D.C., USA.

Mishra, P.R., and others. (1980). *Operational Research Project on Watershed Development for Sediment, Drought and Flood Control*. Sukhomajri, Central Soil and Water Conservation Research and Training Institute, Chandigarh, India.

Mittal, S.K. (1998). *Personal Communication*. Principal Scientist, Central Soil and Water Conservation Research and Training Institute, Chandigarh, India.

Mitti, G. (2001) 'Community-based Seed Supply Systems, Zambia'. Case study for: Dixon, J., Gulliver, A. & Gibbon, D. *Global Farming Systems Study: Challenges and Priorities to 2030*. Consultation Documents, World Bank/FAO, Rome, Italy.

Moench, M. (2001). *The Question of Groundwater and Food Security. Uncertainty, Variability and Risk*. AGLW Technical Paper, FAO, Rome, Italy.

Muñoz, J. (1999). *Los Mercados de Tierras en Bolivia*. Series 61, CEPAL, Santiago, Chile.

Nachtergaele, F.O.N. & Brinkman, R. (1996). 'Identification of Analogous Land for Agrotechnology Transfer in the Savanna Zones of the Developing World'. In FAO. *Integrated Crop Management*. Vol. 1. Crop and Grassland Service, Plant Production and Protection Division, FAO, Rome, Italy. pp. 29-42

Nambiar, K.M. & Ghosh, A.B. (1984). *Highlights of Research of a Long-Term Fertilizer Experiment in India* (1972-1982). LTFE Bulletin 1, Indian Council of Agricultural Research, New Delhi, India.

National Academy of Sciences. (2000). *Transgenic Plants and World Agriculture*. National Academy Press, Washington, D.C., USA.

Norman, D. W., Simmons, E. B. & Hays, H. M. (1982). *Farming Systems in the Nigerian Savanna: Research and Strategies for Development*. Westview Press, Boulder, USA.

Paarlberg, R. (2000). *Governing the GM Crop Revolution: Policy Choices for Developing Countries. Food, Agriculture, and the Environment*. Discussion Paper 33, IFPRI, Washington, D.C., USA.

Pearson, C. J., Norman, D. W. & Dixon, J. (1995). *Sustainable Dryland Cropping in Relation to Soil Productivity*. FAO, Rome, Italy.

Pingali, P., Bigot, Y. & Binswanger, H.P. (1987). *Agricultural Mechanization and the Evolution of Farming Systems in Sub-Saharan Africa*. Johns Hopkins University Press for the World Bank, Baltimore, London.

Pinstrup-Anderson, P., Pandya-Lorch, R. & Rosegrant, M.W. (1999). *World Food Prospects: Critical Issues for the Early Twenty-First Century.* Food Policy Report, IFPRI Washington, D.C., USA.

Ponnamperuma, F.N. & Deturck P. (1993). 'A Review of Fertilization in Rice Production'. *International Rice Commission Newsletter* 42: 1-12.

Prakash, C. (2000). 'A First Step Towards Engineering Improved Phosphate Uptake'. *National Biological Impact Assessment Program News Report* 2-3 May.

Pray, C. E., Ma, D., Huang, J. & Qiao, F. (2001). 'Impact of Bt-Cotton in China'. *Conference Proceedings, International Consortium on Agricultural Biotechnology Research*, August 24-28, Ravello, Italy.

Pretty, J.N. (1995). *Regenerating Agriculture: Policies and Practice for Sustainability and Self-Reliance.* Earthscan, London, UK.

Pretty, J.N. (2000). 'Can Sustainable Agriculture Feed Africa? New Evidence on Progress, Processes and Inputs'. *Environment, Development and Sustainability.* Special issue on sustainable agriculture.

Proyecto Estado de la Región (1999). *Estado de la Región en Desarrollo Humano Sostenible. Informe 1999.* UNDP/European Union, San José, Costa Rica.

Pulver, E.L. & Nguyen, V.N. (1999). 'Sustainable Rice Production Issues for the Third Millennium'. In: *Proceedings of the 19th Session of the International Rice Commission.* FAO, Rome, Italy, pp 32-43

Purcell, D. & Anderson, J.R. (1997). *Agricultural Extension and Research: Achievements and Problems in National Systems.* World Bank, Washington, D.C., USA.

Qaim, M. (1999). 'Potential Benefits of Agricultural Biotechnology: An Example from the Mexican Potato Sector'. *Review of Agricultural Economics* 21(2):390-408

Qaim, M. (2000). *A Prospective Evaluation of Biotechnology in Semi-Subsistence Agriculture.* XXIV Conference of the International Association of Agricultural Economists (IAAE), August 20, Berlin, Germany.

Ramasamy, C. (1996). 'Priority Setting for Rice Research in Southern India'. In: *Proceedings of the Third International Rice Genetics Symposium.* IRRI, Los Banos, Philippines, pp. 978-983.

Rausser, G., Simon, L. & Ameden, H. (2000). 'Public-Private Alliances in Biotechnology - Can they Narrow the Knowledge Gaps between Rich and Poor?' *Food Policy* 25: 499-513.

Reij, C., Scoones, I. & Toulmin, C., (eds) (1996). *Sustaining the Soil: Indigenous Soil and Water Conservation in Africa.* Earthscan, London, UK.

Reijntjes, C., Haverkart, B. & Waters-Bayer, A. (1992). *Farming for the Future: An Introduction to Low External Input and Sustainable Agriculture.* ILEIA & MacMillan, London, UK.

Rodriguez, A., Salahieh, H., Badwan, R. & Khawan, H. (1999). *Groundwater Use and Supplemental Irrigation in Atareb, Northwest Syria.* SSP 7. ICARDA, Aleppo, Syria.

Rolls, M. (2001). *Review of Farm Management in Extension Programmes in Central and Eastern European Countries.* AGSP, FAO, Rome, Italy.

Roy, R.N. & Hardarson, G. (2001). *Technical Expert Meeting on Increasing the Use of Biological Nitrogen Fixation (BNF) in Agriculture.* FAO, Rome, Italy.

Ruthenberg, H. (1971). *Farming Systems in the Tropics.* Clarendon Press, Oxford, UK.

Samayoa Urrea, O. (1994). *Las Implicaciones de la Nueva Tecnología del Comercio Internacional.* UNDP, Ciudad de Guatemala, Guatemala.

Sarin, M. (1996). *Joint Forest Management: The Haryana Experience.* Centre for Environment Education, Ahmedabad, India.

Saunders, J.A. & Matthews, B.F. (1997). *Plant Transformation by Gene Transfer into Pollen.* U.S. Patent 5,629,183, U.S. Patent Office, May 13, 1997. (http://www.uspto.gov/patft/index.html)

Sayre, R. (2000). 'Cyanogen Reduction in GM Cassava: Generation of a Safer Product for Subsistence Farmers'. *Information Systems for Biotechnology News Report.* August 2000.

Schuh, G.E. (2000). 'The Household: The Neglected Link in Research and Programs for Poverty Alleviation'. *Food Policy* 25: 233-241.

Secretaría de Agricultura, Ganadería, Desarrollo Rural, Pesca y Alimentación. (1998). *Datos Básicos.* SAGAR, Distrito Federal, Mexico.

Serova, E.V. (1998). *The Impact of Privatisation and Farm Restructuring on the Russian Agriculture*, USAID, Moscow, Russia.

Shaner, W.W., Philipp, P. F. & Schmehl, W. R. (1982). *Farming Systems Research and Development: Guidelines for Developing Countries*. Westview Press, Boulder, Colorado, USA.

Shmaefsky, B.R. (2000). 'GM Tobacco Requires Less Phopsphorus Fertilizer'. *Information Systems for Biotechnology News Report* 7-9.

Simpson, A.J.G. and others (2000). 'The Genome Sequence of the Plant Pathogen Xylella Fastidiosa'. *Nature* 406: 151 - 157.

Sittenfeld, A., Espinoza, A.M., Muñoz, M. and Zamora, A. (2000). 'Costa Rica: Challenges and Opportunities in Biotechnology and Biodiversity'. In Persley, G.J., and Lantin, M.M. (eds): *Agricultural Biotechnology and the Poor: Proceedings of an International Conference*. October 1999. CGIAR. Washington D.C., pp.79-89.

Somerville, C. & Somerville, S. (1999). 'Plant Functional Genomics'. *Science* 285: 380-383.

Spehar, C. (2001) 'Improvement of Farming Systems in the Savannah Lands of Brazil'. Case study for: Dixon, J., Gulliver, A. & Gibbon, D. *Global Farming Systems Study: Challenges and Priorities to 2030*. Consultation Documents, World Bank/FAO, Rome, Italy.

Spillane, C. (1999). *Recent Development in Biotechnology as they Relate to Plant Genetic Resources for Food and Agriculture*. Background Study Paper 9, FAO, Rome, Italy.

Steele, P. (2001). *Personal Communication*. Senior Officer, Agroindustry and Post-Harvest Service, FAO, Rome, Italy.

Superintendência do Desenvolvimento do Nordeste. (1999). *Região Nordeste do Brasil em Números*. SUDENE, Government of Brazil, Brasilia, Brazil.

Swallow, B.M. (2000). *Impacts of Trypanosomiasis on African Agriculture*. Programme Against African Trypanosomiasis, Technical and Scientific Series 2, FAO, Rome, Italy.

Tabashnik, B., Patin, A.L., Dennehy, T. J., Liu, Y.B., Carrière, Y., Sims, M.A., & Antilla, L. (2000). 'Frequency of Resistance to Bacillus Thuringiensis in Field Populations of Pink Bollworm'. *Proceedings of the National Academy of Science*. 97 (24): 12980-12984.

Takahashi, M. H., Nakanishi, S., Kawasaki, N., Nishizawa, K. & Mori, S. (2001). 'Enhanced Tolerance of Rice to Low Iron Availability in Alkaline Soils Using Barley Nicotianamine Aminotransferase Genes'. *Nature Biotechnology*. 19 (5): 466 – 469.

Tanic, S. & Dauphin, F. (2001). *Global Farming Systems Study: Challenges And Priorities To 2030 – Regional Analysis: Eastern Europe And Central Asia*. Consultation Document, FAO/World Bank, Rome, Italy.

Tanner, C. (2001) 'Community-based Land Tenure Reform in Mozambique'. Case study for: Dixon, J., Gulliver, A. & Gibbon, D. *Global Farming Systems Study: Challenges and Priorities to 2030*. Consultation Documents, World Bank/FAO, Rome, Italy.

Teng, P.S. (2000). *Agricultural Biotechnology: What is in it for Developing Countries - A Perspective from the Private Sector*. SEAMEO-SEARCA Regional Conference on Agricultural Biotechnology, Bangkok, Thailand.

Tiffen, M., Mortimore, M. & Gichuki, F. (1994). *More People, Less Erosion: Environmental Recovery in Kenya*. John Wiley & Sons, Chichester, UK.

Torres, R. (1997). *Linkages between Tourism and Agriculture in Quintana Roo, Mexico*. Unpublished Field Research Report, University of California, Davis, California, USA.

Tran, D. & Nguyen, N. (2001) 'Case Study: Declining Productivity Gains and the Yield Gap in Rice'. In Dixon, J., Gulliver, A. & Gibbon, D. *Global Farming Systems Study: Challenges and Priorities to 2030*. Consultation Documents, World Bank/FAO, Rome, Italy.

Traxler, G., Godoy-Avila, S., Falck-Zepeda, J., & Espinoza-Arellano, J.D.J., (2001). *Transgenic Cotton in Mexico: Economic and Environmental Impacts*. 5th ICABR International Conference on Biotechnology, Science and Modern Agriculture, June 15-19, Ravello, Italy.

UNDP. (2000). *Human Development Report 2000*. Oxford University Press, New York, N.Y., USA.

UNDP. (2001). *Human Development Report 2001*. Oxford University Press, New York, N.Y., USA.

Unidad Sectorial de Planificación Agropecuaria y de Alimentación. (1996). *Estatísticas Nacionales Agropecuarias, 1995-96*. Ministerio de Agricultura, Ganadería y Alimentación. Ciudad de Guatemala, Guatemala.

United Nations Environmental Program. (1997). *Global Environment Outlook – 1. Global State of the Environment Report*. UNEP, Nairobi, Kenya.

United Nations General Assembly. (2000). *United National Millennium Declaration*. UN General Assembly resolution 55/2, Document A/RES/55/2, 18 September, New York, N.Y., USA.

United Nations Population Division. (2000). *World Urbanization Prospects: The 1999 Revision. Key Findings*. United Nations, New York, N.Y., USA.

United Nations Task Force. (2000). *The Elimination of Food Insecurity in the Horn of Africa: A Strategy for Concerted Governmnet and UN Agency Action*. Final Report, FAO, Rome, Italy.

Valdes, A. (2000). *Developing a Rural Poverty Alleviation Strategy for Latin America: Evidence from Case Studies with Emphasis on Brazil*. Seminar in FAO, Rome, on 12 December.

Wambugu, F. (1999). 'Why Africa Needs Agricultural Biotech'. *Nature* 400 (6739): 15-16.

Wang, Z. (2001). 'Innovative Rice-based Farming Systems Development: Zhejiang Province, China'. Case study for: Dixon, J., Gulliver, A. & Gibbon, D. *Global Farming Systems Study: Challenges and Priorities to 2030*. Consultation Documents, World Bank/FAO, Rome, Italy.

Weatherhogg, J., Dixon, J. & d'Alwis, K. (2001). *Global Farming Systems Study: Challenges And Priorities To 2030 – Regional Analysis: South Asia*. Consultation Document, FAO/World Bank, Rome, Italy.

Webster, J. (2000). *Enabling Biotechnology in Africa: Current Situation and Future Needs*. Seminar presented December 8 at FAO, Rome, Italy.

World Bank. (1997). *Rural Development – From Vision to Action*. Study and Monograph Series 12, Environmental and Socially Sustainable Development Department, World Bank, Washington, D.C., USA.

World Bank. (1998). *East Asia and the Pacific*. World Bank, Washington, D.C., USA.

World Bank. (2000a). *World Development Report 2000/2001*. World Bank, Washington, D.C., USA.

World Bank. (2000b). *Can Africa Claim the 21st Century?* World Bank, Washington, D.C., USA.

World Bank. (2000c). *Voices of the Poor*. Oxford University Press for World Bank, Washington, D.C., USA.

World Bank. (2000d). *Social Assessment and Agricultural Reform in Central Asia and Turkey*. Technical Paper 461, World Bank, Washington, D.C., USA.

World Bank. (2000e). *Global Commodity Markets*. Development Prospects Group, World Bank, D.C., USA.

World Bank. (2000f). *World Development Indicators*. World Bank, Washington, D.C., USA.

World Bank. (2001a). *African Rural Development Strategy: Vision to Action Update 2001*. Draft Report, World Bank, Washington D.C., USA.

World Bank. (2001b). *Global Economic Prospects and the Developing Countries, 2001*. World Bank, Washington, D.C., USA.

World Resources Institute. (2000). *Land Area and Use 1982-94*. World Resources Institute, Washington, D.C., USA.

Ye, X., Al-Babili, S., Kloti, A., Zhang, J., Lucca, P., Beyer, P. & Potrykus, I. (2000). 'Engineering the Provitamin A (Beta-Carotene) Biosynthetic Pathway into (Carotenoid-Free) Rice Endosperm'. *Science* 287: 303-305.

Yoon, C. K. (2000). 'Agriculture Takes its Turn in the Genome Spotlight'. *The New York Times. July 18.*

Zhang, H. X. and E. Blumwald (2001). 'Transgenic Salt-Tolerant Tomato Plants Accumulate Salt in Foliage but not in Fruit'. *Nature Biotechnology* 19(8): 765–768.

Zhang, S. P., and others. (1998). 'Expression and Inheritance of Multiple Transgenes in Rice'. *Nature Biotechnology* 16:1060-1064.

ANNEX 5

ACRONYMS, ABBREVIATIONS

AND SPECIAL TERMS

•••

ACRONYMS

AEZ	Agro-Ecological Zone
AFR	Sub-Saharan Africa Region
CDD	Community Driven Development
CGIAR	Consultative Group on International Agricultural Research
CIAT	International Center for Tropical Agriculture
CIMMYT	International Maize and Wheat Improvement Center
CIP	International Potato Center
CIS	Commonwealth of Independent States
CSEE	Central and Southeastern Europe
EAP	East Asia and Pacific Region
ECA	Europe and Central Asia Region
EMBRAPA	Brazilian Agricultural Research Corporation
EU	European Union
FAO	Food and Agriculture Organization of the United Nations
FSA	Farming Systems Approach
FSR	Farming Systems Research
GADP	Gross Agricultural Domestic Product
GDP	Gross Domestic Product
GEF	Global Environment Facility
GMO	Genetically Modified Organism
GNP	Gross National Product
HDI	Human Development Index
HIPC	Highly Indebted Poorest Countries
HIV/AIDS	Human Immunodeficiency Virus/Aquired Immunodeficiency Syndrome
HPI	Human Poverty Index
HYV	High Yielding Variety
IARC	International Agricultural Research Centers

ICARDA	International Center for Agricultural Research in the Dry Areas
ICM	Integrated Crop Management
ICRISAT	International Crops Research Institute for the Semi-Arid Tropics
IDG	International Development Goal
IFAD	International Fund for Agricultural Development
IFPRI	International Food Policy Research Institute
IITA	International Institute of Tropical Agriculture
ILRI	International Livestock Research Institute
IMF	International Monetary Fund
INM	Integrated Nutrient Management
IPCC	Intergovernmental Panel on Climate Change
IPM	Integrated Pest Management
IRRI	International Rice Research Institute
ISNAR	International Service for National Agricultural Research
LAC	Latin America and the Caribbean Region
MIS	Market Information Services
MNA	Middle East and North Africa Region
MOA	Ministry of Agriculture
NAR	National Agricultural Research
NARS	National Agricultural Research System
NGO	Non-Governmental Organization
O&M	Operation and Maintenance
OCP	Onchocerciasis Control Programme
PPP	Purchasing Power Parity
PRSP	Poverty Reduction Strategy Paper
PTD	Participatory Technology Development
SADC	Southern African Development Community
SAP	Structural Adjustment Programme
SAS	South Asia Region
SLA	Sustainable Livelihoods Approach
SME	Small and Medium Enterprise
SSFMI	Small-Scale Farmer Managed Irrigation
T&V	'Training and Visit' (extension methodology)
UNDP	United National Development Programme
UNEP	United Nations Environmental Programme
UNGA	United Nations General Assembly
UNPD	United Nations Population Division
WUA	Water Users Association

ABBREVIATIONS

agric.	agricultural
cult.	cultivated area
ha	hectare
incl.	including
kcal	kilocalorie
kg	kilogram
km	kilometre
km³	cubic kilometre
m	million
%	percentage
popn.	population
pers., p.	person
t	ton
yr	year

GLOSSARY OF SOME SPECIAL TERMS USED IN THE BOOK

Agricultural Population
The agricultural population is defined as all persons depending for their livelihood on agriculture, hunting, fishing or forestry. This estimate comprises all persons actively engaged in agriculture and their non-working dependants.

Annual and Permanent Cropland / Cultivated Area
Sum of land under temporary crops (double-cropped areas are counted only once), temporary meadows for mowing or pasture, land under market and kitchen gardens and land temporarily fallow (land abandoned for less than five years, or as a result of shifting cultivation, is not included in this category.) plus land cultivated with crops that occupy the land for long periods and need not be replanted after each harvest, such as cocoa, coffee and rubber (this category includes land under flowering shrubs, fruit trees, nut trees and vines, but excludes land under trees grown for wood or timber).

Agro-ecological Zones (AEZ)
Agro-ecological zones are defined and delineated by FAO based on the average annual length of growing period for crops, which depends on, *inter alia*, precipitation and temperature. The length of growing period for these zones are: humid, greater than 270 days; moist subhumid, 180 to 269 days; dry subhumid, 120 to 179 days; semiarid, 60 to 119 days; arid, 0 to 59 days.

International Poverty Line / Dollar Poverty

Poverty reference lines set at US$1 and US$2 consumption per capita per day in 1993 Purchasing Power Parity (PPP). The former reference line is generally used when discussing poverty which, when set at this level, is sometimes referred to as *dollar poverty*. Many countries also set national poverty lines which generally differ from the international poverty line.

Irrigated Area

Data on irrigation relate to areas equipped to provide water to the crops. These include areas equipped for full and partial control irrigation, spate irrigation areas, and equipped wetland or inland valley bottoms.

Land Area

Total area of region within the farming system or region excluding areas under inland water bodies.

Total Economically Active Population

This refers to the number of all employed and unemployed persons (including those seeking work for the first time). It covers employers; self-employed workers; salaried employees; wage earners; unpaid workers assisting in a family, farm or business operation; members of producers' co-operatives; and members of the armed forces. The economically active population is also called the labour force.